CATTLE & MEN

Cattle & Men

BY CHARLES WAYLAND TOWNE

& EDWARD NORRIS WENTWORTH

Norman
UNIVERSITY OF OKLAHOMA PRESS

By Charles Wayland Towne

The Foolish Dictionary (Boston, 1904)
Foolish Finance (Boston, 1905)
Eediotic Etiquette (New York, 1906)
The New Foolish Dictionary (Boston, 1914)
Her Majesty Montana (Butte, Montana, 1939)

By Edward Norris Wentworth

Portrait Gallery of the Saddle and Sirloin Club (Chicago, 1919)
Progressive Beef Cattle Raising (Chicago, 1920)
Progressive Hog Raising (Chicago, 1920)
Progressive Sheep Raising (Chicago, 1922)
Marketing Livestock and Meats (Chicago, 1925)
America's Sheep Trails: History, Personalities (Ames, Iowa, 1948)

By Towne and Wentworth

Shepherd's Empire (Norman, 1945)
Pigs: From Cave to Corn Belt (Norman, 1950)
Cattle & Men (Norman, 1955)

Library of Congress Catalog Card Number: 55–9625

Copyright 1955 by the University of Oklahoma Press
Publishing Division of the University
Composed and printed at Norman, Oklahoma, U.S.A.
by the University of Oklahoma Press
First edition

Acknowledgments

No BOOK can be written alone; authors must depend upon the generosity and help of others in locating materials, verifying facts, and interpreting records. Many persons have cheerfully and unselfishly given of their time and knowledge to aid us in the preparation of this book. A few of them to whom we express grateful thanks are J. W. Amschler, Vienna, Austria; Alfred Atkinson, president-emeritus, University of Arizona, Tucson; Henry Bell, secretary, Texas and Southwestern Cattle Raisers Association, Fort Worth; Robert T. Braidwood, Oriental Institute, Chicago; Mrs. Ruth Butler, Newberry Library, Chicago; R. P. Fowler, Tucson; LeRoy R. Hafen, Brigham Young University, Provo, Utah; Miss Lola Homsher, state librarian of Wyoming; Herbert A. Kellar, director, McCormick Collection, Wisconsin State Library, Madison; Carl H. Kraeling, Oriental Institute; Mrs. Gertrude McDevitt, Idaho State Historical Museum, Boise; Mrs. Anne McDonnell, Historical Society of Montana, Helena; the late Governor Manuel Otero of New Mexico, Santa Fé; the late Governor S. B. Packard of Louisiana, long-time cattle feeder in Iowa; Mrs. Edna Parratt, managing director of the California Historical Society, San Francisco; Miss Patricia Paylore, assistant librarian, University of Arizona; William J. Pistor, University of Arizona; Karl Patterson Schmidt, Chicago Natural History Museum; Mrs. Agnes Wright Spring, state historian of Colorado, Denver; E. B. Stanley, University of Arizona; Miss Johanne Vindenas, librarian, Oriental Institute; John A. Wilson, Oriental Institute; and Mrs. Clara Zimmerman, state librarian of California, Sacramento.

We are also indebted to the publishers who kindly gave per-

v

mission to quote from their copyrighted works, which may be identified through the footnotes and bibliography; and to those who permitted us to use illustrations, recognized through credits on the illustration pages.

CHARLES WAYLAND TOWNE
EDWARD NORRIS WENTWORTH

May 17, 1955

Contents

Illustrations

Foreword

MAN CAME into this world a barbarian, surrounded by many natural assets. Some of these he discovered in his early days; others he is still discovering today.

One asset that he recognized very soon in his existence was cattle. First, he hunted and killed them for food and cover; then, he domesticated and raised them for food, clothing, and work. If man conquered and domesticated the smaller races of cattle, or if he captured and raised calves of the larger races, is not known. He is, however, still improving the breed to his changing needs.

Men and cattle developed together; each had a powerful influence on the life of the other. They both started wild, and now most of both are at least semi-domesticated.

Cattle had their origin in Europe and parts of Asia. The men who first raised cattle have gone further and developed more than those who did not take advantage of this opportunity. None of the animals, including cattle, feared man until they learned that he was their enemy. Even then, with proper treatment, this fear may be partially overcome. The gaur, a wild ox of southeastern Asia, is one of the wildest and most fearful of man. However, at the game ranger's headquarters in Malaya salt licks were established near the buildings and gaur there ignore man, his smell, and his noises. The gaur and the banteng have never been really domesticated.

Where man went, there he took his cattle. Over the years they provided him with food, shelter, clothing, transportation, work animals, fertilizer for his fields, a use for surplus grain, and even entered into his religion. In India there are still sacred bulls.

Oxen were the only capable draft animals in the days of the Western freighters. They transported the early settlers and their belongings, and supplied them later with much-needed goods from the East. The lumbering freight wagons were drawn by ten yoke of oxen convoyed by four bullwhackers, and the whole train was supervised by wagon masters and their assistants. The oxen and wagons were usually sold to the settlers at the end of the trips, as it was cheaper than bringing them back empty. This one-trip use created a huge industry of wagon building and ox training in Fort Leavenworth and other Kansas starting points for the Western haul. Today, the railroad, the tractor, and the airplane have relieved the ox of heavy labor in all but the most primitive parts of the world.

When the West was settled, but before the railroads came, the hundreds of owners of the vast cattle ranches in New Mexico, Texas, California, and Arizona employed thousands of men as cowboys and ranch hands. The families of some ranch workers have lived and worked on the same ranch for as many as three or four generations. This is especially true of those of Mexican ancestry.

Aside from assuaging his hunger directly in primitive times, cattle have provided and still do provide, both directly and indirectly, work for many men. From the cowboy to the butcher behind the meat counter, the handling of them, their by-products, and items connected with them provides gainful employment for tens of thousands.

We are apt to associate all cattle, especially the Longhorn, with the West. The best breeds, however, came from Europe and were landed on the Eastern shore, moving west with the settlers. So this book is a history, not only of cattle, but a history of men. It is an appreciation of what cattle have done for man, or really, what man has done *with* cattle. That is, from the standpoint of eatin' cattle, not milkin' cattle. At the present value of steak, or even stew meat, we should all have a respect for cattle. Reading the book will deepen it.

COLIN CAMPBELL SANBORN
Curator, Division of Mammals
Chicago Natural History Museum

CATTLE & MEN

Evolution

CHAPTER 1

From Ancient Aurochs to Baby Beef

THIS IS THE STORY of men and cattle coming up through the ages together, of what they have done for each other, and how they have achieved an association which has produced results quite unattainable had they operated separately.

From the earliest days, even the noun "cattle" has had such an all-embracing connotation in man's affairs as to have become at times an ambiguous and perplexing word, designating many contrasting things. Originally, the word meant property of all kinds, animate and inanimate. In this sense it was identical with "chattel" and "capital." Afterwards, to distinguish livestock from other classes of property, livestock came to be known as "quick" cattle, which included horses, camels, sheep, asses, goats, swine, and all bovines. In the Scriptures and other ancient writings, the word is used in this general sense.

In some languages there was a further breakdown into "large" and "small" cattle. The Spaniards, for example, had their *ganados mayores,* which included horned cattle, mules, and horses; and their *ganados menores,* sheep, goats, swine, and burros. Incidentally, those old Spanish historians who, in referring to cattle, failed to specify "large" or "small" have left many a researcher guessing whether they were writing about cows or sheep, mules or goats.

As for the English, when they talked and wrote about "neat" cattle, they did not mean "tidy." Long ago they borrowed the Icelandic word *naut,* meaning "ox," changed it to "neat," and used it as a label for bovines only. Fourteenth-century Chaucer and sixteenth-century Spenser spoke of herders in the open fields "keeping of their *neat*"; Shakespeare reminded us that

3

"the steer, the heifer, and the calf are all called *neat*"; and in *Cymbeline,* he made Imogen cry in desperation, "Would I were a *neat-herd's* daughter!" There was even a word for the female of the profession—"neatress"—although Herrick gave it a romantic twist in the lines:

> But hark how I can now expresse
> My love unto my Neatherdresse.

Governor William Bradford joyfully welcomed at Plymouth a consignment of "neats"—three heifers and a bull—from England in 1624. And we still have neat's-foot oil from the feet and gristle of neat cattle, and neat's leather from their hides.

If it be true that language develops through "the felicitious misapplication of words, "cattle" has done its share in keeping us enlightened and entertained. In Chaucer's *Canterbury Tales* the Plowman is showered with praise for having paid his tithes "ful faire and wel," both of his own labor and of "his *catel.*" In 1550, King Edward VI bent the royal ear as preacher Latimer pleaded the cause of those who "must have other *cattle,* as horses to draw their plow, and for carriage of things to markets." An English nobleman was once reported to have ridden from Simbla to Umballa in India in one night and back the next day, ninety-two miles each way, "with constant change of *cattle.*"

Not only the man in the street but many of England's eminent writers, in a spirit of ridicule or contempt, often alluded to human beings as "cattle." In *As You Like It,* the Bard declares: "Boys and women are for the most part *cattle* of this colour." Swift tells Congreve that

> Last year, a lad hence by his parents sent
> With other cattle to the city went.

And Byron confessed that nothing grieved him so much

> As that abominable tittle-tattle,
> Which is the cud eschewed [sic] by human cattle.

4

This, however, is a book about cattle of the bovine genus. Furthermore, it treats of beef cattle only, or of the meat-producing merits of more versatile breeds. The milch cow and the dairy industry have no place here. Indeed, an adequate account of the dairy cow would in itself require book-length treatment. It is the aim of this book to trace the progress of the ox from prehistoric times down to the moment it leaves the modern packing house in the form of a prime rib roast or a soup bone. It does not aspire to be a history, an encyclopedia, or a textbook. It hopes to tell a story. It foreswears fiction but cleaves to narrative. Most of all it strives to keep alive the sense of interdependence between men and cattle. For there is little popular interest in merely animal behavior. What people want to know is what cattle have done to, and for, man, and how he in turn has reacted. John Gibson of the famous nineteenth-century cattle-breeding family once wrote: "It is impossible to overestimate the services rendered by the ox to the human race. Living, it ploughs the owner's land and reaps his harvest, carries his goods or himself, safeguards his property values, helps him fight his battles. . . . When dead, its flesh forms a chief source of animal food; its bones are ground into manure or turned into numerous articles of use or adornment; its skin is made into leather; its ears and hoofs into glue; its hair is mixed with mortar; and its horns are cut and moulded into spoons and other useful articles."

For clothing *Cattle* in its garment of praise—and avoiding the spirit of heaviness—there is a pattern. It was cut from the fabric of fact by twin-bladed shears, one blade chronological, the other topical. Like a good workable tool, they aim to deserve Sydney Smith's definition of marriage: "so joined that they cannot be separated, often moving in opposite directions, yet always punishing anyone who comes between them."

Chronologically, the tale begins in prehistoric times, one hundred thousand years ago, when "sub-man" was disputing the right to survive with such creatures as the mammoth, the bison, the wooly rhinoceros, the giant beaver, and the huge hippopotamus. Artists pictured the great aurochs—never domesticated, yet the ancestor of the domestic ox—on cavern walls in southern France and northern Spain twenty thousand or more years ago. These Old Stone Age peoples ate the flesh of the wild desert horse. Their successors, the New Stone Age tribes, reckoned wealth by cows, ate beef, and hitched draft oxen to clumsy wagons with tree-trunk wheels.

In addition to paintings, Aryan epics have left word pictures of stock-raising nationalities. In Sanskrit we read of a fair, beef-eating race which came down from Persia to India and eventually turned vegetarian. *Tain,* the "Irish *Iliad,*" describes a cattle-keeping life. Icelandic sagas are filled with references to the livestock of the sub-polar terrain. Beginning four thousand or five thousand years ago, the story continues through the Minoan, Egyptian, Grecian, and Roman civilizations down to the cultures of Europe and the New World, when the drab descendants of the big, bold aurochs and the little Celtic shorthorn first caught the eye of medieval cowkeepers in search of "bloom."

Chronologically, this volume begins with "Evolution," which treats of the origin and kin of the ox and man's first tentative attempts at domestication. "Admiration" lists bovine contributions to man's religion and sports. "Exploitation" covers the toil and the troubles, the rewards and the punishments which have befallen man and one of the most useful of his many four-footed thralls. So much for the live animal. "Nutrition" reveals what the butcher's pole-ax and the packer's magic have achieved in fabricating hamburgers from heifers and sirloins from steers. In other words, it is a case of televising cattle in four postures—at the altar, in the arena, under the yoke, and on the block.

As a prologue to the performance, perhaps no loftier tribute to the stockman can be found than these lines from the Book of Ecclesiasticus, in the Apocrypha:

6

How shall he become wise that holdeth the plough,
That glorieth in the shaft of the goad,
That driveth oxen, and is occupied in their labours,
And whose discourse is of the stock of bulls?

He will set his heart upon turning his furrows;
And his wakefulness is to give his heifers their fodder.

All these put their trust in their hands;
And each becometh wise in his own work.

Without them shall not a city be inhabited,
And men shall not sojourn nor walk up and down
therein.

They shall not be sought for in the council of the people,
And in the assembly they shall not mount on high;
They shall not sit in the seat of the judge,
And they shall not understand the covenant of
judgment:
Neither shall they declare instruction and judgment;
And where parables are they shall not be found.

But they will maintain the fabric of the world;
And in the handiwork of their craft is their prayer!

We salute the 94,677,000 cattle recently enumerated by the United States Agricultural Marketing Service and their devoted caretakers, "whose discourse is of the stock of bulls," all striving to "maintain the fabric of the world."

CHAPTER 2

The Ox and His Origin

IF EARLY MAN felt any puzzlement about the origin of the animals around him, he was content with the story of the Creation. The flood legends of the Mesopotamian races explaining how they managed to survive—notably the story of Noah—completely satisfied his curiosity. However, when the natural sciences identified more than two million separate forms, living and extinct, it became incredible that even the Ark, with its 450,000 "cubic cubits," could have carried such a cargo. At the very least, the marine-living animals must have taken a postman's holiday in the waters, while the winged forms staged a forty-day marathon high in the air.

With the development of specialized sciences came the classification of every animal known to man. Naturalists now tell us that cattle, buffalo, and bison are all near relatives of the bovine branch of the animal kingdom. Thus, when the farmer seated at the milking stool murmurs, "So-o-o, boss," or when his little daughter summons from the pasture her pet "bossy," they are merely using a name sanctified by science—*Bos taurus*.

Zoologists identify cattle as belonging to the class *Mammalia* (milk-giving animals); the cohort *Ungulata* (hoofed animals); the order *Artiodactyla* (even-toed ungulates); the division *Pecora* (ruminants or cud-chewers); and the family *Bovidae* (called *Cavicornia* or "hollow-horned" by the earlier zoologists). *Bovidae* are apparently the youngest family of the even-toed ruminants and are highly specialized in tooth structure and digestive functioning. In addition to the ox tribe, the family includes antelopes, chamois, goats, sheep, and musk oxen.

To the sub-family known as the *Bovinae* belong our modern

8

cattle and other large, strong, heavy ruminants. One of the *Bo-vinae*, the *Bos primigenius*, was known to the ancients as the urus, or aurochs. At first this animal was confused with the *Bison europaeus*. But thanks to Pliny the Elder and the grammarian Solinus, this confusion was cleared up. And Laurentius flatly declared: "In Lithuania there are Bisons and Uri. . . . Those are in error who call the Bisons Uri; for the Bisons differ from the Uri, which have the form of an ox, in having a beard hanging from the chin!"[1] But in confounding the bison with the urus, the ancient dullards were no stupider than most of us moderns, who persist in calling our American bison "buffalo."

Fossil remains of cattle, dating back to the middle Pliocene era,[2] three to four million years ago, were first found in Asia, afterwards in Europe. The Asiatic species was discovered in the Siwalik ranges along the boundaries of northwestern India. One of the species, well represented by numerous specimens, was a direct ancestor of the ox,[3] heavier, but resembling the European *Leptobos etruscus,* soon to be discussed. Apparently this great beast lived in the forests and grazed in the open glades. Its teeth indicate that it browsed on twigs and shoots. The head was relatively long and narrow, the females being hornless. In the bulls the horns emerged from the head, goatlike, about midway between the eye socket and the top of the poll. In height, the species stood sixteen to seventeen hands (sixty-four to sixty-eight inches) at the shoulder. The horn spread was between six and seven feet.

In Europe, the corresponding form of *Leptobos* showed more slender limbs and was a generalized type. Nearly perfect skulls of this species were discovered in water-borne deposits in the Val d'Arno in Tuscany, west central Italy—hence the name *Leptobos etruscus*.[4] Other specimens were found in southern France.

---

[1] Alvin H. Sanders, "The Taurine World," *National Geographic*, Vol. XLVIII, No. 6 (December, 1925), 638, quotes Laurentius.

[2] R. Lydekker, *The Ox and Its Kindred*, 254–55.

[3] Henry Fairfield Osborn, *The Age of Mammals*, 319, 329.

[4] *Ibid.,* 329; Lydekker, *The Ox and Its Kindred*, 255.

By the end of the Pliocene era, several bovine types were living in southern Asia.[5] These included at least two species of *Leptobos;* the ancestors of the Indian buffalo; a miniature buffalo, *Hemibos,* related to the modern *anoa* of the Celebes; and a primitive bison. During the early Pleistocene, about one million years ago, there were three recognizable forms of the ox in Europe, also a bison and a water buffalo. The most picturesque was the great wild ox, the urus, or aurochs, fossils of which from Europe and western Asia were classified as *Bos primigenius.* This superb specimen stood six feet at the shoulder and roamed the forests of Europe coevally with man.

While the aurochs was quite hardy, during the Pleistocene age it was not able to live as close to the borders of the great ice fields as sheep, goats, and horses. Consequently, the first glaciation of the epoch had advanced and retreated before cattle were found in Great Britain. In the "Forest Beds of Cromer" in ancient Norfolk there were discovered remains of the first true primitive cattle and *Bos primigenius.*[6] Evidently a million years ago Norfolk possessed the qualities of a "cattle country" which made it the home in historic times of the progenitors of the Red Polled breed. It is interesting that true cattle entered Europe along with species adapted to colder climates and survived with them. During the Pliocene age climatic conditions were favorable, but the Pleistocene ushered in a millenium of winters.

With the retreat of the First Glaciation, nearly half a million years ago, new competition appeared. Many of the mighty African-Asiatic types—the elephant, the rhinoceros, and the hippopotamus—moved forward again, together with the broad-nosed moose, the giant stag, and the red deer,[7] all fighting for feedstuffs. Alongside them arrived the westward-moving mi-

[5] Osborn, *The Age of Mammals,* 329.
[6] *Ibid.,* 392, 394–95.
[7] *Ibid.,* 399–400.

grants from Asia, *Bos primigenius* and the primitive *Bison priscus*.[8]

The Second Glaciation, approximately one hundred thousand years later, was most severe. Yet cattle and many other non-Arctic species survived. Probably all were protected by heavy layers of hair, for it seems certain that the cattle of that day had rough, shaggy coats, somewhat on the order of those now characterizing the Scottish Highland breed. After twenty-five thousand years, the weather grew warmer, forest glades and meadows appeared, and cattle and bison multiplied. It was then that wild cattle proved their mettle by successfully withstanding the attacks of the lion, for this predator was then as dominant in the southern European scene as it was in Africa when first discovered by white explorers.

The Third Glaciation, lasting about twenty-five thousand years, was not so severe. The animals of African lineage withdrew before the advancing ice, but our ancestral cattle still had to contend with the great hairy mammoth and the wooly rhinoceros.[9] Then, as these moved northward with the receding ice cap, wild cattle and bison became the dominant "great beasts" of the faunal community. They had definitely become habituated to the cool, temperate climate of central Europe, and for the first time man had become their chief enemy—a hunter in quest of peltries and protein.

During the next hundred thousand years, man assumed further ascendancy over the animals. This stage, together with the Fourth Glaciation, plus 150 centuries—which brought him up to 10,000 or 8,000 B.C.—comprised what is known as the Paleolithic, or Old Stone Age (so called because of the use of implements of flaked or chipped stone). Yet no attempt was made at domestication, this being deferred for many centuries. In fact, during all this period, man's only interest in the ox was for what meat it would yield.

[8] *Ibid.*, 403–407.
[9] *Ibid.*, 414, 418–26.

With the dawn of the Old Stone Age, humans first proved themselves capable of existing and competing successfully in a predominantly animal world. The prevalent race in Europe was Neanderthal man, whose hunters chased the aurochs and the bison, as well as the gigantic elephant and the broad-nosed rhinoceros. It was then that the primitive savage probably learned his first lesson in efficiency—that it paid best to bring down game that provided the largest volume of meat per hunt or per weapon. It is also possible that man was assisted in the chase by his first domestic animal, the wolf or the dog, though direct proof awaited the lapse of many centuries. Anyone who has tangled with infuriated cattle knows how valuable is a dog's help in distracting an enraged steer's attention at a critical moment.

From shallow caves situated on high cliffs Neanderthal man kept watch for game in the valleys below, where aurochs, bison, reindeer, and horses swarmed along the watercourses. While wild cattle were ferocious and wary, they were less difficult to kill when the hunters pooled their resources of men and weapons and launched mass attacks. In another maneuver they often drove their quarry over the edge of a sharp precipice. This method, improved by their successors, the Cro-Magnons,[10] was followed centuries later by our American Plains Indians, who systematically hunted the bison in like manner. And our own aborigines also seem to have followed the Cro-Magnon custom of first eating the internal organs and fat before sampling portions of the back and haunch of the butchered animal. Fossilized bones reveal further that prehistoric man cooked his beef in water forty or fifty thousand years ago, and that even earlier he had acquired the habit of cracking the bones for their marrow.

It was in their cave paintings, first executed about twenty-five hundred years ago, that Aurignacean aritsts bequeathed to posterity the limned likeness of *Bos primigenius*. In the Lascaux caves in southern France are found the figures of the great au-

---

[10] Henry Fairfield Osborn, *Men of the Old Stone Age* (3d ed.), 211–14; Charles R. Knight, *Prehistoric Man,* facing pages 113 and 213.

rochs, bulls, and cows, reproduced so faithfully in some cases, and so suggestively in others, that their relation to the modern breeds of Spanish and French cattle is immediately recognized. In fact, there is a marked resemblance to the best of the Longhorns first brought to Mexico and the southwestern United States by the Spanish *conquistadores*. European tradition tells of matings of tame cows with the aurochs, so blood relationship seems quite plausible.

Bos primigenius was an imposing beast, long in legs and horns and quick and powerful in movement. Compared with the bison, it had a much greater spread of horns and superior stature, speed, and strength. Measurements of ten to eleven feet between the tips of the horns appear not to have been uncommon. One such horn converted into a drinking goblet measured six and one-half feet long[11] and was preserved in Alsace-Lorraine until a century and a half ago. Many skeletons have been unearthed of bulls which attained six or more feet in height at the top of the shoulder.

Various names were given to *Bos primigenius*. From Greek and Latin we get *bos,* with the genitive *bovis,* from which are derived our words *bovine, beeves,* and *beef.* From the Teutonic we get the German *Ochs,* the Danish *oxe,* and the Saxon and English *ox.* Combining this with the old Sanskrit word *ur,* meaning a forest or stony place, we get *urochs* or *aurochs,* which signifies wild cattle. The word *ur* must have been used for centuries in connection with cattle, for it was Latinized into *urus,* the plural being *uri.* This was the word used by Julius Caesar in 65 B.C. when he gave the world the first historical record of wild cattle. From the great Hercynian Forest in Germany he wrote: "There is a third kind of these animals which are called *uri.* In size these are but little inferior to elephants, although in appearance, color, and form they are bulls. Their strength and their speed are great. They spare neither men nor beasts when they see them. The hunters are most careful to kill those which

[11] Lydekker, *The Ox and Its Kindred,* 41.

13

they take in pitfalls, while the young men exercise themselves by hunting them, and are hardened by this toil. Those who kill most receive great praise when they exhibit the horns as trophies of their success. These *uri*, however, even when young cannot be tamed. In the expanse of their horns, as well as in form and appearance, they differ much from our domesticated oxen."[12]

Caesar made no claim to having seen a living urus. His information was evidently obtained from German hunters. On the other hand, he unquestionably saw its great horns and probably drank from them. Long before his day they were mounted with silver and used as drinking vessels. These were supposed to bring good luck to such Teutonic toss-pots as could drain them. Up to a century and a half ago specimens could be found in taverns, castles, and churches. One preserved in southern Germany held three and one-half quarts. There was even a "Brotherhood of the Horns," made up of the two-gallon drinkers living not far from Strasbourg.[13] Seneca wrote of the "fierce uri with wide spreading horns" and Pliny distinguished the "urus, excelling in strength and speed," from the "maned bison." The Romans apparently knew the aurochs as an object of the chase, and a few were introduced to the games at the Colosseum.

Remains of the aurochs have been found in most of the sites of prehistoric man in Germany and the Scandinavian countries. The beast must have been threatened with extinction at one time, for in A.D. 573 the Bishop of Tours referred to the prohibited slaughter of these wild bulls. In the same century a German duke, Charles the Great, is reported to have stalked them, as did Charlemagne, who hunted aurochs near Aix-la-

---

[12] *Commentaries on the Gallic War*, Book VI, chap. 28, lines 1–14.

[13] The use of large horns as containers for beer, particularly, has been a feature of the *Kneipegesellchaft*, a drinking bout usually conducted the night preceding formal dueling, in which one or more German corps take part in German university towns. The *Füchse*, or neophytes, are often required to stand on chairs and drain these horns, which may hold a liter or more, before they take them from their lips. After draining, they are placed upside down on the heads of the *Füchse*.

Chapelle in the ninth century. The Crusaders encountered several aurochs when crossing Germany in the eleventh century.

When the *Nibelungenlied* was taking form about A.D. 1200, a tale was incorporated about a great hunt in the Forest of Worms, wherein were listed Siegfried's heroic deeds:

> *After this he slew in all a bison, and an elk,*
> *Four aurochs strong, and a ferocious Schelch.*

(No one has as yet identified a "Schelch.") Fragmentary accounts of the aurochs have appeared in German, Polish, and Latin literature. Most of these tales come not from eyewitnesses but are secondhand. Those who could write evidently lacked the hardihood of active Nimrods.

Stuffed skins of the aurochs were prepared under primitive methods of taxidermy. Baron Sigismund von Herberstein, distinguished German diplomat, brought from Poland in 1546 the eviscerated carcass of an aurochs and the skeleton and hide of a bison, and the two were mounted and placed at the entrance to his Vienna home. Somewhat later an unknown artist made a drawing from this model.

There seem to have been, from early times, two sizes of aurochs, though it is questionable whether they were more than sub-species. One of the deeper Pleistocene layers in Essex, England, yielded skulls and horns of gigantic cattle having the height and other characteristics of *Bos primigenius*.[14] Yet in English fens and Scottish peat bogs dating many thousands of years later, smaller forms of *Bos longifrons* have been found, no larger than the Polish aurochs, which Herberstein claimed were about the size of domestic cattle.[15] Just how this second variety developed is a moot question among zoologists. For many years it was believed that *Bos longifrons* was a domesticated form, degenerated from *Bos primigenius*. However, the drawings in the Lascaux caves show the two distinct forms ten to fifteen thousand years before the first ox was tamed.

[14] Osborn, *The Age of Mammals,* 406–408.
[15] Lydekker, *The Ox and Its Kindred,* 45, 46.

By the sixth century mention was made of a few wild bulls in France, and by 1170 the small number left in the Rhine district were reserved for the exclusive sport of royalty and the nobility. By the end of the fourteenth century they had practically disappeared west of Prussia, Poland, and Lithuania. After this all records are centered in the Jaktorowka Forest of Mesovia, in Poland, containing the last surviving herd. Here they were being preserved in 1564 by the Duke of Mesovia. In 1596 they were kept alive only by supplemental feeding during the winter. By 1599 the number had been reduced to twenty-four from the original thirty, and to only four by 1602. Eighteen years later the sole survivor was a cow. This last member of the true wild species died in 1627; but for another twenty-five years there were several "half-wild" specimens still living.

The oldest known paintings of the aurochs are in the Lascaux caves.[16] Other representations date from Babylonian and Assyrian times. One is a copper statuette of a bull, found at Tell-al-'Ubaid, tentatively dated around 3000 B.C.[17] Two gold cups found at Amyclae near Sparta date from the Mycenian period about 1500 B.C. These show the capture of uri in nets. One bull is caught, one is fleeing, and a third has knocked down one man and is finishing another.[18] There is an Assyrian drawing showing King Assurnasirpal III (883–858 B.C.) driving three galloping horses attached to a chariot. They are passing over the body of one bull, laid low by four arrows. The King has seized the horn of a second, running with its forelegs over the axle of the chariot, and is about to give it the death blow with a sword held in his right hand.[19] Still another representation of the aurochs appears on a map of the world published at Ebstorf

[16] Fernand Windels, *The Lascaux Cave Paintings;* Alan Houghton Brodrick, *Lascaux: A Commentary.*

[17] H. R. Hall and C. Leonard Woolley, *Ur Excavations al-'Ubaid,* I, Plate XXVII.

[18] Sir Arthur Evans, *The Palace of Minos at Knossos,* III, 179–84, figs. 123–27.

[19] A. T. Olmstead, *History of Assyria,* 92, fig. 49.

near the close of the thirteenth century. Here the figure of a tawny red ox with long, in-curving and upward-curving horns is used to illustrate "Rucia" (Russia). The best of these relatively modern delineations is known as the "Augsburg aurochs," believed to have been drawn between A.D. 1500 and 1525. The picture was copied, by permission of the owner, to illustrate Cuvier's *Animal Kingdom,* published in 1827.[20]

After examination of all these more recent representations of the aurochs, with their conventionalisms and stylistic treatment, particularly those of Assyrian and European origin, one is tempted to conclude that they fall short of reproducing a lifelike aurochs. Only in the Lascaux caves do we find pictures, executed thousands of years ago by the untutored hand of Cro-Magnon draftsmen, which like a candid camera bring to life the splendid physique and the inner fire of this magnificent ancestor of our modern beef animal.

Like *Homo sapiens* himself, the ancient aurochs boasted a family tree. With scores of relatives, close and remote, of kindred blood, all contributing something to its evolutionary development, a study of these species is essential in presenting a true likeness of the domesticated ox.

[20] Lydekker, *The Ox and Its Kindred,* 49–50.

CHAPTER 3

Bos Taurus and His Kinfolk

THE OX OF TODAY is blessed with many relatives of varied characteristics. There is the *anoa*, or pigmy buffalo, of the Celebes: the *bubalis*, including the Indian, the African, and the Asiatic water buffalo; the *Bibos*, to which belong the gaur, banteng, zebu, and the kouprey of India, Indo-China, and the East Indies, as well as the sanga of Africa; the *poëphagus*, or yak, of the Himalayas and Tibet; the *Bos taurus*, or wild ox of Europe, with its related strains of domestic cattle; and the *bison*—misnamed "buffalo"—of the American prairie and its forest-dwelling cousin, the *wisent*, or European bison. The buffalo will not cross with other members of the *Bovinae*, but the bison, yak, gaur, banteng, perhaps the kouprey, and all forms of domestic cattle will interbreed and produce fertile female offspring. Bison and domestic cattle rarely produce fertile male progeny, and only a portion of male yak hybrids can breed successfully.

In stature, the wild forms range from the pigmy buffalo, which stands only thirty-nine inches at the shoulders, to the gaur, which averages around six feet. Among the domesticated varieties, the height of some sacred oxen of Ceylon is but twenty-six inches, with work oxen and buffalo attaining six-feet-four to six-feet-eight at the shoulders. In basic structure, wild and domesticated cattle are quite alike. Since there are now no wild forms which appear to be specifically ancestral to any of the domestic races, it is generally assumed that they were tamed directly from the wild varieties.

Domesticated cattle have changed very little from recognizable fossil forms. Most of them are reasonably gentle or can be made so by careful handling, and they are trustful of their owners and of other animals. But when roused they can be fiercely pugnacious—"on the prod," as American cowboys would say—and will charge the most dangerous beasts, such as lions, tigers, and bears, often victoriously. An outstanding characteristic is the maternal care exercised by the cow over the calf. Today this inherited instinct helps to lighten the labor of the range cattleman in caring for the young.

The pigmy buffalo, or anoa, smallest of all wild cattle (apparently a transition from an earlier form of antelope-like ruminants) lives in the mountainous regions of the island of Celebes. Anoas have the same odor as buffalo and follow the same method of drinking water, drawing long drafts rather than gulping like antelopes.

Naturalists regard the *bubalis* buffalo as the most primitive in structure of all members of the ox tribe, the body being bulky and ungainly, though well rounded in form. The legs are short and heavy-boned. Most characteristic are the head and horns. The face is broad, with a strongly convex, low forehead; the eyes are normally dull, but when the brute is enraged, they become highly bloodshot.

Two varieties show some structural differences. The Indian buffalo has a hairy skin surface over the top of the head between the horns. In the African, the horns are much flattened and more receding, and a large helmet-like mass of horny material spreads out over the poll.

Wild buffalo keep chiefly to level ground and prefer wet or swampy places in which to cool off. They tend to travel in groups of forty to sixty. The African variety, before it was hunted so much, ran in herds as large as four hundred. They have immense courage. If threatened, they will attack lions, tigers, or elephants. If one of their number is attacked, the others come to its aid and usually dispatch the assailant.[1] In India, when a solitary bull or a herd takes possession of a cultivated field, no

[1] Alfred Edmund Brehm, *Life of Animals,* 467.

19

owner dares to enter. In hunting the wild buffalo, it is possible to approach the herd only from the back of an elephant. Even then an infuriated bull will often charge the elephant, sometimes toppling him and putting the rider in grave danger. But the buffalo's greatest accomplishment is swimming. It dives, floats comfortably without stirring, and not only assumes an erect position while doing it but is equally at ease lying on its side or halfway over on its back. It swims straight across a stream and copes well with a strong current.

With most white men the domestic buffalo is a treacherous and belligerent beast, but seems docile and co-operative with Orientals. When American soldiers in the Philippines, China, Korea, or Japan have been attacked, the animal's attention could be distracted by vocal commands from even small Filipino or Chinese children. During the Philippine Insurrection half a century ago our American doughboys composed several songs about the "carabao," or Philippine buffalo, with but one printable verse out of every three or four.

Because there are now so many Brahman cattle in the United States, there is increasing interest in the *Bibos* group in Asia,[2] to which the zebu or Brahman belongs and which includes the gaur, gayal, banteng, and kouprey.

The largest of this group is the magnificent gaur, which is the true wild ox of the area. Its natural haunts are in the low mountain forests extending from India into Burma and the Malay Peninsula. It seems to prefer a dense wilderness, with thickets of wild vines, ferns, bamboo breaks, and well-watered deep ravines. These heavy animals can tear over the broken, rocky acclivities, either up or down slopes, almost as fast as deer. They sometimes descend at night to raid the young crops in the cultivated valleys or to sample the newly sprouted grasses. The bulls often station themselves on heights difficult of access to survey for miles around the prospects for food or a fight. The

[2] The Bibovine group is thoroughly discussed in Lydekker, *The Ox and Its Kindred,* chaps. VII, VIII, and IX.

gaur, a top favorite among big-game hunters, averages sixteen to sixteen and one-half hands at the withers and sometimes attains seventeen to eighteen hands; some have measured twenty hands, or six feet, eight inches, at the top of the shoulders.

Is there a wild gayal, differing from the gaur? Or is the gayal derived from the gaur and modified by selection? There is no doubt about there being wild gayals. But those who hold that these are descended from the gaur classify them as merely feral forms—cattle which have escaped from domestication and gone wild. The gayal, both wild and tame, is found in the country from eastern Bengal through Burma. For many years it was accepted under the name of *Bos frontalis,* but it is now generally conceded that the gayal is a gaur, slightly modified by domestication by certain hill tribes living at the upper end of the Bay of Bengal. Old domesticated bulls have tremendous dewlaps, like the zebu, starting almost from the chin. No wild specimens show this feature. Gayals are kept by the natives for their meat, never for draft purposes or for their milk. The herds roam the forests by day and return to their owners at night, thus reversing the feeding habits of the gaur.

Perhaps the handsomest of all wild cattle is the banteng, indigenous to Java, but also found in Siam, Assam, Yu-Nan, Upper Burma, and the Malay Peninsula. Brehm says that "in gracefulness of form it can vie with the antelope, and its coloring is remarkably attractive."[3] In the banteng and its close relative, the tawny, cream, or grayish fawn-colored Burmese *tsaine,* the adult bulls have a mass of horny skin on the upper forehead, which connects the horns at their bases and passes into the horn structure, providing a cushion against possible concussions while fighting. The skin excretes a yellowish-brown sebaceous substance, similar to that of the zebu. The banteng likes damp or marshy woodland and low-lying, tree-covered valleys traversed by slowly flowing rivers. It usually flees at the sight of man. But if brought to bay and wounded, it will turn on the hunter

[3] Brehm, *Life of Animals,* 478.

and gore him with its pointed horns. Yet the young animal is quite tractable and seems more responsive to kind treatment than any other of the wild oxen.

The zebu, progenitor of the Brahman now widely bred in the United States, is discussed at length later in this book. Nearest to a direct relative of the zebu seems to be the kouprey, or Indo-Chinese forest ox, which became known to naturalists only within the last twenty years. The bull's height at the shoulders is about sixteen hands, three inches, and the spread between horn tips is around thirty-six inches. When the kouprey challenges a rival bull by repeatedly thrusting its horns into the ground, the tips slough off, leaving ragged strips drooping like shredded cuticle. The rest of the horn remains a distinctly polished black. In several respects the kouprey seems ancestrally related to the zebu—the wide, pendant dewlap and the rather narrow head being common to both forms.[4]

Unique among the ox tribe is the yak—a three-letter word familiar to crossword-puzzle fans. It lives normally on the elevated plateau of Tibet, but is found all the way from the northern districts of Ladakh in east central Kashmir to Kan-Su. Northward the range extends beyond Tibet. The yak is definitely adapted to the higher altitudes and seems to thrive best in Rupsu, adjoining Ladakh to the southeast, where the elevation is 13,000 to 16,000 feet. It is considered hazardous to take this pure species as far down as Leh, the principal city of Ladakh, where the altitude is only 11,500 feet. There is more than an even chance of heat prostration on account of the yak's heavy growth of hair all over the body. The hair is so luxuriant over the shoulders as to be mistaken often for a hump. But such hibernal garb is necessary for withstanding the gelid blasts of these elevated exposures. Actually, the yak will lie down in full content, in the lee of the wind, on a bed of glacial snow or ice, its vital organs fully insulated against the cold by its self-made

[4] G. H. H. Tate, *Mammals of Eastern Asia,* 321–22.

hair mattress. Rugs and strong fabrics are woven from the hair, and, in India, the long, bushy tail serves as a fly-whisk.

Purebred yaks are large and powerful animals, but do not attain much height at the shoulder because of their short legs. Wild bulls range from fourteen to sixteen hands high, and their horns are about three feet long. The animal is not particularly prepossessing. Its head is set low, and trailing fringes of long hair make it look awkward—a Sary Gamp in a bedraggled petticoat. Because of this bulky disguise, bulls and cows are difficult to distinguish at a distance, but the bulls are larger, their tails bushier and their horns thicker, while the cows' horns have a definite upcurve at the tip.

The so-called tamed yak of the purely wild species is a burden bearer, but somewhat undependable in that it often becomes surly and vicious. After resting for a few weeks, it rebels against toil and at the first opportunity will jettison its cargo, frequently charging any strangers, especially Europeans, awaiting its services in moving camp and baggage.

To overcome the bad manners of the yak, as well as to permit work at lower altitudes, the male yak has been crossed with the female zebu. This has produced a useful hybrid known as the *zo*—the cows are *zomos*—more docile and tractable than the purebred yak. Both the yak and the zo are the great common carriers in their part of Asia. While the scientific name of the yak, *Bos grunniens,* indicates that it is a grunting ox, most authorities say that only the crossbred zo grunts, an inheritance from the zebu.

Most impressive of all bovines is the bison, which, sad to say, is almost extinct in both Europe and the United States. The European species, or wisent, was more of a forest-dwelling type, the American preferring the plains. Yet on both continents there were woodland and plains varieties. While fossils and early records indicate that the wisent was widely dispersed throughout Europe, it was eventually restricted to the great forest of Bielowitza in Lithuania and to parts of the Caucasus. Extensive hunting seems to have been one cause of its disappearance; other causes being the increase of domestic herds and the decrease in grazing areas on account of the spread of cultivation. A contributing factor was the great epizootic which struck the animals just after A.D. 1700. They were further decimated by poachers' raids on the great estates which were trying to protect them. In this effort the nobility were forced to put them on winter feed, which for some reason seemed to affect the normal balance of the sexes, most of the offspring born under park feeding being bulls.

The wisent often reached impressive size. A specimen long preserved was a bull, slain in Prussia in 1555, reported to have been seven feet tall at the hump and thirteen feet long, and said to have weighed more than nineteen hundred pounds. Modern examples are not more than five feet, eight inches in height, and under eleven and one-half feet long, rarely weighing more than fourteen hundred pounds. Bison hunting was once the sport of kings. In 1860 the Emperor of Russia sponsored a royal hunt in which he killed six bison; his two guests, the Princes Charles and Albrecht of Prussia, killed eight between them.[5]

Near-extinction was the fate of our American "buffalo" also. Three generations ago the great Western prairies and plains contained millions of bison. Now, in all the United States, there are only a few thousand. Early travelers reported great herds roaming the plains, but the most careful estimates of their original numbers vary greatly. It has been claimed that there were a hundred million buffalo at one time, but to anyone knowing their grazing habits and the amount of feed required for so many head, this estimate seems preposterous. Perhaps the best conclusion we can draw is that the population was somewhere between fifteen and thirty million at its height.

The bull of the American bison measures nine to ten feet in

---

[5] A specimen of the European wisent was still to be seen cropping hay in the Munich, Germany, zoo as late as the 1930's.

length from muzzle to tail root, the tail and brush adding about two and one-half feet more. It is stockily built, and its height at the withers ranges from five feet, eight inches to five feet, ten, although some specimens have attained six feet, four inches. Weights range from twelve hundred to two thousand pounds. Cows are significantly smaller. The neck is deep and proportionately narrow and leads abruptly upward to high and rather sharp withers, which are covered with long hair that accentuates the hump and extends like a long coat over the neck, shoulders, and forelegs to the knees. Because of this protective cover, bison always face into a storm, instead of turning their backs and retreating before it as do domestic cattle. In winter the hair grows to a great length, and in the spring the animal, like the European species, sheds in such large matted locks as to make it look like a four-legged rag-bag.

This heavy coat is a lifesaver for the bulls in their frequent battles during the rutting season. John Bradbury, the English naturalist, came on a herd 140 years ago in the midst of the breeding period. "Such a scene opened to us," he wrote, "as will fall to the lot of few travelers to witness. This plain was literally covered with buffaloes [bison] as far as we could see, and we soon discovered that it consisted in part of females. The males were fighting in every direction, with a fury which I have never seen paralleled, each having singled out his antagonist. . . . There were many hundreds of these battles going on at the same time, some not eighty yards from us. . . . A shot was fired amongst them, which they did not seem to notice. . . . The noise occasioned by the trampling and bellowing was far beyond description."[6]

The great climax to a similar contest is described by E. Douglas Branch in his paraphrase of the memoirs of the famous Western freighter Alexander Majors: "Each herd had discovered the other at about the same time, and came to a standstill

[6] John Bradbury, *Travels in the Interior of America in the Years 1809 . . .* , 190, 191.

for a moment; then . . . began again to crunch the grass in a slow march forward. The space separating the herds was slowly reduced; and the two leading bulls approached each other like two freight engines determined to run head-on. The bull whose herd had been first on the prairie announced his rage, pawing the earth, and with his horns tossing up bunches of sod that silted down into his mane. The later arrival likewise curved up plumes of dirt with his hooves, and tore into the earth with his horns. The two bulls came nearer, and the herds left off their crunching to watch.

"After much circling and side-stepping for position, the fighters made the rush—with a heavy collision of skulls and a crash of horns. Then they pushed, head against head; muscles bulged out on thighs, and hooves wrenched into the earth. They pushed, until one of them went down on his knees. That settled it. The conquering bull scraped his horns into the hide and flesh of his victim; and he left off the taunts to meander into his adversary's herd.

"But as he strode, another bull moved his monstrous bulk out of the herd, and snorted another challenge. The contestants squared off and plunged. The thud of the collision threw them both to their knees; but both were instantly on their feet and locked horns with the same swiftness. The cords stood out like great ropes on their necks; the muscles on thighs and hips were like huge welts. We were quite near these fellows and could see the roll of their blood-red, fiery eyes. They braced and shoved with perfectly terrible force. The froth began to drip in long strings from their mouths.

"Both relaxed a moment for breath, then sank their hooves into the sod and renewed the struggle. A sound came like the crack of lightning as one of the legs of the champion crumpled under him. The challenger lunged toward him to finish the fight; then the earth trembled, the fighters reeled, the bluff on which the two buffaloes were standing dropped into the Missouri, and the current bore both the actors downstream."[7]

The melodramatic death of these two individuals may well stand as a symbol of the ultimate near-extinction of the wild American bison. What a contrast to the ever expanding herds of tame meat cattle now populating the prairies and the plains of their dispossessed predecessors!

[7] E. Douglas Branch, *The Hunting of the Buffalo,* 9–11. Branch has edited the quotation from Alexander Majors, whose original account appears in his *Twenty Years on the Frontier* (Chicago, Rand, McNally, 1893), 194–200.

CHAPTER 4

The Bullock Goes to Work

WHILE BISON BULLS BATTLED for a harem on the bluffs above the Big Muddy, yoke-fellows Buck and Bright were patiently plowing a two-acre plot bordering the quiet Connecticut in New Hampshire, far to the east. This contrast in applied power raises the question: Why did the ox decide to "join up" with man? Surely wild cattle had the instinct and the power to resist subjugation. But unlike other wild forms the ox was normally patient, good natured, and co-operative. On the other hand, man chose the ox as his co-worker because no other animal could offer him so much physical and inspirational sustenance. As Thomas Bewick put it, a century and a half ago, "The ox is the only horned animal that will apply his strength to the service of mankind; and in general is more profitable than the horse for the plough or draught."[1]

Historical records have yielded less knowledge of domestic cattle than the remains of prehistoric man. Between 8000 and 6000 B.C., migrations of New Stone Age races began pressing into Europe from western Asia. Three types advanced over three routes. A broadheaded people from the high plateaus of Asia penetrated the central continent via the Danube, a longer-headed kind came into southern Europe along the Mediterranean, and a more primitive specimen entered along the Baltic. These migrants brought cattle among other domestic animals. Remains of the northern race, with bone relics from their livestock, have been found in the kitchen middens and shell heaps of Denmark, and the central races left definite records in the lake dwellings of Switzerland, where they probably arrived some time after 6000 B.C.

[1] Thomas Bewick, *A General History of Quadrupeds* (5th ed.), 36.

Here two species of horned ruminants—the stag and the ox—are found in such abundance as to equal the total of all the other exhumed animals. Easterly the stag bones outnumber those of the ox, but in the western lakes area the reverse is true. These lake dwellers had two species of domestic oxen, one being aurochs, the other Celtic shorthorns. Amschler is logical in showing that in northern Iran, where these immigrants supposedly originated, all cattle remains were of the Celtic shorthorn type.[2] But Dürst follows Rütimeyer in assuming that the cattle brought by the lake dwellers may actually have been of zebu descent.[3]

Domestic cattle were probably kept in the wooden homes built over the waters. This arrangement would afford safety from raiders and provide animal warmth, avoiding the hazard of indoor fires. The movement of these heavy animals into the huts called for a lot of piling—about one pile to every three square feet of floor—to insure strong construction. Not far from these wooden dwellings were cultivated fields where oxen dragged the heavy, awkward, wooden plows through the hard, resistant soil. Beyond the fields, grazing in the glades and on the edges of the forests, were cattle, sheep, and goats. Swine ranged the woods for mast and policed the shores for the householders' garbage.

The domestication of such grass-eating animals as the ox marked the decline of the hunter and the rise of the herdsman. These "civilized" nomads had no fixed dwellings, but roamed the plateaus and plains with their wives, children, and servants, lodging them in tents of hides or wool. The first herdsman to reach good pasturage merely drove his cattle and sheep onto it and, after grazing it bare, moved on. The village snobs prob-

---

[2] J. W. Amschler, *"Tierreste der Ausgrabungen von dem 'Grosse Königshügel'
Shah Tepe in Nord Iran,"* in *Reports* from the Scientific Expedition to the Northwestern Provinces of China under the Leadership of Dr. Sven Hedin, *Publication 9*, p. 96.

[3] J. V. Dürst, "Animal Remains from the Excavations at Anau," in R. Pumpelly's *Explorations in Turkestan*, 71–91.

ably looked down their noses at these "barbarians" who had no conception of land ownership, fixed boundaries, or the social amenities. But they were strong and warlike, and between the fifth and the third millenia they despoiled the Near Eastern terrain, recognizing no law but that of force.

In the center of a region where these conditions prevailed, between the eastern end of the Mediterranean and the deserts and dry plains of Persia and Arabia, are found the oldest remains of domestic cattle. Here the ox became the real foundation of agriculture. James Breasted, foremost authority on Egypt and western Asia, dubbed these intermediate lands the "Fertile Crescent."[4] Struggle for their control continued over the centuries as one vigorous pastoral tribe after another drove from mountain or desert to create the historic cultures of the Sumerians, Babylonians, Assyrians, Chaldeans, Medes, and Persians. The mountain and desert men domesticated the trailable species, the "hoofers"—dogs, sheep, goats, cattle, camels, donkeys, and horses. The farmers of the plain tamed the less migratory types—cats, pigs, chickens, ducks, and geese—and drove them inside their village walls at night for protection.

The day of the Biblical patriarchs probably began about 2000 B.C. when there was a considerable hegira of Semites from the Arabian desert into the valley of the Euphrates. They were known as the Amorites, from whom the patriarch Abraham may have descended. Then, a little before 1700 B.C., Canaan (Syria-Palestine) and Egypt were overrun by a race of pastoral origin which founded the dynasty of the Hyksos kings in Egypt. It was under this regime that Joseph came to power.

In spite of the numbers of his cattle and the size of his menage, Abraham did not invade Canaan with the idea of winning new pastures for his herd; rather, he was fleeing from the non-Semitic tribes who about this time expelled the Hebrews from their homes on the middle Euphrates. After defeating an expedition which tried to drive him out, the venerable leader

[4] James H. Breasted, *Ancient Times: A History of the Early World,* 101, 104.

was later joined by other patriarchs, who gave him sufficient strength to protect and hold his range. But he had family troubles. In trying to divide his grazing lands with his nephew Lot, Abraham offered and Lot accepted grazing acreage on the plain of Jordan and forthwith departed for Sodom and Gomorrah. With Lot went his extensive herds and his numerous household.

Two generations later, Abraham's grandson, Jacob, outwitted his father-in-law, Laban, in a cattle deal that antedated but did not surpass some of those manipulated by one Daniel Drew, nineteenth-century Yankee drover, smug churchman, and "city slicker."[5] In dividing the livestock, Jacob agreed to take as his share all the "ringstraked, spotted, and speckled" cattle. To multiply their number, he then set peeled and unpeeled poplar rods for fences surrounding the watering and breeding places; he figured that impressionable females would give birth to more calves of his own markings than of those of Laban. Whether or not all this prenatal maneuvering was successful, at least we have the word of the Holy Writ that "the man increased exceedingly and had much cattle."[6] Apparently Jacob felt no guilt in connection with this transaction, nor was he ever ashamed of his lowly vocation. At the age of 130 years he was presented at court by his son Joseph, the prime minister. When Pharoah asked him, "What is your occupation?," the old man straightened up and proudly replied, "Thy servant's trade hath been about cattle from our youth, both we and also our fathers." And this despite the fact that at that time herdsmen were "an abomination unto the Egyptians."[7]

In Biblical lands the ox may have preceded the sheep and goat as the small family's sole domestic animal. Here it was actually the symbol of the family, the poorest having at least one head. Job implies that even a widow was entitled to one indis-

[5] See Bouck White, *The Book of Daniel Drew.*
[6] Gen. 30:43.
[7] Gen. 46:34 and 47:3.

31

pensable ox and condemned those who would take it from her for a "pledge."[8] The Old Testament is full of allusions to oxen, from their grass-eating habits to their skill as transport animals. There was King Nebuchadnezzar, condemned to roam the fields, where he "did eat grass like oxen";[9] but after seven years the vegetarian resumed his customary diet of palace-prepared meats. It was a select yoke of oxen which hauled the Ark of the Covenant after the Israelites quit Egypt and entered the Promised Land. The Chosen People did not raise oxen primarily for food, although they enjoyed eating a joint from a sacrificed bullock as part of their religious ritual.

Evidences of domestic cattle in the Near East range from dried dung found in the early Sumerian mud-plastered homes to drawings, paintings, and sculptures executed by the civilizations which followed. In portraying ancient life along the Nile, Egyptian pyramids, tombs, and temples reproduce all phases of man's daily contact with cattle, whose domestication apparently followed the methods still used in taming five- to seven-year-old renegade steers fresh from the mesquite thickets of Texas. From Sumerian, Egyptian, Cretan, and Greek art, and from tools and other artifacts, we learn that the one basic piece of equipment was a rope.

Although no evidence of domestic animals other than the dog is found among the remains of the Old Stone Age peoples,[10] yet their food requirements were such as to call for a more uniform meat supply than they could get from hunting. Many students of pre-history regard planned food production as humanity's first economic revolution, which became significant in the Near Middle East about 6000 B.C. Early traces of cattle are found in Iraq at Hassuna and at the earliest site of Nineveh; in north central Iran at Sialk; near the Cilician coast in the vicinity of Mersin, not far from Saint Paul's Tarsus; in the in-

[8] Job 24:3.
[9] 1 Sam. 6:7.
[10] Osborn, *Men of the Old Stone Age* (3d ed.), 474, 486, 488, 497–99.

terior of Palestine around Jericho; and in Egypt at the lowest excavated level at Fayum, southwest of Cairo.[11] While all these sites show evidences of cattle, it is not always clear that the cattle were domesticated.

By the time man had learned to write, it was several millenia too late for the scribe to record the early techniques of domestication. But in Egypt the gap was filled to some extent by pictures showing various stages of cattle management. Some exhibit boastfulness and others are amusing, suggesting the handiwork of both comic and commercial artists. Some time before 2625 B.C., in the Fifth Dynasty, there was placed on the east wall of the corridor of the tomb of Akhethetep a series of engravings showing some boys playing with calves whose forelegs are hobbled, while a worried cow watches the tethered dogies struggling to break away. In the rock tombs of Deir, dating before 2500 B.C., is a picture titled "The Delivery of a Calf by the Herdsman Ka-user." This male midwife is assisted by a comrade, Perneb, who keeps the mother quiet by "allowing her to lick his hand." The "Superintendent of the Gang" watches the operation. Near by is another picture wherein a herdsman tries to induce a young animal to drink from a large vessel. This one is labeled "Causing the Calf to Drink."[12] Still another shows a cowherd carrying a calf, while a disproportionately small dam, obviously worried, follows behind.

During the earlier dynasties, Egyptian nobles loved to inspect their herds. Several miniature models perpetuate in clay or bronze the joyful scene as these nobles of the Nile scrutinize their potent bulls and patient cows. Scribes are sometimes shown totting up the numbers of each kind in the herd. About a generation ago the world was electrified by the news that archaeologists had discovered and opened the tomb of King Tutankhamen, which yielded fabulously rich treasure. Not so widely

[11] Robert J. Braidwood, "Jarmo: A Village of Early Farmers in Iraq," *Antiquity*, Vol. XXIV, No. 96 (December, 1950), 189.
[12] Norman de G. Davies, *The Rock Tombs of Deir el Gebrâwi*, I, 24.

publicized were the monarch's adventures in stock growing, disclosed by exploration in the tomb of Huy. Here men are depicted branding cattle with the prenomen of Tutankhamen. Huy is known to have been in charge of the royal herds. Scribes are also shown taking a census of the King's livestock, including—besides oxen—horses, donkeys, and goats. In the tomb of Auta, of the Fifth Dynasty, there is a picture showing a bull branded on the left rump with the number 113.[13]

The Prodigal Son, gorging himself on home-grown veal on his return, must have recalled his wastrel days amid the fleshpots of Egypt, where he ate beef which was fattened before slaughter. Proof that the cattle were fattened is available in scenes from the Fifth Dynasty which show servants feeding cattle from a large pottery bowl, stuffing the nourishment down the mouths of the animals. In a later model of a feed barn, we see four cattle eating normally from a trough and two being fed by hand, one of the latter stretched on the floor.

Throwing cattle before branding or slaughter was evidently a major operation. From the tombs of Deir comes a picture of a bull with wide-spreading horns and pained expression being cast by a rope tied around the left fore-cannon bone, carried over the back and across under the belly to encircle the left hock and deprive him of all support on the left side. Earlier pictures show more cumbersome operations, requiring from four to eight men. Always, there is one man grabbing the horns and another twisting the tail. Usually one "bulldogger" is working on the foreleg and another on the hind leg on the same side. Sometimes a superman is shown twisting the head by grasping the jaw or muzzle with one hand and a horn with the other. Then there are men with ropes to hold the animal, while another man stands by with a lariat in case the bull should break away from his tormentors.

Slaughter was also a complicated process. One or two early drawings depict a servant apparently stunning an ox, to judge

13 Nina de G. Davies, *The Tomb of Huy,* 21.

from the animal's expression of pained astonishment. But the executioner is wielding what looks like a puny swagger-stick instead of an authentic pole-ax. However, there are several pictures of cattle tied for slaughter, the tie being the same that rodeo contestants use today, with one front leg and the hind legs "in the bundle." Apparently one of the first cuts was the removal of the shoulder—or perhaps this operation was easiest for the artist to depict, for nearly all of the drawings include this procedure. Skinning operations are also shown. One drawing portrays the butcher boning beef, with his helper carrying away the choicer cuts, the ribs of the carcass standing out distinctly. There are also models of slaughter houses with a killing floor and balcony for hanging the beef, and likewise of a smokehouse and meat shop.

There are many representations of oxen at draft. From the tomb of Huy comes the portrait of a princess, with a parasol of ostrich feathers growing out of her diadem, riding in a chariot drawn by oxen. According to Davies it is "not impossible that the oxen were dwarf cattle."[14] Again, in the rock tombs of Deir there is a group in which six yoke of oxen are plowing, attended only by a plowman who grasps the handles. Though the simple plow is without cross-pieces, it seems to have sufficed for the easy task of breaking the soft Nile mud.[15] The plow, of course, was a development of the hoe, with the handle lengthened and turned forward so that the oxen could be attached to it. Short handles were affixed to the upper part of the "hog-plow" blade so that the plowman could control it.

Probably the first step was teaching the animal to "lead." Earliest pictures show one man leading an ox which is attached to the plow by a thong around its neck. To improve the draft, the next step was to fasten the "tongue" of the plow to the horns of the ox by ropes—later to a straight cross-bar roped to the animal's horns. Eventually the cross-bar was moved back to

14 *Ibid.*, 24.
15 Norman de G. Davies, *The Rock Tombs of Deir,* II, 7.

the neck as a kind of yoke, or a curved piece of wood was carried across the horns which fitted against the brow of the ox or the base of its horns. For draft purposes, the Egyptians seem to have preferred bulls. In western Asia, when cattle were worked singly, loops were placed around the ox's neck with ropes extending along both sides of the animal to the plow.

The early humans in Crete, who seem to have come from the south and who dominated the Aegean area from 3000–2400 B.C., left fossilized remains which suggest the presence of a few humped cattle. However, Cretan art depicts only cattle of the northern or aurochs type. Since mariners, bent on trade or plunder, scoured the Aegean from Crete to the Hellespont and the Black Sea, Crete must have acquired a real hodge-podge of cattle types. When Crete fell in the fourteenth century B.C., the center of power shifted to Mycenae at the head of the Gulf of Argolis, in the Peloponnesus. Here oxen were evidently used mostly for work, as was the case in Asia. Along the mainland and island coasts, commercial craft unquestionably plied a flourishing trade in live cattle, dried and salted beef, fats, and hides.

In Greece, an ox once aided a draft dodger; and sacred cattle, impiously slaughtered, foretold a shipwreck. When the Greeks came to draft Ulysses under his agreement to rescue Helen of Troy, he feigned madness by yoking an ox and an ass to a plow, furrowing the sand, and sowing salt. Failing to qualify as a lunatic, however, Ulysses went to war. When the war was over and he was homeward bound, he ran out of provisions. Landing on the island of Thrinakia—grazing ground for the sacred cattle of the sun god Hyperion—his crew defied his orders and slew some of the sacrosanct animals, whereupon the bloody hides began to writhe on the ground and joints of beef bellowed like bulls while roasting on the spits. These baleful portents were soon fulfilled. Shortly after the Greeks set sail, a tremendous hurricane arose. Lightning struck the mast. In falling, the mast killed the pilot, the vessel was broken to bits, and the entire crew perished. Only Ulysses, who fashioned a makeshift raft from the salvaged keel and mast, was saved.

To the Greeks, cattle were most profitably employed in barter or as co-laborers in scratching the hard, clayey gumbo of their valleys and hillsides, so that grain might be grown and olive trees made to yield their precious oil. Except as a favorite sacrifice to the gods, cattle meant little as food or milk.

Pre-Roman colonizers—who may have reached the Italian peninsula as early as 3000 B.C., after migrating from Greece to the lower Danube basin five hundred years earlier—possessed cattle. By 1000 B.C. they were occupying the hills above the Tiber, living in straw huts or straw-thatched adobe dwellings. When the republic was established five hundred years later, livestock were common in the fields surrounding Rome. A large area between the Capitoline Hill and the Tiber was probably the site of the world's first large cattle market. When Trajan built his great forum in the first century A.D., one of its ornate decorations was a marble balustrade featuring sculptures of the boars, rams, and bulls which were sacrificed in the Suovetaurilia, a ceremony designed to purify the fields. These sculptures reveal an advanced stage of breeding for the production of edible meats.

Thirty years before the birth of Christ, Roman stock raisers got expert advice on breeds and range management in four poems called *Georgics*. They were written by Publius Vergilius Maro—Virgil—farmer's son, poet, and small-time husbandman. "On Selecting a Cow" the author advised:

> *Whoso breeds . . . brave and strong-pulling oxen,*
> *First be it his to pick out the mothers. Best shaped will a*
>   *cow be,*
> *Grim-looking, ugly-headed, whose stout neck mostly*
>   *commends her*
> *While from chin to leg downward there falleth a dewlap.*
> *Next, to the flank's long range be no limit; all hath a largeness*

> *E'en the foot and shaggy ears where horns curve o'er*
>   *above them;*
> *Nor shall me the dapple displease—distinguishing ensign—*
> *Nor one averse to the yoke, whose horn gives token of anger,*
> *More as a bull to behold: of a tow'ring stateliness is she,*
> *And flicking, as she moves, her tail sweeps closely behind her.*

This is still a rather good blueprint for American range management, albeit such an animal might never win a prize at a livestock show.

Some lines later, Virgil advises:

> *Next, when calving is o'er, men's whole thought goes to the*
>   *offspring;*
> *And they stamp them anon with brands distinguishing each one*
> *As preference dictates: these for maintaining a true breed,*
> *These for sacred office, and these as laboring oxen*
> *Upturning the rugged loam-clods and straining across them,*
> *While the others at grass go forth as an army to pasture.*

Then, after telling his readers how to train young oxen, the poet goes into feeding:

> *Meanwhile not on hay thou'lt feed thy apprentices only,*
> *Nor yet upon the sallow's thin leaf and watery sedge-grass,*
> *But corn freshly gather'd: nor let thy cows as in old days*
> *Spend their creamy supplies avalanche-like into the milk-pail:*
> *Be their teeming udders to the dear calves wholly devoted.*[16]

The four books of the *Georgics* were confessedly an imitation from Greek originals, particularly Hesiod's *Works and Days;* and in the field of natural philosophy the style followed that of Virgil's fellow countryman Lucretius, who wrote *Of the Nature of Things.* Among his fellow husbandmen, many of these precepts were matters of common knowledge, but not until the *Georgics* were they committed to written form. A century later appeared *De Re Rustica (Of Rural Things)* in twelve books;

[16] C. W. Brodribb translation, pp. 45–49.

in one of these Columella, the author, laid down more specific dogma on the management of cattle.

By the end of the Roman Empire, the ox was being used for work or food from western Europe to eastern Asia, and from the icy lands of the north to the deserts and jungles of Africa. Today there is scarcely a nation or people, savage or civilized, rural or urban, which does not acknowledge a historic debt to these useful ruminants. And rare indeed is the modern American stockgrower who does not envy the kind of social and economic security enjoyed throughout the ages by those who, by "working ahead of the roundup" became "wealthy in bulls, rich in fat oxen."

But in their long association with man, cattle have played an important role other than economic. In ministering to his mystical lore and spiritual rites, they have helped to create and perpetuate imperishable religions, legends, miracles, and myths. This significant contribution to the annals of history must not be overlooked.

CATTLE & MEN

Admiration

CHAPTER 5

Cattle in Magic, Mythology, and Religion

WHEN THE CHILDREN OF ISRAEL, impatient at Moses'
prolonged stay on Mount Sinai and clamorous for new
gods, prevailed upon Aaron to fashion a molten calf for
them to worship, they did something more than break the First
and Second Commandments. Actually they reverted to the older
magico-religious animal cult of the Egyptians from whose servitude they had so recently been freed. The impact of 430 years
of bondage under a mighty nation whose principal idols were
the sacred bulls Apis and Mnevis was not to be denied. Faith
in an unsubstantial Jehovah was wavering, likewise confidence in
his invisible vicar, mewed up on a mountaintop for forty days
and forty nights.

We may well forgive them their apostasy. These dispossessed
helots had but lately come from a land where reigning Pharaohs
proclaimed themselves "mighty bulls" and four million fellahin
rendered divine honors to their plow cattle. Animal cults before
and since the Jews' captivity flourished among pre-Sumerians,
Babylonians, Persians, Phrygians, Hindus, Greeks, Romans,
Celts, Teutons, and Slavs. But it was in Egypt that this type
of religion reached its highest development. Here the reverence
for cattle was such that cows were never killed, and bulls only
by priestly permission.

At the top of the long list of Egyptian gods towered the dominant figure of Osiris, believed by some to have been born of a
cow impregnated by either a stroke of lightning or the divine
influence of moonshine. His *alter ego* was the sacred bull Apis,

43

regarded as an image of the soul of Osiris and worshiped at Memphis. The bull-god Mnevis, of equal stature with Apis and similarly regarded as containing the soul of Osiris, was worshiped at Heliopolis. The Apis bull was always black, with a white triangle on his forehead, the figure of an eagle on his back, in his tail a double hair, and under his tongue a beetle—or scarab-shaped growth—the sacred object which proved his holiness. His tenure of office was limited to twenty-five years, insuring continued virility. If still alive at the end of that time, he was summarily drowned by the priests in the holy spring from which he had been accustomed to drink, since he was never allowed to imbibe the waters of the Nile.

Hunting a new Apis was a chore for the priests. When he was finally selected, pure white oxen were sacrificed to him, the owner of the herd from which he came was rewarded, and the dam of the bull was allotted a second sanctuary at Memphis. Here Apis himself was housed in a palace of his own, surrounded by beautiful parks. He was fed on cakes of flour and honey, was regularly bathed, and slaked his thirst at his own private spring. A harem of cow-wives completed the picture of domestic tranquility.

On his birthday, Apis appeared in public, flanked by a squad of youths who assisted in the task of keeping all women from approaching him. However, during the bull's four months of education, women were permitted to expose themselves before him; if he gave them so much as a look, their fertility was assured. When drowning ended his quarter-century reign, his mummy was buried with elaborate ceremonies. Subsequently, in response to the demand of the ignorant masses, an oracle was established for Apis. The suppliant, after asking a question of the bull, went away. Then a group of boys, instructed by the priests, announced in prose and verse the bull's decision.

In the fullest sense of the word, Apis was sacrosanct. Whoever killed or wounded him was hanged with cruel torture. Foreign conquerors who offended him suffered an early death. So widespread was his influence that even the Roman emperor Titus once assisted at the introduction of a new Apis.

Osiris was the most popular of all the Egyptian deities, and his legend dates before dynastic times, or prior to 3200 B.C. In the Upper Nile, he was said to be the offspring of Set, the earth god, and Nut, or Hathor, the sky goddess, with whom for a long time he had to share divine honors. Hathor was represented in the form of a cow and was hailed as the "Lady of Heaven, Earth, and the Underworld, the Cow Goddess of the House of Horus."

The nation-wide veneration of Apis and Mnevis put them in a class by themselves. There were other sacred animals, but these were worshiped only locally. The Egyptians originally regarded all cattle as sacred, cows as well as bulls. Cows were never sacrificed and bulls only when they had passed the priests' inspection and had been certified as divine scapegoats. If the bull had the proper marks, the priest put his seal on the animal, indicating that it might be sacrificed in atonement for the people's misfortunes. If a man sacrificed a bull which had not been sealed, he was put to death. All bulls which died a natural death were carefully buried. Later their bones, gathered from all parts of Egypt, were interred in a single spot.

Egyptian worship of bulls and cows stems from the great strength of the bull and his headlong rush and invincible belligerency, which excited fear and admiration, while his reproductive powers, to these primitive peoples, made him an enviable type of the generative principle in nature. For hundreds of years every successive Pharaoh boastfully called himself a "mighty bull." Many of them inscribed the title on their *serekh,* or cognizance, which displayed their names as descendants of the divine Horus, the son of Osiris and Isis. Unas, a king of the Fifth Dynasty (about 2750 B.C.), asserted that he was "The Bull of Heaven, which overcometh by his will and which feedeth upon that which cometh into being from every god—a man eater!"

45

This deification of the bovine was a natural, almost inevitable, fruition of an economy which placed cattle at the apex of national wealth. From prehistoric times Egypt had excelled in the selective breeding of two animals—a naturally hornless kind of cattle and the Egyptian greyhound. During the Twentieth Dynasty, which began about 1000 B.C., the priesthood practically ruled the country, and the temples owned towns, gardens, vineyards, orchards, shipyards, and shipping—and half a million head of cattle. John A. Wilson estimates that at that time the temples owned one person in every ten and one acre in every eight. The god Amon had more than 400,000 cattle, large and small; one herd in the eastern Delta was attended by 971 Meshwesh, a conquered tribe of western Libya. The successes of empire greatly augmented the gods' vast holdings. When Rameses IV took 40,000 cattle from the defeated Meshwesh, two-thirds of them were turned over to Amon.[1] As for privately owned property, every year there was a fiscal census of all arable land, cattle, and gold. On the basis of this accounting, taxes were levied, payable in kind. When famine struck, this system was inexorably exploited by a shrewd Israelite named Joseph.

Appointed by Pharaoh to rule the land, he gathered up and stored all surplus grain accumulated during seven years of plenty. During the seven succeeding years of dearth, he first sold stored corn to the Egyptians and to the starving peoples of neighboring nations for gold; when the gold failed, he took cattle in payment; when the last big roundup had stripped the people of their livestock, the famine still continuing, they again came to Joseph and cried, "Our money is spent; my lord also hath our herds of cattle. . . . wherefore shall we die before thine eyes, both we and our land? Buy us, and our land, for bread and we and our land will be servants unto Pharaoh."[2] And that is exactly what Joseph did—with the significant exception of the lands of the priests, for "the priests had a portion assigned them

1 John A. Wilson, *The Burden of Egypt,* 228ff.
2 Gen. 47:18, 19, 22, 24.

of Pharaoh, and did eat their portion which Pharaoh gave them."
Foreseeing the end of the famine, Joseph gave them seed and
told them to sow the land, with this proviso: "In the increase,
ye shall give the fifth part unto Pharaoh, and four parts shall
be your own, for seed of the field and for your food, and for them
of your households, and for food for your little ones."

On the religious side, the peripatetic Hebrews repeatedly
relapsed into the idolatrous habits of other nations, notably the
Canaanites, whom they had conquered but did not exterminate.
Again they abandoned Jehovah and turned to worshiping the
Canaanite god Baal, or Moloch. In his honor they made molten
images. To him they offered their offspring to be burned alive.
Their children were laid on the hands of a calf-headed idol of
bronze, from which they slid into a fiery oven, while the people
danced and banged cymbals to drown the cries of the burning
victims. Here was another bovine monster which was apparently
just as potent in luring the Chosen People into idolatry as the
Golden Calf of Aaron's day.

These horrifying rites were apparently practiced in other
lands, including Sicily and Crete. From the latter came the well-
known legend of Minos and the Minotaur. Queen Pasiphae,
wife of King Minos of Knossus, was said to have fallen in love
with a glamorous white bull which rose from the sea. To gratify
her passion, the artist Daedalus fashioned a hollow wooden cow
and covered it with a real cowhide. To the lovesick Queen, hidden within, came the bull rampant. The fruit of their unholy
union was the Minotaur, a monster with the body of a man and
the head of a bull. This repulsive creature the King shut up in
the Labyrinth, a building full of tortuous passages so baffling
that a prisoner might roam it for years without ever finding his
way out.

In spite of its revolting character, this legend was periodically acted out by the king and queen of Knossus, the object being
to symbolize the mythical marriage of the sun and the moon.
For the simple Cretan islanders, accustomed to seeing the sun

rise daily from the sea, it was easy to compare it with a white bull emerging from the waves. In fact, the Cretans actually called the sun a bull. A similar fancy possessed the people of Heliopolis, "City of the Sun," where the sacred bull Mnevis was frequently hailed as the sun god. Pausanias identified Pasiphae with the moon, "she who shines on all." The horns of the waxing or waning moon so resembled the horns of a white cow that the ancients represented the goddess of the moon being drawn by a yoke of white cattle.

There is also the story of how Zeus tricked Europa by assuming the disguise of a bull. Deceived by his tame and peaceful appearance, she mounted the animal, whereupon Zeus plunged into the sea and swam with her to Crete. The scene was reproduced in embroidery by the maiden Arachne while competing at her specialty with the goddess Athena. So skillfully was it done that the bull looked like a living thing, the water really wet, and Europa appeared actually shuddering at the sight of the heaving waves. Spenser and Garrick apostrophized Arachne in verse, and in his "Palace of Art" Tennyson alluded to the embroidered picture wherein *"Sweet Europa's mantle blew unclasped from off her shoulder, backward borne. From one hand drooped a crocus, one hand grasped the mild bull's golden horn."*

Dionysus, or Bacchus, the Greco-Roman god of wine, was another deity often represented in the form of a bull, or at least wearing a bull's horns. Types of the horned Dionysus are found in many ancient ruins. On one statuette he wears a bull's hide, with head, horns, and hoofs hanging down behind. In Arcadia men used to pick out a bull from the herd and carry it to the sanctuary of the wine god, who was supposed to have inspired them to choose the right animal. The women of Elis hailed him as a bull, crying "Come hither, Dionysus, to thy holy temple by the sea; come with the Graces to thy temple, rushing with thy bull's foot, O goodly bull, O goodly bull!" In their practice of animal cults the ancients did not worship the animal as such, but only when a divinity assumed its shape. At all other times the beast was the object of no special veneration.

To cattle, however, were often ascribed supernatural powers. The destruction of Pompeii was foretold by an ox; another ox solemnly warned of the battle of Pharsalia and of the assassination of Julius Caesar. A cow is said to have led Cadmus to the site upon which he founded the city of Thebes, in Boetia of ancient Greece. In the Vosges Mountains of France, cattle acquired the gift of speech on Christmas Eve. But the natives never tried to eavesdrop after hearing what happened to a farmer of Vecoux who hid in the corner of his stable to listen to the animals talk. Said one beast to the other, "What shall we do tomorrow?" Replied the other "We shall carry our master to the churchyard." Sure enough, the farmer died that very night and was buried the next morning.

All through the three great stages of society—the hunting, the pastoral, and the agricultural—superstitious respect has been paid to cattle. In Africa we see the Dinkas of the White Nile placing extraordinary value on their herds; even their dung is saved and burned to ashes for sleeping in and for smearing their bodies; the urine is used in washing and as a substitute for salt. Cows are never slaughtered, and only those that die a natural death, or by accident, are used for food. Indra, the great god of battles in India, had the form of a bull, and cows are everywhere held so sacred by the Hindus as to pose a serious agricultural problem. Here two hundred million head of cattle, one-quarter of the world total, are never killed but are allowed to wander at large, denuding the fields in search of feed, robbing hucksters' stalls of vegetables unchallenged, and contributing to the soil none of their revitalizing manure, which the natives collect and dry for fuel or for mixing with earth and flooring their huts. There is even an official "Cattle Preservation Day," there are three thousand "old cows' homes" financed by private protective federations, and each year the government

49

allocates forty times the amount appropriated for family planning and population to ameliorating the condition of India's cattle.[3] Too many people and too many cows are more than India's ravaged soil can stand.

In North America, the Minnetaree, or Hidatsa, Indians believed that the bones of those buffalo which they killed and divested of their flesh would rise again, clothed with new flesh and quickened with life so that by the following June they would be fat enough for slaughter.

In nearly all the nations of antiquity the favorite sacrifice to the gods was cattle. In Greece it was said that no smell was more pleasing to the gods than that of roasting ox shanks. A sacrifice periodically made at the Temple of Zeus on the Acropolis at Athens dated from the time one Sopratus, a stranger, slew one of his oxen which had eaten of the sacrificial corn. Sopratus killed the beast, but, stricken with remorse, he buried it and fled to Crete. A dearth fell upon the land, and to remove the curse, a sacrifice known as the Bouphonia was instituted. At the annual festival oxen were driven around the altar, and whichever animal tasted the oblational cereals became the sacrificial victim. An ax was dipped in water brought by maidens to the altar and handed to the sacrificer. The victim's throat was cut, and all the people made to taste of its flesh. The hide was then stuffed with grass and sewed together, and the reconstructed ox yoked to the plow. Although all the participants loudly accused each other of ox murder, the matter was finally resolved by putting the blame on the ax, which was cast into the sea.

The Grecian goddess Demeter, patron of animal husbandry, accepted both male and female cattle as sacrifices; Pluto and Persephone, deities of the lower world, favored black steers and sterile cows as offerings. In Rome, on the first of the year, a white steer was slaughtered by the chief consul, and a triumphal

[3] Population Reference Bureau, Inc., *Population Bulletin,* Vol. IX, No. 1 (February, 1953), 7–8.

Above: Skull of *Bos primigenius*

Right: Skull of *Bos longifrons*

British Museum of Natural History

Below: *Leptobos falconeri Rutimeyer*—skull
partially restored

American Museum of Natural History, New York

Humped bull from the reliefs on the eastern stairway of the "Apadana" building at Persepolis, showing the Babylonians bringing their tribute, about 475 B.C.

Supposed *Bos urus*

The Gaur

A Banteng

The Yak

Chicago Natural History Museum

The European Bison

American Museum of Natural History, New York

Painting of a bull from the Lascaux Cave, France

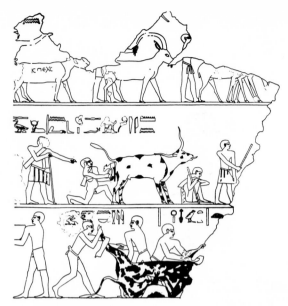

Delivering the Calf

From A. M. Blackman, *The Rock Tombs of Meir,* I, plate X

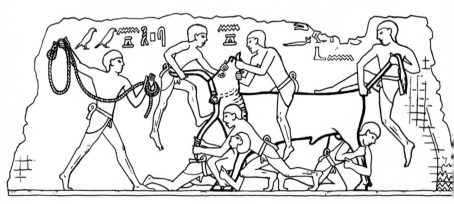

Throwing the Calf

From a drawing by Othmar J. Hoffler

Preparing Hides in Early Nineteenth-Century England

From an old print, published January, 1805
By William Miller, Albemarle Street, London

Bull Baiting. From an old print (1820).

A Banderillero "Nails the Darts." From a painting by J. Suárez.

R. P. Fowler

march followed. There was a mass slaughter of cattle when Scipio returned in triumph from his defeat of Hannibal. Cows were sacrificed to mature goddesses, heifers to maiden goddesses. To Tellus, goddess of the earth, cows and calves were sacrificed. In Rome, said to have been founded by shepherds and herdsmen, many personal names reflected belief in this tradition. Common examples include Porcius, "pig man"; Ovinius, "sheep man"; Caprillius, "goat man"; Equitius, "horse man"; and Taurius, "bull man."

MANY OF THE EXAMPLES of magico-religious cults so far cited date back as far as 5000 B.C. But they are almost modern compared to the antiquity of the cave paintings of southern France and northern Spain. Some authorities date these back twenty or thirty thousand years, thus proving that men of the Old Stone Age had a superstitious regard for wild cattle, including the aurochs, the bison, and the bulls and cows of other species now extinct. More than forty painted caves in France and thirty-five in Spain tell the story. Outstanding among these are Altamira and Lascaux.

One Marcelino de Sautola, who owned some land near Vispieres in northern Spain, discovered Altamira in 1875 and explored it further in 1879. One day as he was groping about in the dark, damp passages, his five-year-old daughter, whom he had brought with him, after fearlessly penetrating an even gloomier area, rushed up to her daddy shouting, *"Toros, toros, hay muchos, muchos toros!"* In such fashion was discovered the world-famous vault of Altamira, the sensational news of its marvelous frescoes of "bulls, many bulls" being heralded by a five-year-old moppet.

These pictures cover a ceiling measuring 35 by 140 feet. They are predominantly polychrome paintings of bison—with blacks, browns, reds, and yellows skillfully blended in most of them. They show intelligent use of light and shade, and the irregularities of the walls are utilized to give the effect of relief. There are semi-human figures wearing animal masks, with arms uplifted as if in prayer, suggesting the practice of mask-magic. There are also checkers, squares, lines, dots, encircled crosses, and other semi-geometrical symbols, strongly suggestive of wizardry and enchantment. The great bison vault shows scores of these animals in all sorts of postures, mostly belligerent.

Marvelous as they are, the paintings at Altamira were eclipsed by those at Lascaux, in France, which were discovered in 1940. Here the frescoes date even farther back than those at Altamira, and give the archaeologist a clear picture of the evolution of paleolithic painting. Again, as at Altamira, the preferred subjects were "bulls and more bulls." And again, this great cave yielded its secrets to the wandering foot of youth. Only in this case, instead of a little Spanish *muchacha,* five French lads and a dog stumbled upon the great discovery.

These youngsters—the oldest was only seventeen—were hunting rabbits near the ruins of an old house known as the Chateau de Lascaux, not far from Montignac, when they lost their dog. They began to whistle for him and were answered by faint barks issuing from a hole in the ground, left by an uprooted fir tree. Down this opening scrambled the leader. He landed on a sandy level some twenty-five feet below the surface. Striking a match, he grabbed his pup and called for his companions.

Presently they were all standing in a grotto opening into darkness. With the aid of matches, they fumbled their way through the gloom until they found themselves in a vaulted hall, some sixty feet long by thirty feet wide. On the sloping walls were colored pictures of animals—horses, stags, oxen, bulls, cows, deer, and beasts now long extinct in western Europe. Open-mouthed, these rabbit hunters of the twentieth century gaped in stupefaction at this primeval art exhibit. With awe they contemplated the work artists had wrought twenty thousand years ago, which had been hidden from human eyes for possibly fifteen thousand. In less than a year the cave was thoroughly explored by experts, and in 1942 there appeared the first published accounts of the discovery, with interpretive comment by scholars.

The caves at Lascaux have several divisions—antechamber, main hall, axial gallery, lateral passage, nave, apse, and crypt. There are no pictures in the antechamber. In the hall and gallery are depicted great, black, plunging bulls, intermingled with other beasts. There are also small figures traced in thin red lines, identified as three horses and a stag's antlers. In another group are four bulls' heads; in still another, ponies, horses, and an ibex. Elsewhere are oxen, bulls, and cows. From the back of one of the big black bulls emerge the muzzle, horns, and other parts of a large crimson bull.

Among the most striking figures in the gallery are a black male aurochs and a black cow with her hind legs drawn up as if hurdling a couple of ponies depicted below—a perfect prototype of the cow that jumped over the moon. The head and shoulders of the bull are magnificently drawn, radiating brute strength. The large, prominent eye and distended nostril are emphasized by unpainted patches, making them strikingly realistic. Beneath this male aurochs are two *longifrons* wild oxen. Elsewhere are four more of these "long-faced" beasts, all cows. Another painting, showing the forepart of an aurochs, is peppered with small dots, signifying a speckled, but probably roan, specimen of the species.

The paintings in the Lascaux caves are the handiwork of men who lived in different eras, thousands of years apart. In size they vary from thirteen inches to seventeen feet in length. The most imposing figure is that of the great aurochs in the main hall. Near by are three others. All four are beautifully colored, reflecting the master talent of great artists. Another painting merits the title "the dying bull." Here is a big aurochs whose hams seem to buckle, while his forelegs sprawl, his head droops, his muzzle sags to the ground, his eyes are closed, and his limbs seem to be stiffening. Facing the expiring brute are a cow and a calf of the aurochs family.

All these pictures are in the main hall and gallery. In the passage, nave, apse, and crypt are other bovine paintings, in contrasting postures and actions. Two large black figures of oxen show curiously hairy, shaggy bellies. There is a dark brown bison with a ridiculously small head and seven barbed projectiles scratched on its side. Experts think that these were superimposed long after the picture was drawn, and point out that wherever javelins or arrows are shown, they are never pictured as piercing or wounding the beasts. A black *longifrons* cow, heavy with calf, waddles across the scene. Powerfully delineated are two male bison, their onrushing charge indicating the primal urge of the rutting season in Aquitaine two hundred centuries ago. Two blackish-brown males of the *longifrons* species, each twelve feet long, parade one behind the other.

In the crypt is a painted scene dramatizing a prehistoric tragedy. To the right is a bison. In front of him lies the supine figure of a man, wearing a bird-mask. To the right of the bison is a black wooly rhinoceros. The bison's flanks are transfixed by a javelin (a unique occurrence in cave paintings). Its belly is ripped open and the guts sag bloodily in a great sack. The brute's head is lowered as though trying to stab the body of the man; its legs seem to quiver as if in the death throes. At a little distance below the man is a stick with a bird fixed to its top and an object that may represent a "propulsor," an implement made of wood, bone, or ivory with which to irritate wild animals.

The story behind this scene is a matter of plausible conjecture. The man has gone out hunting, wearing his bird-mask and carrying his bird stick. He has wounded the bison with his javelin, and the wounded beast has turned and gored the man to death. Before he can trample his victim, a great wooly rhinoceros has ripped open the bison with his murderous horns.

This scene, painted not less than fourteen thousand years ago, provides a dramatic climax to the magico-religious saga implicit in all these paintings. It should be emphasized that these prehistoric pictures were all executed in dark, damp, almost inaccessible caverns, wholly unsuited to human habitation. If any number of people had ventured to live here, the stench, discomfort, and disease would have killed them off. On the other hand, it is obvious that they were the sites where men of the Old Stone Age practiced magic rites, sorcery, hunting wizardry, and weird enchantments.

As Hugo Obermaier says, "An invincible superstitious force must have surged into recesses of the caverns from the men who made these pictures. This force must have been hunting-magic, based upon the belief that the hunter acquires power over an animal as soon as he has dominated, by magic arts, its image."[4] Alan Brodrick points out that "some of the beasts are just touched by missiles, have missiles imposed, but in no case [save in the 'prehistoric tragedy'] is there any representation of wounds."[5] This British authority on cave art further suggests that the hunting-magic precedes the chase. The quarry is implored to let himself be captured or killed, and excuses are often made that he has to be slain. But the pictured animal is already half-overcome, and missiles imposed upon his image make his doom still more certain. Another commentator called this "wishful painting."

Call it what you will, these engraved and painted caves were indubitably the precursors of all the subterranean shrines of later times—of the underground sanctuaries of Sumeria and Egypt, of the rock temples of Buddhist India, of the catacombs, of the painted grottoes strung along the Silky Way of the caravans through central Asia, and of the frescoed crypts of our Romanesque churches. And, as we have seen, it was from the taurine world of the aurochs, of the bison, and of other bovines now extinct that these talented artists of the late Old Stone Age drew their greatest inspiration.

[4] Alan Houghton Brodrick, *Lascaux: A Commentary,* 90.
[5] *Ibid.,* 91.

CHAPTER 6

They Took the Bull by the Horns

"SUBLIME" was Edmund Burke's word for a bull. Britain's greatest political thinker wrote: "I know of nothing sublime which is not some modification of power. . . . An ox is a creature of vast strength; but he is an innocent creature . . . and not at all dangerous; for which reason the idea of an ox is by no means grand. A bull is strong too: but his strength is of another kind; often very destructive; the idea of a bull is therefore great, and it has frequently a place in sublime descriptions."[1]

"Sublime" he may have been, but the bull's sublimity began to be tested, both in the countryside and in the sports arena, at least four thousand years ago. And the challengers were not only men, but women. The time: midway of the Bronze Age, which spanned the years 2500 to 1400 B.C.; the place: an oval, fenced arena before the palace of Minos, legendary king of Crete, at Knossos; the occasion: a sports program attending religious ceremonials performed under the patronage of the local goddess, whose shrine overlooked the scene of combat; the animals: bulls of established pedigree, reared in special herds and carefully trained as in Spain today.

Because the events were of a religious character, it was quite proper for girls, apparently of the First Families of Knossos, to join the ranks of the professionals at the rugged pastime known as "bull grappling." From the records which have been recovered through the excavations of Sir Arthur Evans, the British archaeologist, it is clear that these highly skilled females were of gentle birth and breeding. They wore bright-colored bandeaux on their foreheads, their hair was fashionably curled, broad armlets en-

[1] Edmund Burke, "On the Sublime and Beautiful."

56

circled their upper arms, and heavy necklaces hung over their bosoms and down their backs. Incidentally, it was also the female of the species who always had the choice seats at the show. Women from the highest social circles filled the front rows of the grandstand. And it was their great Minoan goddess who occupied the divine station afterward assigned to Zeus. The whole organization at Knossos was strongly suggestive of gynecocracy. But, petticoat rule or not, the acrobatics of the lady bull grapplers were good enough to merit the plaudits of the spectators—male as well as female.

Scenes from the world's first rodeo have been preserved in frescoes, bas-reliefs, and statuettes, cast in imperishable bronze. One fresco shows a female tumbler doing a back somersault over the bull's body and being caught by another performer standing behind the animal. In another, a youth is doing the tumbling and a female the receiving. In still another, a single piece cast in solid bronze, a youth—not a girl—is in the act of a revolution while somersaulting from the back of a bull, his head supported by the bull's forehead, his feet gaining purchase from the animal's back, preparatory to landing on the ground. Another develops the whole act of bull grappling from start to finish, in four stages: (1) the charging bull is seized by the horns near their tips; (2) the bull's head is raised in an effort to toss his assailant, this movement at the same time giving an impetus to the turning figure; (3) the acrobat, having released his grip on the horns and after completing his back somersault, has landed on his feet on the bull's back; (4) the performer makes a final leap to the ground from the bull's hindquarters.[2]

The Minoan scene has not been overlooked by modern historians and writers of fiction. In his monumental series outlining *The Story of Civilization,* Will Durant comments: "The Cretan's greatest thrill comes when he wins his way into the crowd that fills the amphitheater on a holiday to see men and women face death against huge, charging bulls. Time and again he pic-

[2] Evans, *The Palace of Minos at Knossos,* III, 207ff.

tures the stages of this lusty sport: the daring hunter capturing the bull by jumping astride its neck as it laps up water from a pool; the professional tamer twisting the animal's head until it learns some measure of tolerance for the acrobat's annoying tricks; the skilled performer, slim and agile, meeting the bull in the arena, grasping its horns, leaping into the air, somersaulting over its back, and landing feet first on the ground in the arms of a female companion who lends her grace to the scene. Even in Minoan Crete this is already an ancient art; a clay cylinder from Cappadocia, ascribed to 2400 B.C., shows a bull-grappling sport as vigorous and dangerous. . . . For a moment [we] catch a glimpse of the contradictory complexity of man as we perceive that this game of blood-lust and courage, still popular today, is as old as civilization."[3]

In Mika Waltari's novel of the pre-Christian era the physician Sinuhe expresses amazement at first seeing Minea dancing before wild bulls: "In this town there was a field in which wild bulls were kept. . . . and the youth of the place were wont to display their litheness and valor in encounters with these beasts, hurling darts into their shoulders and leaping over them. Minea was overjoyed to see them and desired to test her skill. . . . It was like nothing I had ever seen before, and my heart froze as I watched. For a wild bull is the most terrible of all savage beasts . . . and its horns are long and sharp as brad awls; with one stroke it will slit a man's body or toss him high in the air and trample him underfoot.

"But Minea danced before them wearing only a flimsy garment, and she stepped lightly aside when they lowered their heads and charged at her with dreadful bellowings. Her face was flushed, and with growing excitement she threw off her silver hair net so that her hair floated in the wind. Her dance was so rapid that the eye could not follow all her movements as she leaped up between the horns of an attacking beast, held fast to them and then, thrusting with her feet against its forehead,

[3] *The Life of Greece,* 12–13.

threw herself upward in a somersault, to land on its back. I gazed spellbound at her performance . . . [and] with my body steaming with sweat, I could not sit still, although those who sat behind me on the benches swore at me and tugged at my shoulder cloth."[4]

Turning to scientific evidence, archaeologist Evans states that "in northern Greece (Thessaly) riders wearied their animals by driving them around the arena and then brought them down by jumping on them and seizing their horns, in the Minoan fashion, a method still practiced in the 'Wild West of America.' "[5] Thus Thessaly's cowboys, long after the Minoan civilization had given way to that of Mycenae, in Greece, adopted as their own the bull-grappling sport of their predecessors.

Just as our modern rodeos originated in the every-day work of Mexican *vaqueros* and American cowpokes, so were the circus sports of ancient Crete the outgrowth of skill acquired by Minoan herdsmen. There the job of both males and females was to herd or catch wild and half-wild cattle by gathering them throughout the countryside and driving them into narrow defiles beset with obstacles and ambushes. These adventurous drives and "roundups," involving all kinds of danger and excitement, provided excellent training for the specialized feats of the arena. Naturally a considerable amount of personal risk attended these performances. It is fortunate that, along with its athletic achievements, Crete of the Bronze Age developed artists capable of depicting these contemporary spectacles in pictographic and linear writing, in engraving on copper, silver, and gold, and in modeling in clay and casting in bronze, the realistic and enduring records which have rewarded the efforts of modern historians and archaeologists.

From Crete and Greece, these exhibitions spread to Rome, where the amphitheaters staged hunting scenes known as the *Venationes.* Here also wild cattle were sometimes matched

[4] *The Egyptian,* 188–89.
[5] Evans, *The Palace of Minos at Knossos,* III, 207.

against the weapons of skilled swordsmen, and here they were turned loose, along with lions, on unarmed Christians, before the converted Emperor Constantine abolished gladiatorial combats and the mass slaughter of martyrs.

Yet long after Christianity was firmly established and Rome had become the Holy City, carnival sports, regulated by law or custom, were staged in more than one amphitheater. In September of A.D. 1332, according to Gibbon, a bull-feast in the fashion of the Moors and Spaniards was celebrated in the 80,000-seat Colosseum. Some two-score high-born youths, including a few from the rival houses of the Ursini and the Colonna, with maids and matrons of the nobility looking on, were sent into the pit on foot, armed only with a spear, to battle wild cattle. In turn, each challenger faced a single bull. It was a dangerous and bloody business, with victory going to the bulls. Only eleven of them were left on the field, against eighteen killed and nine wounded among their human opponents. The aristocracy might mourn, but the pomp and ceremony of the funerals held in the churches of St. John the Lateran and Ste Maria Maggiore afforded a second holiday for the crowds.

In Sienkiewicz' novel, *Quo Vadis,* laid in the first century A.D., with the bloodthirsty Nero as the villain, there is a description of a titanic tussle between an aurochs and the Christian giant Ursus, a native of Lygia, whose queen of the same name is the heroine of the story.

"Suddenly . . . a grating opposite Caesar's podium was opened, and into the arena rushed, amid shouts of beast-keepers, an enormous German aurochs, bearing on his head the naked body of a woman. 'Lygia! Lygia!' cried Vinicius [her betrothed who sat in the stands].... When he [the Lygian] saw his queen on the horns of the wild beast, he sprang up, as if touched by living fire, and bending forward he ran at the raging animal . . . [seizing] the wild beast by the horns. The man's feet sank in the sand to his ankles, his back was bent like a drawn bow, his head was hidden between his shoulders, on his arms the muscles

60

came out so that the skin almost burst from their pressure; but he had stopped the bull in his tracks. . . . The bull sank his feet as well as did the man in the sand, and his dark shaggy body was curved so that it seemed a gigantic ball. . . . Which . . . would fall first, that was the question. . . . But the man and the beast continued . . . their monstrous exertion; one might have said that they were planted in the earth. . . . People thought themselves dreaming till the enormous head of the bull began to turn in the iron hands of the barbarian. The face, neck, and arms of the Lygian grew purple; his back bent still more. It was clear that he was rallying the remnant of his super-human strength, but that he could not last long. Duller and duller, hoarser and hoarser, more and more painful grew the groan of the bull as it mingled with the whistling breath from the breast of the giant. The head of the beast turned more and more, and from his jaws came a long, foaming tongue. A moment more, and to the ears of spectators sitting nearer came as if it were the crack of breaking bones; then the beast rolled on the earth with its neck twisted in death. The giant removed in a twinkle the ropes from the horns of the bull and, raising the maiden, began to breathe hurriedly. . . . a moment he stood as if only half-conscious; then he raised his eyes and looked at the spectators. The amphitheater had gone wild."[6]

The well-remembered story ended happily. Nero was forced to spare the lives of maid and man, fearing the vengeance of the mob if he should refuse. And Lygia and Vicinius were reunited.

A modified, and more humane, form of bull fighting is still practiced in the south of France, where the Roman influence has persisted to this day. In the Department of Bouches-du-Rhône, there lies an island, La Camargue by name. Here the Marquis of Baroncelli-Javon has bred splendid specimens of fighting bulls which periodically appear in the arena at Arles to test their mettle against the prowess of the local youths. La

[6] Pages 498–500.

Camargue cattle are quite primitive and are esteemed not for their milk or meat, but for their strength, courage, agility, and speed as fighters. They have nearly straight backs, strong legs, and well-formed hooves, small and firm. In color they are usually rusty black, and between the horns the long, curly hair is much like that of the ancient aurochs. They are never stabled, but live altogether in the open, subject to the hottest suns and the biting winds of the dreaded mistral.

On nearly every spring Sunday, in the towns and villages, there is a bull fight. Here, however, the object is not to kill the animal, as in the Spanish sport, but to pluck from each of the bull's horns a small colored woolen tassel and from the forehead a bright cockade. Twenty agile young men, known as *razeteurs*, are chosen for each contest from among the hundreds of eager applicants. Lutz Heck, the German zoologist—who after fifteen years of selecting and crossing half-wild types of cattle, claims to have succeeded in recreating the ancient aurochs—was once a spectator at one of these contests. Translated from the German and paraphrased, this is his story:

The first time I ever saw such a bull fight was on a cloudless Sunday, Ascension Day, in the famous Roman arena at Arles. An hour before the performance, 20,000 people from town and countryside crowded the arena, sitting on chairs, balcony seats, and the stone steps leading up to the top of the surrounding wall. It was to be the concluding fight of the season, with the "golden cockade" going to the victor. The best stock of the Camargue breeders was to be opposed by the most famous *razeteurs* in the country. Presently, in the runway behind the fence, there appeared the bullfighters—twenty youths wearing white shirts and white trousers, with their hands in their pockets, their caps jauntily poised on the back of their heads.

At four o'clock the Mayor entered the official box, a trumpet sounded, and from an opposite gate the first bull stormed in—a black, fiery animal with pointed horns, ominously sharp. Quickly it crossed the arena, looked all about, and began to paw the earth. At a given signal, the *razeteurs* dashed in and the contest began. Excitement ran high as the black beast charged his white-clad tormentors in movements as quick as thought. Racing in front of the animal's head, a single fighter, wielding a short iron rod, attempted to lift the cockade from the bull's brow or retrieve a tassel from its horns. The animal tried to charge the attacker, but its attention was immediately distracted by another fighter, who ran up to protect his friend; whereupon the bull had to turn suddenly to meet the new threat. This run-around was repeated until the brute paused momentarily for breath and, with sides heaving, let out a defiant bellow, challenging his persecutors. When pursuit was resumed, one *razeteur* was chased to the fence, over which he jumped just in time to escape being gored. For a long time no one had succeeded in making way with a cockade or a tassel. But eventually from the now tired and slow-moving animal the three prized trophies were secured and the lucky winners and their companions retired behind the barrier.

But the bull didn't want to leave the arena. He pawed the earth, bellowed, and faced his youthful victors, who stood grinning behind the fence. Whereupon a peaceful ox, wearing a bell around his neck was led in. At the familiar sound, the wild one trotted to the side of the "gentled" beast and strolled from the arena as meek as a lamb.

Six fighting bovines competed during the afternoon. One was a cow, whose agility and belligerent attacks kept her tormentors at bay so successfully that they failed to lift a single trophy. The triumph of beast versus man aroused the crowd's unbounded enthusiasm. Her courage and determination were shown when she butted the fence behind which the *razeteurs* cowered, lifted a section with her horns, and tossed it three feet into the air. Through this hole the animal stormed into the runway, where some spectators were seated. Screaming, they went away from there in a hurry. But displaying a rare sense of showmanship, the cow about-faced and returned to the arena. From

20,000 throats and twice as many hands arose shouts of approval and thunderous applause.

Once again the buckaroos in white sallied forth and resolutely renewed the contest. As time went on and still no cockades had been gathered, the mayor sought to raise the lads' spirits by boosting the cash rewards. "Five hundred francs for the first one," he shouted, "seven hundred francs, one thousand francs." But like a black she-devil, the cow dashed hither and yon, sending the fighters again scurrying for protection behind the barrier. Amid screams from the crowd, she overtook and tossed one unlucky youth, then lowered her head to gore him; but with great skill and alacrity the boy rolled his body beneath the fence and was saved. After that the fighters became more cautious, so much so that the bold, brave bossy was allowed to leave the arena amid the plaudits of the spectators, unconquered and undespoiled of her ribbons.[7]

Although it was the dream of every spirited youth in Provence to become a *razeteur,* Heck thought that for risking one's life, the pay of six to twenty dollars a performance was small reward. Incidentally, Heck's claim of resynthesis of the aurochs has been widely disputed by geneticists and naturalists, most scientists believing such a feat is not possible. Indeed, statisticians have calculated that it would take millions of generations before, by the law of averages, one aurochs could be born.[8]

IN SPAIN, contesting with wild and half-wild cattle dates from the earliest times—before there were any "Spaniards," ethnologists classifying the natives as "Iberians." As already noted, bull grappling had been practiced in Crete forty centuries before, had spread to Thessaly, and from there to Rome, where, according to Pliny the Elder, Julius Caesar is credited with introducing the sport during his dictatorship. Because no reliable records

[7] Lutz Heck, *Auf Tiersuche in Weiter Welt,* chap. IX.

[8] *Washington Post and Times-Herald,* November 25, 1954. Article by David Jones.

have established the real origin of taurine sports in Spain, these questions remain unanswered: Were they brought in by the Roman legions in the first century A.D. or by the conquering Moslems in the seventh? If it is contended that the Cretan performances within an enclosure were merely field exercises, practiced by cowboys while doing their daily chores, one is led to conclude that the Iberians could have found means to capture live bulls, perfect themselves at taming them, and eventually make of their pursuit a sport to arouse the liveliest emotions, after developing the qualities of speed, beauty, and power in their fighting animals.

In the eleventh century A.D. documents mentioned for the first time that in Spain Christians and Mohammedans were competing against bulls. There were two kinds of combat—one a plebeian, full of brutality and crudeness, with no rules or regulations; the other, tilting from horseback, favored by the nobles, who organized their own privately presented jousts, in which the rider attacked the bull with a lance. (In Portugal this kind of sport is still in vogue). Towards the end of the thirteenth century these two kinds were merged when the nobility took in hand the organization of public bull fights, celebrated on the occasion of all-important festivals. The apex of equestrian combat was reached in the seventeenth century, when the cavaliers replaced the long and heavy lance of their ancestors with the shorter *rejón*, a javelin set in flexible wood. When Philip V, founder of the Bourbon dynasty in Spain, came to the throne in A.D. 1700, he notified all and sundry that he was opposed to bull fights. Whereupon the nobility withdrew their support— and their horses—from the *plazas de toros*. It was then that bull fighting entered a new phase: the sport became commercial, with paid professionals; wooden amphitheaters were replaced by masonry structures; and fighters on foot were elevated to the principal role, where previously they had been mere auxiliaries of the mounted cavaliers.

Specialized breeding of Spanish bulls began about the time

rebellious Yankees rose in arms against an unloved John Bull, their overseas oppressor—that is, between 1775 and 1780. The qualities then specified as indispensable in fighting animals at such famous breeding farms as those of Count de Vistahermosa, Vicente José Vásquez, and Juan Conradi have been maintained in an unbroken line to this day. Courage and vigor are prime requisites, and these objectives require the breeder to reproduce, generation after generation, animals which "have what it takes" in conformation and fighting spirit and which suggest unbroken descent from the ancient aurochs.

Such a bull is a wild beast. His chief instinct is to fight. And he is conceded by experts to be one of the fiercest and bravest animals in the world. Compared with a creature reared for beef, he is as the wolf is to the dog. To meet Spanish regulations governing the sport, a bull must weigh a minimum of over half a ton—specifically 1,197 pounds. He must have a very fine but tough hide, with glossy hair, almost always black, a small head with a wide forehead, crest over the neck well proportioned, nostrils large and well distended, muzzle small, elastic, moist, and black, horns well set, pointing to the front, short, thick neck with a great hump of muscle which stands up when he is enraged, wide shoulders, small, sharp hooves, long, slender tail ending in a tuft, eyes large, lively, and intelligent, and ears small and capable of great mobility. Since his principal weapon is the horns, they should be turned neither too high nor too low, and not too open nor too closed, for the best arena performances of man and animal. In Mexico, where North Americans have easier access to bull fights than in Europe, the bulls are somewhat smaller, supposedly on account of the continuous crossing of native stock with sires imported from Spain.

Among English-speaking peoples there is but one word for the uncastrated ox, and that is "bull." But in Spain, up to three years of age he is a *becerro;* between three and four, a *novillo;* beyond four, he becomes a *toro* and a preferred combatant at the big *corridas* (bull fights). At the great breeding farms young

66

bulls are repeatedly subjected to proddings with blunted lances by cowboys on horseback to test their fighting abilities. One or two out of every ten are accepted, the rest being discarded as unfit and sold for beef. The cows, being prospective dams of fighting stock, are similarly tested. At one examination, from thirty-six only six were chosen, although to the untutored bystanders even the weakest seemed to have done very well.

Said one Spanish stockman, "A breeding establishment of wild bulls ought not to be a business. It is an expensive luxury. It is true we are paid four or five times as much for a fighting bull as for the others, but then see what it costs to rear!"[9] Constant watchfulness is mandatory. The bull's food and water must be carefully chosen, his movement from place to place, depending on changes in temperature, must be attended to, so that the expense of rearing one animal equals, or at least approximates, the cost of maintaining a family. When at last the mature *toro* is brought to perfection, this pampered brute must be constantly safeguarded right up to the moment he enters the arena. Breeders have been known to refuse to let their bulls perform until band music, blaring above the runway, has been silenced.

As an industry, Spain's breeding and matching of bulls against men bulks large. There is an Association of Fighting Bull Breeders, with over one hundred members, of which eighty own about forty thousand bulls, each bearing the owner's brand burned on the flank. In Spain and other countries, including France, Mexico, Peru, Ecuador, Portugal, Venezuela, Colombia, and other Latin-American nations, between 450 and 500 bull fights, employing four- and five-year-old bulls, are held each year. For these fights about 8,000 four-year-old and 3,000 five-year-old bulls are required annually. There is a famous school in Seville established by Ferdinand VII in the eighteenth century which attracts students hoping to graduate as Doctors of Tauromachia. The American, Sidney Franklin, worked for and earned such a title.

[9] Vicente Blasco-Ibáñez, *Blood and Sand,* 154.

Probably the two most distinguished Spanish matadors of the past sixty years were Juan Belmonte and Joselito, exponents of two dissimilar styles of fighting. Belmonte, before his retirement, had taken part in 750 *corridas* and killed 1,550 bulls. In 1913 he performed in Mexico at the capital city, Vera Cruz, Guadalajara, San Luis Potosí, and Nogales. Joselito's brilliant record of an equal number of bulls killed in 680 *corridas* was terminated when he was fatally gored in 1920, at the age of twenty-five by the bull *Bailador*. Probably an all-time score was made by Pedro Romero of the famous Romero dynasty, who, between 1771 and 1799, killed 5,600 bulls, and died in bed at the age of eighty-six.

But of equal importance to the *aficionados* are those bulls which make a name for themselves as outstanding combatants. Of the Conradi breeding, the bull *Monudo* in 1892, at Algeciras, sustained twenty wounds from the lances of the *picadors* (mounted fighters) and killed eight horses; *Trompetero* in 1889 at Madrid killed seven horses and was acclaimed the best bull of all time. Another taurine quartet, engaged for a charity performance, killed sixteen horses, of which the bull *Sombrero* killed seven.

The Spanish bull is intelligent and learns fast. When released from his gloomy pen under the stands, he dashes into the blazing sunlight thinking he is being returned to the fields from which he had been driven only a day or two before. When he sees that this is only another, although bigger, enclosure fencing him in, he is mad, fighting mad. Men on foot—to which he is unaccustomed—start waving large, colored capes at him. He charges—and what he hits is nothing substantial. Heretofore, he has been accustomed to toss into the air and gore something solid. Now it's like tilting at a shadow. Only when the *picadors* ride in and their horses provide a familiar target can he thrust his head and horns into living flesh.

Incidentally, there is a far greater mortality among horses than among *toreros*.[10] With the withdrawal of the horses at the sound of the trumpet, the animal is teased and fooled by the men with the capes and by the matador with the *muleta*. But not for long! Unless brought to earth within ten or fifteen minutes after his entry into the arena, any bull becomes unplayable and unkillable, for he has mastered the mystery behind the flimsy cloth—it is the man holding the *muleta* who must be attacked. Prolonging the combat an additional ten minutes is too dangerous for the tormentor. A trumpet sounds, and the victorious brute trots off at the side of the lead ox which has been brought in for escort. Being "wise," he can never be played again and must be slaughtered for beef or returned to the breeding herd.

Among its followers, bull fighting is regarded as not merely a lethal sport; it is an art, comparable to ballet dancing or fencing in its display of grace and beauty, besides providing imminent hazard in attempting scores of different kinds of "passes" with the *muleta* and the expert sword play of the matador.

Unfortunately, bull fighting, which had already yielded to football as the favorite sport with the Spanish masses, reached a fresh crisis in 1952 when it was revealed that the *toreros* had been fighting undersized bulls with filed-down horns. As a result the government passed a law penalizing cattlemen who send bulls into the ring weighing less than 470 kilograms (1,036 pounds), or with their horns "shaved." This latter practice throws the animal off balance—like a cat with its whiskers cut—and when it lunges at the enemy, it falls a couple of inches short of hitting the target. If the shaving is drastic, the horn tips become sensitive enough to make the animal "favor" its only weapon against the matador. The scandal reached such proportions that many *toreros* who refused to fight "regulation" weight

[10] All professional bullfighers are *toreros;* the group appearing in the ring is a *cuadrilla* and includes the *matador* (killer) ; two or three *bandilleros,* who affix the bright-streamered, barbed darts in the bull's shoulders; and two or three *picadors*—riders on worthless horses—who attack the bull with lances. Also assisting are two or three *peones,* fighters on foot, and a *punctillero,* or dagger man, who, when other means fail to kill, drives his weapon between the animal's skull and atlas vertebra to sever the spinal cord. The *cuadrilla* is under the orders of the matador, who pays its members according to an official wage scale.

or non-"filed-horn" bulls were fined 15,000 pesos or more, and breeders 20,000 pesos for sending underweight or "tampered" animals into the arena.

Although foredoomed to death, a brave and resolute bull can claim his share of the applause bestowed by the critical *aficionados*.

CHAPTER 7

Calf Scrambling and Bulldogging

T HE CONTINUITY OF CONTESTS between men and beasts in the arenas of the world has paralleled that of civilization itself. Centuries after the Cretans, Greeks, Romans, and Iberians first came to grips with the bullocks of the Eastern Hemisphere, history continues to repeat itself in similar New World sports, such as steer wrestling, Brahman-bull riding, and "calf scrambling."

The calf scramble is a modern addition to the outdoor programs of many of our livestock shows. The participants are youngsters of the 4-H Clubs and the Future Farmers of America, to whom is given the opportunity to distinguish themselves in "show business" and to start a career in animal husbandry. In Denver the National Western Stock Show annually in January stages a "4-H Catch-It Contest." For fun and fury this unrehearsed spectacle is hard to beat.

To the spectator it seems to be just as amusing and no more "organized" than an old-time greased-pig chase. But there are rules which limit the age, the behavior, and the eligibility of the contestants. Boys are admitted from 4-H Clubs in Colorado, Wyoming, Kansas, Nebraska, New Mexico, and Oklahoma, who can be certified by their county agent. The rules require contestants to be at least twelve and under twenty-one years of age. Altogether there are fourteen rules to which the applicant must subscribe before being entered, in addition to having the signed permission of his parent or guardian and the county agent.

Before a boy enters the arena, he draws a number from a hat to determine his place. One calf is released for each pair of boys, and that ratio is maintained in each day's contest. When a boy gets hold of an animal, no other boy may touch it until it breaks away. If he can hold it long enough, the winning lad attaches a halter with a ten-foot rope to the calf's head and leads it to the gate, without assistance. The calf becomes his property, but he must feed it and condition it for sale at the next year's show, meanwhile writing a letter monthly to the sponsor of his calf. The boy gets 90 per cent of the prize and sale money, the remaining 10 per cent going into the general fund. This "scramble" is financed by the Stock Show, with each breed association contributing $30 a head towards expenses. Forty calves are used, including eight Shorthorns, eight Aberdeen Angus, and twenty-four Herefords, which matches percentage-wise the number customarily exhibited both at the Show and at the Christmas sale immediately preceding.

In Iowa, nine 4-H Club boys and nine Future Farmers of America—vocational agriculture students—are selected on their merits to enter a similar catch-it-and-keep-it run-around. At both Denver and Des Moines, the number of calves released in the arena is just half the number of contestants, which leaves a 50–50 ratio of winners to losers. At the Iowa State Fair, held in August, three Aberdeen Angus, three Herefords, and three Shorthorns, each weighing between 240 and 300 pounds, are used.

The scramble begins when the eighteen boys lined up at one end of the arena are turned loose on the nine calves simultaneously released at the other end. For the contest there are nine judges—each closely following the fortunes of one particular calf. Barehanded, each lad tries to catch an animal—leaping, plunging, and nose-diving in an attempt at "necking" his chosen hunk of veal-on-the-hoof. If a boy can get a good "holt" on a calf—good enough to control it—no other contestant may touch it unless it gets away. If a calf "outscrambles" a boy and escapes, it is a free agent, but no one else may attempt to catch it until the lad who lost it returns to the side of the arena and joins the others who lost out on the first attempt; they may

72

then resume their pursuit of any uncaptured calves. Each boy has a rope halter with which, if he is successful, he leads the calf to the judges' stand, where he gets a winner's certificate.

This scramble is something more than an acrobatic feat. During the succeeding sixteen months each winner must feed and train a young animal—not the one he captured but a suitable steer of show-beef type which he receives in October, since August would stretch the feeding season too long if the "scrambled" animal were used. The county agent, club leader, or F.F.A. instructor makes periodic visits to the boy's home, and members of the staff of Armour's Livestock Bureau, sponsor of the contest, proffer assistance and advice in the development of the project. When the boys show their calves at the International Livestock Exposition in Chicago fifteen months later, all proceeds from their sale at auction go to them. Of the nine calf-scramble winners, the boy who does the best job of training, caring for, and feeding his animal receives a $300 scholarship at his state agricultural college; the second best wins a $100 scholarship.

At most of the county fairs scheduling calf scrambles, these are the rules: The calf is turned loose, and the boy is given a certain number of seconds in which to catch and halter it. If he succeeds in doing so within the time limit, the calf is turned over to him as a project for the season. When it is sold at the fair the following year, the boy will repay 60 per cent of the cost of the animal. If the calf should die, the sponsor loses the cost of the calf and the boy whatever he has spent in rearing it. In some cases such losses are covered by insurance. Sponsors are readily secured from the ranks of local merchants, chambers of commerce, or livestock associations. These scrambles do not interfere with the scheduled programs of the boys' clubs; they are merely supplements and added incentives. Sponsors agree that capturing and haltering a calf quickly and unassisted is a necessary skill wherever cattle are handled, and also that the successful raising of the high-grade animal he has won gives a boy a good start as a producer of quality livestock. As for the spectators, the holiday crowds watching bull grappling in a Cretan amphitheater forty centuries ago could have had no more fun than does the grass-roots audience at an Iowa calf scramble in the twentieth century A.D.

Not all the young "scramblers" become cattle kings. Some of them grow up to be college professors of animal husbandry, or county agents, advising agriculturalists what to plant or breed. And an occasional amateur participant becomes a professional rodeo performer. For those with a wandering foot and a yen for exhibitionism, it is a natural transition from scrambling for veal to calf-roping for money. Those who become expert in this specialty usually earn more money than those who go into teaching. A boy who is a "whiz" with a rope can gross $10,000 a year, even up to $25,000. For example, twenty-four-year-old Del Haverty of Benson, Arizona, 1951 world champion cowboy, won $6,550 in prize money for one week's work: including $3,620 for bareback riding, $1,680 for calf-roping, and $1,250 for bull-dogging. The 1954 world champion was Buck Rutherford, of Lenepah, Oklahoma, who won $40,404 for his year's work. Runner-up was another Oklahoman, Jim Shoulders, of Henryetta, whose arena winnings totaled $28,700.

But a roper, to make the rounds of the rodeos—which stretch from Canada to Mexico and from New York to California—must have a good car, a dependable and speedy horse, and a stout trailer. He often travels forty thousand miles during the season, performing at some forty profitable shows. At a big rodeo he may rope as many as six or eight calves, each bringing a substantial reward.

Calf-roping is divided into "go-rounds." When each contestant has had a chance to rope his first calf, a go-round has been concluded, and the winners, down to fourth place, are paid off. Following nine or ten such rounds, the winners of the final averages get into the concluding award of prize money, from first to fourth places. If a roper wins several go-rounds, he collects a tidy sum of money.

According to the rules, a mounted contestant dashes from the side of the chute as the calf breaks the barrier, swinging a menacing rope toward the calf in an attempt to loop it about its neck. If successful, he must dismount on the run, throw the calf by hand, and while his trained horse takes up the slack in the rope fastened to the saddle horn, the cowpoke must tie any three legs together (usually one front and both hind) with his piggin' string. This accomplished, he raises his hands, the judge's flag drops, and the timers scrutinize their stop-watches. Sixteen seconds is considered good time at most shows, but some of the speedier snaggers finish the job in about ten seconds. When a full-grown steer is substituted for a calf and two mounted ropers operate as a team in bringing it down—one roping it around the neck, the other around a hind leg—the event is scheduled as "team tying."

In the modern arena, a stunt known as "bulldogging" seems to repeat many a *beau geste* from four thousand years ago, all performed in the spirit of good, clean fun. In our own country, the origin of this sport is credited to Bill Picket, a Texas Negro cowhand, who, fifty years ago, while pursuing a runaway steer, leaped from his horse, seized it by the horns, dug his boot-heels into the ground to serve as a brake, and brought the critter down by twisting its neck, after taking a bite out of the animal's lip, in the same fashion that big bovines once succumbed to the tenacious teeth of a bulldog—hence the rodeo word "bulldogging."

Probably without realizing it, the Texan, was following a precedent set by the old-time sport of "bull baiting." In this gentle pastime of England, dating from the fourteenth century, a bull was let loose in the ring, or tied to a stake by a short rope connected to a heavy collar around his neck, sometimes after his nose had been blown full of pepper to infuriate him. A clever bull would sometimes paw a hole in the ground into which he

75

would stick his muzzle. Specially bred dogs with pushed-back noses and forward-thrust under jaws were then set upon the bull in an effort to get a firm grip on his nostrils. The game was won by the dog which could not be shaken off, in spite of horns and high welter. This was called "pinning the bull." The sport probably reached its peak of popularity in 1575, on the day when a number of bulls and bears were "baited" for the entertainment of Queen Elizabeth I. It is not known whether or not they gained the royal favor. But certainly John Evelyn, the noted diarist, was no enthusiast. Under the date of June 16, 1670, he wrote: "I went with some friends to the bear garden, where was cock-fighting, dog-fighting, bear and bull baiting, it being a famous day for all these butcherly sports. . . . The bulls did exceedingly well, but the Irish wolf-dog exceeded— . . . One of the bulls tossed a dog full into a lady's lap, as she sat in one of the boxes at a considerable height from the arena. . . . I most heartily weary of the rude and dirty pastime."[1]

A variant known as "bull running" was popular in provincial towns, among them Stamford, where on every November 13 a bull provided by the local butchers was released and the townsfolk invited to chase it. Eventually the winded beast and his panting pursuers reached the point of exhaustion, whereupon the bull was slaughtered for whatever meat remained on the shrunken carcass. However, a humane rule prohibited the mob from using "sticks or staves shod with iron." In 1835 both sports were suppressed by act of Parliament.

When Bill Mauldin, the artist, was sent to England in 1953 to cover the coronation of Queen Elizabeth II for *Life* Magazine, he chose to sketch the folk activities of St. Keverne in Cornwall (population 300). Here was staged the age-old ceremony of roasting a "coronation ox" and distributing free barbecued beef to the villagers. Preceding the feast, the populace crowded into the church where a radio described the ceremony in Westminster Abbey. Afterwards everyone rushed to the square where

[1] *The Diary of John Evelyn* (ed. by William Bray), II, 53–54.

a huge ox, having been spitted at six in the morning, had been roasting for hours under the supervision of three butchers. The concrete block supporting the spit and the fire-pit were the work of a local mason and his three sons. Some two thousand country-men fought for quarter-pound pieces of meat. "Pity the Queen's so young," mourned one trencherman. "We shan't see another of these for fifty years!"

In Spanish California, in the brave days of the Dons, a little more than a century ago, there was "bull running" by mounted men, performing within a large, fenced arena, with high plat-forms for spectators just outside. In the ring, one hundred or more of the most highly skilled *rancheros*, waving *serapes* and occasionally pricking the bull with a four-foot lance, baited the animal until, filled with weariness and fury, it was driven through the open gate. Here, augmented by other horsemen outside the arena, they pursued the beast at full speed. The object was to seize and throw the bull by the tail, which was no easy task. In the general melee, horses often collided and riders were un-horsed in this *corrida de toros*—suggestive of the sport as prac-ticed in Portugal to this day. Sometimes the Californians staged a contest in which the performers, mounted or on foot, tried to place barbed darts exactly between the bull's shoulders, in the fashion of the *banderilleros* of Spain. Those who succeeded were applauded, while those who failed to hit the exact spot were jeered at for their awkwardness.

Another entertainment indigenous to California was the bear-and-bull fight. Into the ring was led the bull, a strap around one foreleg. The bear, which had been lassoed in the mountains with rawhide *reatas*, was then released in the arena. A long piece of rope, attached to one of its hind legs, connected it with the strap around the bull's foreleg. "It was a soul-refreshing sight," said one spectator, "to see the growling beast of blood, tied with a long *reata* on one of its hind legs—so as to leave it free to use its claws and teeth—to one of the bull's feet, leaving it free for attack or defense. . . . The bull was generally the first to attack.

77

The bear stood on the defensive, and either put his paw in the face of the bull or seized him by the knee, which made the bull lower its head and bellow, whereupon the bear seized its tongue. They were, at this juncture, usually separated to save the bull."[2] Certain of the horsemen stood by with loaded guns and *reatas* in case the bear should leap the barrier. It often happened that both animals were killed.

In Brazil, where all cattle are worked in corrals with ten- or twelve-foot wire or timber fences to prevent their jumping out, a unique kind of bull-baiting is practiced by fearless Paraguayan cowhands—never the less venturesome Brazilians. This exciting pastime—a comic interlude in the day's work—was once described by the late John Mackenzie, one-time manager of the Matador Land and Cattle Company, as it existed three decades ago in South America.

"During the corral work," he wrote, "whether branding calves or sorting cattle, a zebu bull sometimes showed signs of fight. On seeing this, the men kept teasing him to keep him annoyed. After the work was done, all cattle were let out except the bull. He was then teased some more, until he was really 'on the prod.' At a signal from the *capitas* (foreman), ten or twelve men took their positions around the pen and at another signal closed in on all sides. Each took hold of some part—head, legs, tail, etc.—and threw the beast, tying or holding him down. Then the boss stepped up, planted one foot on the bull's head and gave him a wordy, Latin-American tongue-lashing, with gestures: 'You thought you were big and mighty, but look where you are now. We men work together using our heads. You, poor fool, use only your brawn.' While the orator shouted and thumped his chest, the men laughed and cheered. Sometimes they got so excited they forgot to hold the bull. When he started to get up, this called for another tussle to throw him, a completely new performance and another speech."[3]

---

[2] H. H. Bancroft, *California Pastoral*, 433–34.
[3] Letter to the authors from John Mackenzie, February 14, 1952.

In our modern rodeos, bulldogging is now generally listed as "steer wrestling." At a given signal the steer is released from the chute, and the moment it crosses a designated line two riders dash out in pursuit—a "dogger" and a "hazer." If either breaks out before the steer crosses the line, a ten-second penalty is assessed. The hazer's job is working on one side to keep the steer running in a straight line. On the other side, the dogger's horse is matching the pace of the steer. As quickly as possible the rider leans from the saddle, grabs the steer's horns, leaps to the ground, digging in his heels to stop the brute, and twists its neck until it falls. When all four legs are parallel with the ground and pointing in the same direction, the judge drops the flag and the time is recorded and broadcast by the announcer. Fast time for "dogging" a steer from behind a barrier is between eight and eighteen seconds. In the so-called "lap and tap" method, hazer and dogger may rush the steer the instant it leaves the chute. In this way some phenomenal records have been made, perhaps the fastest being 2.8 seconds flat. This is possible only when the steer is caught before it starts to run.

Another rodeo feature, provoking gales of laughter, is the "wild cow milking contest." A lot of range mothers, with puny udders, are let loose in the ring. Then an equal number of cowpokes carrying empty milk bottles move in, their plunders to perform. In the midst of the ensuing commotion, the blattings of the mammy cows are punctuated with grandstand cries of "Hook 'em, cow" and "Grab her tail, cowboy." The first to extract even a few drops and rush with it to the judge's stand is declared the winner. The sum total of all this uproar is a minimum amount of milk and a maximum number of discontented cows. Sometimes each contestant is assisted by a "gunsel"— usually an amateur who helps by distracting the attention of the cow long enough for the milk to be extracted.

Probably the severest test a cowpoke can undergo in trying to maintain his seat on any bucking animal, bovine or equine, is to ride a Brahman bull bareback, with one hand clutching a rope attached to the beast's girth strap. These huge, humped cattle, some of them weighing a ton, can twist, lunge, and leap into the air with such speed and vigor as to unseat almost any human who tries to "stay aboard" within the time limit of a mere eight seconds. Especially dangerous is the "spinning" bull —one which, instead of bucking straight away, twists in fast, tight circles, and then, when the rider hits the dirt, often whirls and tries to gore him with its horns. Here is where the professional clown, indispensable at all rodeos, rushes in and baits the maddened bull, drawing it away from the fallen rider, who is more than likely stunned by his fall and unable to scamper to safety. Just as a matador caught in a tight situation at a bull fight is saved by his mates with the capes, so does this courageous, fleet-footed acrobat and athlete act in a similar emergency. All cowboys appreciate his timely services. "I'd just as soon come out of the chute on a loco mountain lion," said Gus Thompson, an old-time rider in the Buffalo Bill show, " 'cause I'd know the clown would get it off me."

On one occasion back in 1904, when he had no rescuing clown, Gus tried an even more dangerous stunt. Colonel Cody had purchased a couple of bull buffalo to cross with domestic cows on his Carter Ranch in Wyoming. It fell to the lot of Roy Myers and Gus to drive them from the railhead to their destination. After they had proceeded some distance, Gus thought one of the pair should help work its passage by carrying his two hundred pounds of bone and muscle. With Roy's help in roping and holding, Gus finally managed to get on deck, grasp the girthing rope, and order the lariat loosed. With a terrific snort and a great bellow, the buffalo started a wild race across the prairie. For almost ten miles he ran at break-neck speed, turning, twisting, jumping, bellowing, and heaving Gus first onto his shaggy neck, then onto his short-haired rump. In spite of these maneuvers, he failed to unseat the rider. Finally, when the maddened animal reached Diamond Creek, he plunged in, drove his head against the opposite bank, and threw Gus into the air, depositing him forty-seven measured feet away. Gus later admitted that the buffalo was the toughest thing he had ever tackled, but vowed he'd have him saddle-broke within thirty days.

In spite of their resentment at being molested, Brahman cattle are otherwise quiet, gentle, and easily handled. At stock shows one often sees little children patting these floppy-eared, mild-eyed creatures in their pens. They are easily trained to jump. One Illinois breeder has a herd of thirty, some of which he sends to rodeos to toss unhappy waddies from their backs, others he trains to clear a five-barred gate like a high-bred hunter. A powerful animal can clear six feet at one graceful, effortless bound.

To the Spaniards we are indebted for the word "rodeo," meaning roundup. South of the border and in California it is pronounced *ro-day'-o,* but generally, if you are talking to a bow-legged poke who makes his living at riding broncs and bulls in the United States, you'll never win his friendship unless you call it *ro'de-o.* It is an important branch of American sports, the number of its paying patrons annually ranking third, just behind basketball and baseball. And the major part of its program consists of what is done to, and by, cattle.

CHAPTER 8

Ox-Pulls in Yankeeland

FOR CENTURIES, plowing has always required more power than any other farming operation. It remained for our Yankee forefathers to emphasize ox-drawn plowing and pulling matches. As early as 1820 spirited contests were held at several New England cattle shows. Later came competition for "points" between plowmen driving teams of mules or horses. Today the struggle is between tractor-drawn implements of the machine age.

"Open to the United States" proclaimed the big three-sheet announcement of the seventy-sixth annual plowing match near Wheatland, Illinois, on September 12, 1953.[1] Just 101 years earlier, on September 3, 1852, back east, sturdy Vermonters were excitedly competing for similar "points," hoping that their oxen and those newly-invented steel walking plows could win a five-dollar prize at the Rutland State Fair. Almost thirty years before that, at Brighton, Massachusetts, the annual "Ploughing Match" was promoted in the news columns of the *New England Farmer,* which announced that a "suitable piece of ground" had been furnished by Mr. Francis Winship, "north of his house, on the road leading from Cambridge to Brighton Meeting-house." The theater of operations, "laid out by a careful surveyor," consisted of eleven lots of one-eighth of an acre each, to be plowed by one yoke of oxen, and nine lots of one-quarter of an acre each, to be plowed by two yokes of oxen, "with a margin for the accommodation of spectators"—no mention of

[1] The score card at Wheatland listed the "points" on which the match was to be judged: 25 each for opening, conformation, and straightness of furrows; 15 for evenness; and 10 for neatness. Prizes ranged from $25 for first place to $15 for fourth place.

a grandstand or bleachers, so indispensable to the effete "fans" of later generations.

To the clanking of chains, the creaking of yokes, the suspiration of panting bullocks, and the shouts of struggling sodbusters plying lash-tipped hickory switches, the battle was on. To those driving a single pair, plowing an eighth of an acre, went three prizes; to the first plow, $15; to its plowman, $8; and to the driver $4—a total of $27; second place, with a similar division of the prize money, won a total of $18; and the third, $11; all these "having performed the best work with the least expense of time and labor." Those driving two yoke of oxen plowing a quarter of an acre, also "with the least expense of labor," were awarded cash premiums identical with those driving single teams. Since not all contestants employed a driver, this portion of the prize money went to the plowman who could control his oxen vocally, with no need of driver, goad, or switch. That was October 16, 1823.

In September, 1827, at the fourth annual Grand Cattle Show at Stockbridge, Massachusetts, oxen were still being hitched to iron-patched wooden plows or plows made of cast iron. It was not until the 1830's that the revolutionary all-steel plow was invented, with braces, beams, and handles of wood. It reduced by one-third the amount of animal power needed for turning the soil. The earlier wooden plows required at least four oxen to pull them through the tough sod of the prairie states—often six and eight teams were needed—and an acre a day was considered successful plowing.

Under these conditions it is not surprising that plowing even a little competitive plot of one-eighth of an acre, "with furrows not to exceed ten inches in width," called for the most strenuous exertions of man and beast. And so there was great excitement among populace and performers when the teams lined up to turn the rain-sodden soil at Stockbridge a century and a quarter ago. Among the spectators was Captain Basil Hall of the British navy, who bequeathed to posterity this account of the event:

"The ploughmen, who showed a great deal of spirit in this amusing competition, all drove oxen excepting one man, on whose ridge horses were used. I have such an obscure idea of what good ploughing is, that I cannot tell how this trial ought to rank with similar exhibitions elsewhere; in truth I soon ceased to watch the details of the match in the personal interest I was led to take in one of the competitors, whose vehement anxiety to win the prize enlisted the sympathy of most of the spectators. He was a small and rather handsome negro, who drove a team of oxen as diminutive, in proportion, as himself. His whole soul was absorbed in the enterprise. He looked neither to the right nor to the left, nor anywhere indeed but to the heads of his cattle, whose slightest deviation from the straight line he watched with a quickness which excited the admiration and sometimes the applause of the bystanders. In his hand he wielded a little whip, or more generally he laid it across the plough, using it only when his voice failed to direct his team. Even then he merely touched one or the other of the oxen with the end of the lash, not rudely and with a volley of angry reproaches, but gently, and more as a hint to the animals than as a punishment. Accordingly as in duty bound, they seemed to enter fully into their master's anxiety and tugged and panted along in gallant style.

"After the match was over, the umpires kept us a long time in suspense before they decided which ridge was the best ploughed, for it appears that expedition in these matters is only one of many points which determine the real merit of the work done. But the judges at last decided in favour of our sable friend—a result with which the whole field seemed satisfied. Poor blackie indeed has very seldom such occasions of triumph, for even in these non-slaveholding States of America this fatal shade, by marking out the negro as a totally different race, gives him little or no chance of placing himself upon any permanent equality with the white lords of the creation who on their part would as soon think of sitting down to eat Indian corn leaves or chopped pumpkins with their cattle, as of entering into social intercourse with a 'negur,' with whom, however, it would seem they have no objection to engage in manly but temporary competition."[2]

Today it is doubtful if such competition, with oxen pulling the plows, is being staged anywhere in the United States. There is, however, another kind of contest with cattle in the stellar role. For this, one must go to New England when the leaves begin to turn and "fair time" lures the local yeomanry to the annual ox-pull. Here bearded old-timers and middle-aged farmers of five states guide their leisurely animals to the drawing pits, each certain that his particular team can out-pull all others and walk away flaunting a blue ribbon from the horns of the nigh ox.

The test consists of the ability of a yoke of oxen to pull a "stone boat"—a kind of dry-land toboggan built of timber and planking and loaded with rocks—a specified distance in a straight draw. The rules differ in the several states. In Massachusetts, Vermont, and New Hampshire the distance is six feet straight ahead in one continuous pull, within a three-minute time limit. In Connecticut it is two feet;[3] and in Maine, as far as possible—the winner being the pair that covers the longest distance without stopping.

In the Granite and Green Mountain states there are several classes, each grouped according to weight. In the first class are all cattle weighing under 2,700 pounds; in the second, those between 2,700 and 3,100; and in the third, 3,100 to 3,500. There is also a free-for-all class, with no weight limit. Heavy stones, aggregating perhaps four tons, are placed on the boat, and when all competitors in the preliminary "draws" have hauled this much, 500 or 700 more pounds are added to the load. The procedure is repeated over and over, until the failures are eliminated, and the blue ribbon is given to the pair which has moved the heaviest weight six feet within the prescribed time limit.

[2] Capt. Basil Hall, *Travels in North America, 1827–28*, II, 75–77.
[3] At the Danbury Fair in 1951 this was increased to six feet.

Most fairs award second-, third,- and fourth-place ribbons; some, five or six. Any team which fails to pull the load six feet is ineligible to hitch again, with the exception of the finals, when the pulling of a staggeringly heavy load may be decided by inches—for example, one yoke might pull it fifty-two inches, another thirty-five, and the next, twenty-four.

Americans may be interested in the weight record for a six-foot pull. Around the first of this century, Jim Avery, of Buckland, Massachusetts, hitched a mighty pair of Holsteins, each standing six feet at the shoulder and weighing over two tons apiece, to a stone boat at Brattleboro, Vermont, where they drew 11,200 pounds of granite blocks to establish a world record—years later bettered by his driver, Earl Purington, of Buckland.

Maine stages a different kind of ox-pull. Here the cattle are classified not by weight, but by "girt," as the ox fanciers say. For this a "girting chain," of very fine links and from seven and one-half to eight feet long, is used. Every six inches, from the fourth to the eighth foot, is marked by a wire ring. Put around the body just behind the front legs, this chain is supposed to indicate the size and weight of the animal. However, on account of different builds of various breeds of cattle, it is not an absolute gauge. For example, Durhams are rather accurately measured, while Devons are smaller around the heart and as a rule overweigh what the chain indicates. Depending on breed, flesh, length, and quality, five feet generally means a weight of 1,200 to 1,300 pounds, with increasing weights for every six-inch increase in the chain length, culminating in 3,500 to 3,800 pounds for a seven-and-one-half foot measurement. Under this system, Maine may classify in one group all oxen under six feet, four inches, another six feet, ten, another seven feet, two with a free-for-all which has no limit in girth. For each class the stone boat is loaded proportionately, and the team that pulls it the largest number of feet in three minutes wins.

Training oxen for pulling contests entails a lot of time, work, and patience. Bovine muscles have to be developed and hardened, and driver and beasts must establish mutual understanding and confidence. A number of New England farmers make a specialty of breeding, training, and exhibiting oxen. Such a one is Glen Parker, of Norwich, Vermont. He and his partner, A. E. Maxham of Woodstock, who own a string of twenty to twenty-five teams, were brought up with steers and oxen, as were their fathers and grandfathers. At Maine, Massachusetts, Vermont, and New Hampshire fairs the Parker and Maxham ox teams have frequently been exhibited and have won many blue ribbons. Some of them perform tricks such as kneeling and lying down at a command. In a parade around the race track others, without yoke or harness, are driven by young girls. In a letter to the authors, Mr. Parker thus comments on the method of breaking and training the oxen.

"They are like children, handle much easier and learn more quickly when calves six to ten months old, and once broken they never forget. With patience, and taking time, one can teach them to go side by side with no yoke, kneel, lie down, and so on. . . . In driving them, no two men have the same method. Here in Vermont we use a lash whip, in Maine a goad stick, and in other countries reins. Drivers even use different language. But in any case each ox must know his name. Favorites in New England are Bright & Broad, Joe & Tom, Dick & Dan, Star & Roan, Jim & Jerry, Duke & Dime, Pat & Mike.

"The driver always stands back of his oxen, or on the left side, this 'nigh' ox usually being 'handier' than his mate, the 'off' ox. Dropping his whip gently on their shoulders, the driver calls 'whoo-hish,' and off they start. In 'hawing' them, or turning left, he steps nearer the nigh ox's hip, swinging his whip to shoulder or forelegs, then touching the off ox on the rump, crying 'woo-haw' (come here)![4] By so doing, he can turn the team in a complete circle. In turning to the right, or 'geeing' the pair, the driver steps up by the nigh ox's head, gently using the whip in

[4] Among the Indians of the Great Plains, the oxen and other cattle accompanying the emigrant trains were known as "Wo-haws."

87

front of the legs or head of the off ox, then hitting the rump of the nigh ox with the whip and commanding them to 'Gee!' To back the pair the whip must be applied to all four front legs repeating the command 'Back!' This takes a long time and much practice. Younger cattle require the use of the whip but eventually the driver can stand back and they will obey by merely using the proper commands. Most important is their stopping promptly at the word 'whoa.' If patience is used, they will understand, but if the driver loses his temper and uses too much whip, the animals will become frightened, and often run away. In mating them as pairs, they must match as near as possible in conformation, height, length, color, and set of horns; even in disposition. I have a pair of three-year-old roan Durham steers, identical twins, the only pair I ever had that I have to look at twice to tell them apart."

A State of Maine neighbor of John Gould, the author-farmer, is described as one who has so intimately lived with oxen as to establish an indissoluble bond between man and beast. According to Gould, his friend Elmer Keith loves his oxen devotedly and is such a successful blue-ribbon winner at ox-pulls that competitors strive only for second place. "He doesn't say he trains them," reports Gould, "he says he 'plays around' with them. But in playing round, Elmer has taught them to obey his slightest wish instantly. . . . His only commands are whispered whoas and gees, and a friendly sucking through his teeth. Elmer can suck just so, and his steers will turn on a dime and leave eight cents change. . . . His opponents even train down heavy oxen to make his class, and he still beats them. They yell and holler and wave their sticks, and sometimes brad and thump, mostly to put on an act because they love their steers too, but Elmer comes walking in and sucks his tooth and trims them. . . . Elmer sold a prize-winning yoke last year when a farmer met his price, and the farmer tried to team them in the ring but they wouldn't budge. Elmer stood back in the crowd with the money in his pocket and laughed, and after a bit the oxen walked over to where he was and stood there. Elmer felt bad because he'd sold them. . . . 'The main secret of winning all the time,' says Elmer, 'is a knack of getting closer to your steers than the other fellows. . . . As for pulling, the steers love it, the way a boy chins himself on a limb to show off in front of his girl. Steers like mine are only unhappy when they're tied up in the barn.' "[5]

Another story demonstrating the integration of teamster with team comes from Connecticut. According to writer Norman Myrick, a driver once brought his cattle into the drawing pit at the Danbury Fair, where the official hauling distance was two feet. This chap "was having a rugged time with John Barleycorn, with the decision obviously going to John. Officials attempted to dissuade him from drawing, but he was there and he was going to draw. He could scarcely stand alone and hung onto the horn of the nigh ox for support. How he ever hooked on will remain one of those unfathomable occurrences that belong somewhere between miracle and fantasy. Hook on he did and then, lurching up to the security of the nigh ox, he took off his cap and threw it down on the ground two feet in front of his team. 'There' he said to his cattle, 'want you should draw up to there. Now git.' Why they did it or how they did it will never be known, but they did it. Lifted their great shoulders into the yoke, moved up to the cap, and stopped. Up to the cap the man had said and up to the cap they would go, that far and no farther."[6]

There are certain phases and procedures peculiar to draft cattle. An animal which is castrated when a few weeks old grows up to be a steer; after working a season it becomes an ox. If the operation is deferred until the animal is somewhat more mature, it becomes a "stag," tougher but less tractable. Well-broken pairs need little more than voice and brains for successful handling. However, a driver usually carries some kind of a "persuader." And here's where Yankee provincialism as-

[5] John Gould, "The Pull in the Pulling Contest," from an undated clipping from the *Christian Science Monitor.*

[6] Norman Myrick, "The Lord Made 'em Capable: A Story of Oxen," *Yankee Magazine,* Vol. XI, No. 5 (May, 1947), 32.

serts itself. In Maine, they use a goad-stick, or "gad," with a darning-needle tip; in Massachusetts, New Hampshire, and Vermont, a short hickory switch with a thin rawhide lash; in Connecticut, a long sapling, scornfully referred to by northern neighbors as "fish poles." When the use of a whip is indicated, a driver will "touch up" a horse, but he "hoes down" an ox. When a yoke fits snugly on the neck, it is "bowed up." A driver always takes his stand at the shoulder of the left-hand, or "nigh" ox, the one on the right being the "off" ox.

"Go to the drawing pits," advises Myrick, "and see the great cattle swing into the ring with yokes creaking, chains jingling. Watch the driver hook on. Notice how he hitches as close to the boat as he can stand and still have clearance left for his cattle. He stands back now and looks the team over. That nigh ox, the driver hitches him two inches closer to his mate. The right hind foot of the off ox needs to come up a hair. The driver taps the hoof with his whip and makes the adjustment. They are standing well now, ready to lift into the yoke when he gives the word. With something akin to a caress they take up the slack in the chain. It is part of the ritual, part of that tense moment of expectancy when man and beasts stand poised for that one mighty instant when flesh and blood are turned to the task. Then—'Git up you black-hearted sons o'Satan. Hi-hi-hi-hi-hi-hi' Two thundering bodies boring into the yoke, heads up, shoulders lifting, steel-shod hooves churning the red clay in a turbulent pattern of power. Yes, it moves. Two feet in Connecticut, six feet in Massachusetts, as far as you can go in Maine. It makes no difference, for the end is the same. A driver mopping his brow with a red bandana. A pair of cattle standing under the yoke, their flanks heaving like a blacksmith's bellows, and over the public address system come the golden words, 'It's a draw, Mr. Guildford, an up an' down honest-to-God draw and ninety-eight hundred on the boat.' That's all there is to it. Two oxen and a man moving five tons of stone on a draw. No parimutuels, no colored silks and dazzling prima donnas—two oxen and a man."[7]

[7] *Ibid.*, 32–34.

Too bad Edmund Burke never witnessed an ox-pull in Yankeeland. If he had, he could hardly have written, "An ox is a creature of vast strength; but . . . the idea of an ox is by no means grand."

CATTLE & MEN

Exploitation

CHAPTER 9

Europeans Blazed the Trail

ALL PRESENT-DAY BREEDS of cattle in the New World are descended from the two types which were known in Europe from prehistoric times, the large, or *Bos primigenius* type being represented by the aurochs and the small, or *Bos longifrons*, by the Celtic shorthorn. It may well be that some of the original stock of *Bos longifrons* entered the Mediterranean area of Europe along with Neolithic man migrating from Asia. But undoubtedly other local strains were tamed directly from the Celtic shorthorn by some of the northern European tribes. In Spain, in Gaul, and in Britain the cattle of the native tribes carried blood of comparable derivation.

The Alps and the great forests of central Europe supposedly constituted a natural barrier between the aurochs of the north and the *longifrons* types to the south. But the cows of this latter kind, ranging near the woods, could easily mate with the great aurochs bulls when they burst from their leafy glades in the rutting season and begat prototypes of Paul Bunyan's Great Blue Ox. The Germanic, Helvetian, Gallic, and Belgic tribes would have benefited by the increased size of such hybrids. But aside from debatable questions as to just when and where certain types originated, one fact is indisputable: Cattle evolved in Europe contemporaneously with prehistoric man, and later when the course of empire moved relentlessly westward from the Near East of Babylon, Egypt, and Persia, their leaders established the cultures of Greece, Rome, Spain, Gaul, and Britain. Meanwhile cattle participated in three general waves of dispersion.

The first was that of the small hardy breeds kept by the Celtic tribes, which ultimately blazed bovine trails to the

outer frontiers of Europe. W. Boyd Dawkins points out that
when the Romans conquered Britain, there was no need to import cattle from Italy to a land where there was already present
"a breed used to the climate and to the half-wild life which, in
a country for the most part uncleared, must have been their
lot."[1] Characteristic traits persist to this day in the older Irish
breeds; the mottled Glamorgan and sturdy Pembroke races of
Wales; the shaggy Scottish Highland and other strains of mountain cattle; the double-coated Galloway along the southwestern
coast of Scotland; the small Brittany race of western France and
the combative Camargue at the mouth of the Rhone; the hardy,
primitive stocks on the islands off the northern coast of Europe,
such as the Orkneys, Faroes, and Shetlands; the muscular breeds
of the Scandinavian peninsula; and the undersized, peasant-
owned strains along the Baltic.

The second wave was a movement of Mediterranean breeds
and was caused by religion rather than economics. When the
Christians vanquished the Moors and drove them out of Europe, they anathematized not only the Moslems but also their
cattle. Apparently several proved varieties of "infidel" work
oxen of African blood were purged along with their owners.
This loss of quality stock called for replacements, requiring the
importation from the Italian peninsula of a number of specimens
of the old Roman and Iberian breeds.

The third was a kind of double wave, part Germanic, part
Norse. German breeds cut into the cross-current of Mediterranean strains moving northward into France and the Low Countries. Norse cattle shared the venturesome voyages of the Vik-
ings to the northern islands, ranging from Ireland and Britain
to Spitzbergen, Iceland, Greenland, and even to the "Vineland"
of an unexplored North America. There was a renascence of
Norse bloodlines in Britain's Irish, Devon, and Norfolk breeds,
while the red cattle of the Angles, Jutes, and Saxons left trade

[1] W. Boyd Dawkins, "1. On the British Fossil Oxen. Part II. Bos longifrons,
Owen," *Quarterly Journal of the Royal Geological Society*, Vol. XXIII (February 20, 1867), 183.

marks in the bigger-framed modern stocks along the shores of
the North Sea from Lincoln to East Anglia.

Stronger evidence of the spread of the Germanic type appears in the large-framed cattle of the Lowlands, extending
from Belgium to Denmark, where the more massive build of
the "forest-type" varieties seemed better adapted to the semi-
marsh conditions than did the lighter-weight, more delicate types
from the Mediterranean.[2] Aurochs blood predominated in the
Flemish, Dutch, Friesian, and Red Danish strains, revealing the
characteristics which appealed to certain nobles with agricultural backgrounds who crossed western Europe at the time of
the Crusades.

Under the feudal system, helmeted knights and belted earls
gave little thought to the improvement of cattle. Theirs was a
war-horse rather than a draft-ox obsession. However, a few
English noblemen with large holdings became interested in the
large-framed cattle of Middle Europe and, through royal favor,
were occasionally able to obtain well-bred bulls from central
France and the fertile areas of Savoy. Some which reached the
shores of Albion were allegedly ancestral to the sizable Holder-
ness cattle and the mellow-fleshed Teeswater strain of York
and Lincoln in northeastern England. As most of these were imported before the public became interested in cattle improvement, their origin remains a matter of conjecture rather than of
authentic record.

The Romans were probably the first people to discover the
principles of good farming and stock raising. In the fifth century B.C. it was the noble Cincinnatus who left plow and oxen
in the field to fight his nation's foe, and in *De Agricultura* Cato,
the original "grasslands stockman," went all out for fertilizing
the soil to provide forage during the dry seasons. Varro, Virgil,
Columella, and Pliny the Elder added enough of their own advice to give the Roman farmer a solid background for raising
quality cattle. The breeders themselves were able to establish

[2] Lydekker, *The Ox and Its Kindred*, 53.

firmly their great silver-gray breed of oxen—the cattle of the Campagna.

Then came the barbarians. These hooligans butchered and scattered the herds, nullifying the achievements of centuries and setting cattle breeding back a full millenium. In remote areas some of the better blood persisted, but in the devastated fields the superior types could no longer be reproduced because of lack of feed and the master's control over breeding.

When Spain and Gaul became Roman colonies, there was some importation of better-bred Roman cows and bulls. Columella's vigorous writings on agriculture also encouraged the breeders. With the expansion of the Roman Catholic faith among the barbarians, its priests commended the quality of work animals. In fact, certain priests, such as St. Francis of Assisi, were canonized because of their inspired influence over animals and birds.

Although Julius Caesar is often credited with having originated the bull fight as a sport, this, as we have seen, had been a prime attraction in the arenas of ancient Thessaly, Crete, and Egypt. It was nearly fifteen hundred years after Caesar that the cattle breeders of Spain and southern France began to demand animals with the fierce combative spirit essential to the bull ring. Their Roman imports notably increased the efficiency of their work oxen.

Most present-day strains of improved cattle in America are of British origin. Regardless of how the prehistoric breeds of Great Britain looked, the first records indicate that the contemporary cattle, while numerous, possessed "no great bulk or beauty."[3] Caesar noted in 55 B.C. that the Britons neglected tillage and lived on meat and milk. But if a people anywhere had to live thus, it was on these islands. For five hundred years the soil was reddened by the blood of battling barons and petty kings, no fixed property was secure, and the sower of grains

[3] W. Youatt and W. C. L. Martin, *Cattle: A Treatise on Their Breeds, Management, and Diseases,* 11.

never knew whether he could reap his harvest or not. Naturally what he most prized were his "goods and chattels"—property which could be removed quickly or secured within the walls of the castle, where immense stocks of provisions were stored for the sustenance of all the besieged, from churl to chatelaine, from plow-oxen to poultry.

Roman domination of England lasted from the first to the fifth centuries. During this time, and for centuries after, "rugged individuals" of the bovine species continued to fend for themselves in field and forest. In the words of our Western stockmen, they were "great rustlers," foraging for themselves and defying sporadic attempts at domestication. The death of one such, a "wild cow" which had been a tenth-century devastating scourge and had been killed by the Duke of Warwick, inspired these lines:

> *On Dunsmore heath I also slew*
> *A monstrous wild and cruel beast,*
> *Called the dun cow of Dunsmore heath*
> *Which many people had oppressed.*[4]

As the forests were cleared and humans multiplied, wild cattle became increasingly scarce. Finally only a few herds survived. Under the protecting aegis of the British nobility, the so-called Wild White, or Park, cattle, descendants of the original types, could still be found at Chillingham Castle in Northumberland, seat of the Earl of Tankerville; at Cadzow Park in Lancashire, property of the Duke of Hamilton; at Chartley Park in Staffordshire, home of the Lords Ferrers; and at parks in North and South Wales.

These survivors of a primitive stock are small and their coats long and shaggy, notably over the head and neck of the bulls. Although they are of the beef type, the quarters are rather shrunken but muscular. In color, they are white, with a pigmented skin, but vary from black through brown into red at the extremities—as around the eyelids, ears, muzzles, tips of tail,

---

[4] John Storer, *The Wild White Cattle of England*, 56–57.

and ends of teats and horns. When not crossed with domestic cattle, they possess a disposition that is distinctly belligerent, or, as George Culley, writing in the eighteenth century, expressed it: "These, from being untamable, can only be kept within walls, consequently a very few of them only are to be met with. . . . They are so absolutely wild, that those I have seen could not be come so near to, as to form a proper judgment of them. . . . As soon as we came near them, they fled to a considerable distance, then turned suddenly round, and set themselves in battle array, facing us, and knocking their horns one against another.

"We were told by the park-keeper, that they always conceal their calves from the first dropping of them, which would be very difficult to find, if he was not to watch the dam early or late, when she goes very privately to give it suck, after which it immediately claps down again amongst brakes, rushes, etc., while she steals away with great caution. . . . When the park-keeper wants to castrate a calf, having previously well marked the place where it is hid, he goes very softly till he seizes his prey, then after making as short work as possible, he runs to his horse, which is hooked as near as he can be, and rides for his life; for the first noise of the calf not only brings the dam, but the whole herd, instantly; and he told us he sometimes escaped very narrowly, as it makes them quite outrageous."[5]

Some forty years later Youatt corroborated Culley's description, adding that "the dams allow no person to touch their calves, without attacking them with impetuous ferocity. When any one happens to be wounded, or is grown feeble through age or sickness, the rest of the herd set on it and gore it to death."[6] Although this statement is questionable, it does parallel accounts of similar alleged behavior on the part of wolves in killing decrepit or wounded companions.

Concerning the origin of these white cattle, two theories have been advanced. One suggests that they are the direct descend-

[5] George Culley, *An Essay on the Breeding of Livestock*, 23.
[6] Youatt and Martin, *Cattle: A Treatise*, 12.

ants of the original *Bos longifrons* or *bos primigenius,* all except
the white specimens having been killed off. Another conjecture
is that they descended from Celtic or Roman domestic stock
which strayed from the herds during the embattled existence
of the early roving Britons, and became wild, even ferocious.
This seems plausible when one considers that after a stabilized
government had taken over, allowing the grain grower to harvest
his crops in peace, the farmer was freed from the care of his
herds, whereupon his cattle took to the woods and went feral.

The long-standing interest of the nobility in the Park cattle
stems from the remote possibility of their being direct, but de-
generate, descendants of the aurochs or of the Celtic shorthorn.
No proven connection substantiates this theory, and most geneticists consider them merely feral strains developed after escape
from domestication. Youatt places the weight of the wild white
ox at 490 to 630 pounds and the cow from 350 to 490. He says
the six-year-old ox made very good beef, "whence it may be
fairly supposed, in proper situations, they would feed well."[7]

Although Roman invaders chased the old Celtic strains to
the frontiers of Ireland, Scotland, and Wales, their own cattle
had to retreat when Norsemen brought in their polled and horned
cattle and their black, red, and white specimens. The Angles and
Saxons, too, introduced some "red-coats," ancestors of the modern Red Polled breeds of Norfolk and Suffolk. Following the defeat of King Harold by William the Conqueror in 1066, many an
English shire found its livestock superseded by meaty, multi-
colored cattle from Normandy. Then some of the Crusaders—
and later pioneer English cattle improvers—imported Flemish
stocks. The ensuing mixture of Flemish and Norman bloods
produced the old English Longhorn, the primitive Shorthorn,
and the Hereford.

A preview of colonial stock raising in the Americas, is provided in regulations relating to the public pastures, or "commons," in England. For example, all the cattle of a village, even

[7] *Ibid.*

if of different ownership, had to be pastured in one herd, under the direction of one person, whose sworn testimony was decisive in all disputes about livestock.[8] During the sixteenth-century reign of Henry VIII, laws were enacted which forbade the running at large of bulls, rams, and stallions which failed to meet size and other specifications. Before being freed on the commons, those which fell short had to be castrated.

The curious laws which governed the farmer disclose the primitive state of early British agriculture. About the end of the seventh century, King Ina of the West Saxons approved a law whereby a farm consisting of ten "hides," or plow-lands, was required to pay the following annual rent: ten casks of honey, three hundred loaves of bread, twelve casks of strong ale, two oxen, ten wethers, ten geese, twenty hens, ten cheeses, one cask of butter, twenty pounds of forage, five salmon, and one hundred eels.[9] Our modern tenant farmer, struggling to solve the mechanical mysteries of power farming, should be thankful that in order to pay the rent he does not also have to be an expert apiarist, brew-master, baker, fisherman, dairyman, and general husbandman.

For a stock-raising career, the eighteenth-century rustic could choose from six types of "black cattle,"[10] listed by Culley as the wild white cattle, the Scotch and Welch kyloes (mountain breeds), the Alderney or French stock, the humbled, or polled,

---

[8] Thomas G. Fessenden, *The Complete Farmer and Rural Economist, iii.*

[9] *Ibid., iv,* quotes Wilkins' *Leges Saxon.*

[10] The term "black cattle" seems to have been used as a synonym for "cattle," but sometimes implied sturdiness and vitality, at other times primitive origin. Culley wrote: "In all accounts of cattle relative to this island [Britain] which I have seen either in deeds or law statutes, they are called black cattle. . . .[Before] our seacoasts and low country was improved or enclosed . . . is it not probable that we had mostly the small black cattle which are still to be met with in all the wild mountainous parts of Wales and Scotland?" (*An Essay on the Breeding of Livestock,* 25–26.) And Hale, in *A Compleat Body of Husbandry,* stated: "The Lancashire Breed were famous for their calves; and they were generally black; thus *a Black Cow* and *a Lancashire Cow* [*italics ours*] became two expressions for the same Thing, in the same manner as we have shewn a red Cow, and a Wiltshire Cow, meant the same."

breed (Galloway), the Longhorns, including the Herefordshire "brown cattle" (designated as "a mixture between the Welch and a bastard race of longhorns"), and the Shorthorn or "Dutch kine."[11]

Praise for the last-named breed came from J. W. Gent, who in the seventeenth century boasted that "the best sort is the large Dutch cow that brings two calves at one birth, and gives ordinarily two gallons of milk at one meal," declaring that "these worthy sort of beasts are in great request with husbandmen, the Oxe being useful at his Cart and Plough, the Cow yielding great store of Provision both for the family and the Market."[12]

As a publicity man, promoter Gent ran a poor second to William Harrison, who, a century or so earlier, in Hollinshed's Chronicles (1577) solemnly testified, "I heard of late of a cow in Warwickshire, belonging to Thomas Breuer of Studley, which in six years had sixteen calves and twice twins, which unto many may seem a thing incredible." It does!

While Britons were sounding off with prideful cow and ox talk, in southern Spain there were cattle destined to play a vital role in American agricultural history. Andalusia was breeding a sturdy type of ox whose origin dated back to the days of prehistoric Iberia. A traditional incident reported by Herodotus concerned a Greek trading ship which was said to have passed the Pillars of Hercules in 630 B.C. during a severe storm and taken refuge in the port of Tartessos—frequently identified as *Tarshish* of the Old Testament.[13] Here the astonished mariners found dried beef, grains, olive oil, and other feed products, as well as lead, tin, and iron. Their hosts were Iberians, later described by Roman writers as small-framed, alert, wiry, with dark complexions and unkempt hair, prominent cheek-bones, and projecting lower lips. They had horses and excellent work cattle, since most of their sales to visiting mariners came from

[11] Culley, *An Essay on the Breeding of Livestock,* 10–24.

[12] J. W. Gent, *Systema Agriculturae: The Mystery of Husbandry Discovered* (2nd ed.), 161.

[13] Ezek. 27:12.

crops requiring maximum tillage. The Greeks and Romans successively contributed to their agricultural development, interrupted by Carthaginian conquests, which nullified much of the cattle-breeding progress on the plains of Andalusia.

This ancient kingdom was divided into two parts, the geography and climate of which favorably pre-conditioned the cattle brought to America by early Spanish colonists. In the popular mind, Andalusia begins with the sharp descent from the east-west range of mountains, the Sierra Morena. The wide and undulating lowlands that separate the mountains from the Guadalquivir River valley constitute Upper Andalusia. Here the summers are hot, with scanty rainfall, the pastures dry, and the cattle hardy—descendants (quite direct) of *Bos primigenius*. Schmid describes them as being bred for draft and beef and showing strongly pigmented red or black color.[14] All of the subordinate varieties were described as being horned and of great stature. The cattle of Upper Andalusia provided some work animals, but in general were developed as beeves.

Lower Andalusia had even more excessive heat and drought in summer, with no irrigation, but the winters were milder than in any other section of Spain. The olive groves and their culture, west of Seville, were famous, and the vineyards of Jerez de la Frontera supplied famous Spanish wines. Both of these crops, because of the dry summers, required cultivation by the plow and the ox.

This proven strain of cattle provided the stock that accompanied Columbus to the Indies and Villalobos to the coast of Mexico. It was the hardy ancestor, acclimated before arrival, of the Texas Longhorn and the trail herds of the Western plains. Fortunately, in the genial clime of the Southwest, they were able to fulfill the Biblical prophecy: "Their bull gendereth, and faileth not; their cow calveth, and casteth not her calf."[15]

[14] A. Schmid, *Rassenkunde des Rindes*, I, 132; II, 58.
[15] Job 21:10.

CHAPTER 10

Greenland Grass and "Catel"

IT IS AN ARRESTING FACT that five hundred years before Columbus landed his Andalusian bull and some heifers at His-
paniola, a bold Norseman named Erik the Red put ashore
on the coast of Greenland a nondescript assortment of domestic
animals, including cattle and a score or two of human custodians. This occurred in A.D. 981.

The livestock thus introduced eventually petered out and
bequeathed nothing to bovine posterity. However, their early
vicissitudes and those of their owners make a unique contribution of mixed fact and folklore to the story of animal husbandry
in the New World. Scandinavian sagas supply the chronological
flashback, inviting a deliberate shift from documented history
to tradition.

It is difficult to determine what were the exact headlands and
shore lines of Greenland a thousand years ago, so drastic have
been the climatic changes during the intervening centuries. This
has had the effect of confusing the historians and throwing many
of the narratives into apparent conflict with each other. Faulty
translations and fantastic romanticism have also distorted some
of the sagas so as to make them seem improbable, challenging
the credulity of the reader. Yet, stripped of fantasy, the tales of
the North relate matter-of-fact experiences which plain but
virile men would naturally undergo in new and unfamiliar lands,
including versions of strange happenings in conformity with
their superstitions and legends. One such tale has something
to say about cattle.[1]

[1] For a modern study of the sagas, see Arlington H. Mallery, *Lost America*,
and Edward Reman, *Norse Discoveries and Explorations in America*. The latter

In Norway, well before the middle of the tenth century, a boy named Erik the Red left the Jaeder district, in company with the exiled family of his father, Thorvald Asvaldsson, who had been found guilty of manslaughter in connection with a feud. About A.D. 950 they settled at Drangar, on the northeast coast of Iceland. Here Erik married and settled near a wealthy farmer named Valthjof. One day some of Erik's thralls caused a landslide which engulfed Valthjof's field. A kinsman promptly slew the slaves, and Erik retaliated, killing the murderer and a famous duelist who came to his aid. Thereafter Erik, compelled to leave home, settled on South, later on Ox, Island. Becoming involved in a quarrel with one Thorgest, who refused to return some borrowed property, Erik slew two of Thorgest's sons and was banished from Iceland for three years.

As a return to Norway would have required diplomatic hocus-pocus, Erik determined to seek land to the west which had been sighted and described by Gunnbjorn Ulfsson. But if he had climbed a certain peak in the right kind of weather near one of his own west coast farms, Erik himself could have spied the rocky cliffs of Greenland. Apparently reversing the course described by Gunnbjorn, he sailed from Snaefellsness in the year 981, commanding a ship probably between seventy and one hundred feet long. The craft was partly decked and was equipped with oars and a mast carrying a square sail that could be stepped down. Erik took with him his wife and children, his slaves and their offspring, and perhaps some freedmen and their families. There may have been neighbors also, with their dependents.

Slaves, freedmen, and some others were probably of straight Irish blood, but most of the company were Icelanders of Nor-

---

gives both Icelandic and Greenlandic versions of the same sagas. In 1906 the Norroena Society republished *The Flatey Book,* containing several sagas and some Vatican manuscripts concerning America as early as the tenth century. Popular versions and interpretations appear in Vilhjalmur Stefansson's *Iceland: The First American Republic* and *Greenland,* as well as in Einar Haugen's *Voyages to Vinland.* The oldest account, Thormodus Torfaers' *History of Vinland,* was published in Iceland in 1705.

wegian ancestry or of mixed Norwegian-Irish descent. They numbered between twenty and forty persons. With them sailed specimens of most or all of the Icelandic domestic stock—cattle, horses, sheep, goats, pigs, dogs, and perhaps fowls. Hay was carried for the animals and some grain for feed, also dried and smoked fish, probably supplemented by fresh fish caught over-side. There was little cooking on shipboard; when there was, food was prepared over an open fire laid on flat stones on the deck.

Constantly battling the drifting, southward-moving, close-packed ice floes, they made the first determined attack upon sea ice in the recorded history of European civilization. Several weeks must have elapsed before the party was able to round Cape Farewell and make landfall somewhere beyond, in what is now the Julianehaab District. Erik hove his vessel broadside to the land. The animals jumped or were pushed over the gun-wale, and swam or waded to the beach. The adventurers landed, built houses and barns, made hay for the stock, and spent the winter in Icelandic fashion, milking their cows, ewes, and goats, butchering some animals for food, and shearing sheep or pluck-ing them for wool.

That they could have accomplished this if the climate char-acteristic of the sub-polar regions today had prevailed, is doubt-ful, but modern Danish and Icelandic research shows that at the time of Erik's discovery the land was thoroughly adapted to a medieval livestock husbandry. Grass was abundant in the fjordland, and the conditions for a grasslands agriculture, as advocated today, seem to have prevailed. The temperature was distinctly warmer.

During his three years of banishment, Erik explored the coast from Cape Farewell west and northward to what is now the Godthaab District; that is, from the sixtieth to the sixty-fourth parallel north latitude. One can imagine an adventurer's ambition in such a land—here he could literally be emperor of his own world. But Erik the Red was a sociable, friendly man at heart, eager to share his gains with friends in Iceland and bring them to his newly found land. Here were no greedy souls preceding him, and a new fatherland could be established where all could be true neighbors. Hence with a modern realtor's shrewdness he christened his new domain *Green Land,* arguing to himself that "People will all the more want to go there, if the land has an attractive name."

Returning to Iceland about 984, Erik convinced so many people of the desirability of emigrating that the following spring no less than twenty-five ships started with him. Some were lost and others turned back, but fourteen won through, thus starting a colony of around 350 people. Settlements were along pastoral lines, with most of the farms lying at the heads of the fjords. Two major settlements were established, one in Julianehaab, the other in Godthaab, with some ninety farms between, although an uninhabited region known as Obygdir intervened which required six days' rowing to pass.

It was only the southern section of the west coast of the vast island continent—as big as all of our states east of the Mississippi River—which Erik the Red christened Greenland. Here, on a narrow strip along the coast line, the chief occupation was animal husbandry, attended by dairy manufacture, crude spinning and weaving, leather working, and fish drying and curing. With their cattle, horses, sheep, goats, pigs, hens, and geese, the colonists fared very well. Herds and flocks were driven into higher lands for the summer. Stables have been excavated which possessed as many as 104 cattle stalls under one roof, and there were corresponding accommodations for other animals—sheep, goats, swine, horses, and fowl. The grasses and herbage on the near-by slopes above the barns provided the essential feed for the cows. Hay was put up each season and held under cover. Horses were used as pack animals, and their flesh was esteemed for food until the advent of Christianity. Because of the Biblical injunction that one must not eat of a beast unless it splits the hoof and chews the cud, heavy penalties were levied against horse eaters. Cattle were chiefly dairy animals, although calves and some steers and bulls were eaten. As in most northern countries, butchering was done in the fall and enough meat laid up to last all winter. Storage of dressed meats, butter, cheese, and dried fish was provided in caves and pits underground.[2]

During the early seasons all went well—no hardships and no loss of life. By the fifteenth century, however, the whole colony, which at one time numbered 9,000 in population, had been wiped out. Some authorities attribute this to a worsening of the climate, others to the Black Death, despite the fact that no ship came from Norway during the year the plague ravaged northern Europe.

And now another accident actually brought the hoofprints of European cattle to mainland North America. Erik the pagan had a son Leif who was a Christian. King Olaf of Norway persuaded the young man to take two priests to Greenland to convert the settlers there. Sailing from Norway in the spring of the year A.D. 1000, he chose the direct route to Cape Farewell. Apparently he was blown off his course and finally landed on a coast that he did not recognize. Going ashore, Leif found grapes, self-sown wheat, and trees called "mausur." Taking samples of these products, he proceeded to Greenland where he succeeded in getting converts to the Christian religion. Some present-day scholars believe that Leif sailed directly from Norway to Greenland, and that in 1003 or 1004, stimulated by Bjarni Herjulfsson's experience, he deliberately set out to explore lands to the southwest. Discovering the grapes, he called the place Vinland and spent the winter there.

It is now generally accepted that Leif Ericsson was an early white discoverer of the North American continent. But just where was the Vinland of "Leif the Lucky"? Its location has provided food for endless speculation. Complicated theories have been evolved for many sites, all the way from Labrador to Vir-

[2] Stefansson, *Greenland*, 158.

ginia, with Newfoundland, Nova Scotia, Maine, and Massachusetts the favored locations.

The real colonizer of the mainland was Thorfinn Karlsefni, who brought to Nova Scotia 160 men and several women, including his wife Gudrid and an illegitimate daughter of Erik the Red named Freydis. When the adventurers landed, their cattle, sheep, horses, and goats spread out and wandered widely while grazing. This was the year 1004 and these were the first farm animals to settle on the mainland of the Western Hemisphere. The next spring the group and their livestock moved farther south, finally locating in Vinland, where they found evidences of Leif's previous visit. In the year 1012, they were visited by natives whom they called "Skraelings"—sometimes Eskimos, at other times forest-dwelling Indians.

Early one morning, as they were scanning seawards, they caught sight of a great fleet of skin-covered craft. The men in the approaching boats were waving in a "clockwise" direction pieces of wood, the "waving" being the circular motion made in propelling their boats with double-ended paddles. Karlsefni's men raised their white shields in token of friendliness, the Skraelings landed, and trading commenced.

Mostly the visitors craved red cloth. They also wanted spears and swords. But traffic in any kind of weapons was forbidden. In exchange for the cloth the savages offered untanned furs and gray pelts. For each fur they got about a span's length of cloth—nine inches. This they gleefully tied about their heads. After brisk trafficking, the Norsemen began to run short of cloth, so they cut what they had left into smaller strips until each strip was only about one finger wide. Yet the Skraelings gave just as much for this meager portion as they had for the larger swatches.

All this happy huckstering was suddenly and rudely interrupted. One of the bulls belonging to the Norsemen burst from the woods, trotting towards the open-air emporium, bellowing lustily. The terrified Skraelings, never having seen such a beast, took to their heels, jumped into their boats, and hastily vanished to the south. Nothing more was glimpsed of them for three weeks.

At the end of that time Karlsefni's people one day saw a mighty fleet coming from the south, with the paddles waving "counter-clockwise," and all hands shrieking at the tops of their voices. The Norse clansmen raised a red shield and carried it toward the beach. The visiting foemen promptly jumped from their boats and joined battle. Presently they raised a huge sphere on a pole and hurled it over the heads of the Norsemen. It looked like an inflated sheep's belly. As it struck the earth, it made such a terrifying groaning noise that Karlsefni's poltroons bolted, retreating upstream along the river. They kept up their running until they reached the cliffs, where they made shift to reform their ranks and try to withstand the enemy.

At the sight of this shameful retreat, out from her house strode the woman Freydis. "Why do you flee from these wretches?" she shrieked. "Such stout fellows as you are, it seems to me you could butcher them as if they were cattle. If I only had weapons I think I could fight better than any of you." The men paid her no heed.

Freydis tried to follow them, but made heavy work of it for she was with child. Bravely she struggled along into the woods. The Skraelings started after her. Presently in front of her lay a dead man, Thorbrand, his head crushed by a flat rock. Beside him lay his sword. Freydis stooped, picked up the sword, and prepared to defend herself. As the savages approached, she pulled her ample breasts from under her dress and began to strop the naked weapon on them. This gesture so appalled the superstitious Skraelings that they turned and ran for the beach, where they jumped into their boats and paddled away in panic. Karlsefni's warriors then came forward and, red-faced, congratulated Freydis on the astonishing success of her hidden weapons.

Although to many the word "saga" means folklore or fiction, it is the considered judgment of leading authorities that the *Saga of Erik the Red* is a historical document of importance, with any bits of possible fiction too trivial to affect the essential truth of the main theme. Sagas have always been the chief source material for these Norsemen's adventures up to about 1500, when they succumbed to illness and were wiped out with all their livestock. But for half a millenium the Greenlanders were America's only cattlemen.

IN CONTRAST to the tragic disappearance of the Norse herds from the American scene was the discovery of a few hundred head of European cattle which had been put ashore sometime in the sixteenth century on Sable Island, off the southern tip of Nova Scotia, and which later achieved a vigorous though feral survival. When the Marquis de la Roche planted a colony of Frenchmen on the island in 1598, they were astonished to find sizable bands of wild cattle and sheep. Near the shore were the gaunt skeletons of wrecked Spanish ships, melancholy memorials of an expedition which had been sent to colonize Cape Breton. The natural inference was that the livestock had escaped from these ships. The marooned Frenchmen knocked together some boats from the ships' timbers, in which they managed to escape and sail to France.

These Sable Island cattle apparently went unnoticed thereafter until a shipwrecked Englishman named John Rose was cast ashore in 1633. Rose estimated the herd at eight hundred head and so reported to the French when he succeeded in reaching the mainland. Two years later, two vessels, the *James* and the *Rebecca*, were fitted out and sailed from Massachusetts Bay to hunt for sea horse and to search out the wild cows. On arriving at Sable Island, the crews found fourteen Frenchmen who had slaughtered many of the cattle. The visitors described the animals as solid red in color and their numbers "not above 140 and but two or three calves."[3]

Not only did the New Englanders seek to replenish their dwindling herds of neat cattle here, but the French of Canada and the islands of the Gulf of St. Lawrence also tapped the same source of supply. Even Captain John Smith, while scouting the New England coast in 1609, is said to have known about these out-of-the-way herds and in later years advised his fellow Virginians to get a few before the supply was exhausted. Possibly that was in 1613 when certain English gentlemen from Jamestown raided M. de Champlain's French settlement at Port Royal —present-day Annapolis—in Nova Scotia.

Port Royal, founded in 1605 by the colonizers Count de Monts and Samuel de Champlain, was the first settlement in Canada. It is not recorded that the colonists brought livestock. But to Quebec, founded in 1608, came settlers from the west coast of France, whose importations of Normandy-Brittany type cattle twelve years later provided the foundation herds. This stock was closely allied, in blood, appearance, and quality, to the Alderney cows of the Channel Islands. Their descendants have survived to this day without appreciable "improvement." Chiefly milch stock, they are also tolerable as beef animals and for work under the yoke.

Neither the Norse nor the French cattle left any imprint on our own northern herds. However, the introduction of French cattle to Biloxi on the Gulf Coast by d'Iberville in 1699 had a prolonged effect on Mississippi stock raising. French cattle also infiltrated the Middle West when St. Louis was founded in 1764 as a home for French exiles, from Vincennes on the Wabash to Kaskaskia on the Mississippi. These animals had arrived from Canada gradually by way of fur-trading posts and flatboats via the Wisconsin, Illinois, or Wabash rivers. They were mostly scrubs and had little effect on breeding practices.

[3] Lyman Carrier, *The Beginnings of Agriculture in America*, 104 (quoting Winthrop's *Journal* [ed. by James Kendall Hosmer], I, 162).

One interesting fact for the student of livestock history is the apparently superior survival qualities of Spanish cattle, compared with those of other national origins, when abandoned by their human custodians. The English cattle left by the fleeing starved-out colonists of Virginia, the Norse cattle abandoned when pestilence supposedly wiped out the Greenland settlements, the mixed herds set free whenever Indians destroyed the farmers' herds of New England or the middle colonies—all these vanished as soon as they lost their caretakers. Only the Spanish "foundlings" managed to survive.

Those derelict cows that persisted in staying alive on barren Sable Island were of the same strain as the descendants of Coronado's cattle, which gave to the world the indestructible Texas Longhorn, thus illustrating Darwin's concept of the "survival of the fittest"—and inciting Evetts Haley, Texas cattleman and historian to do

A Bit of Bragging About a Cow

"THE cow to which I propose a monument established no blood-lines, set no butter-fat records, and produced no prize-winning beeves for the International Show. But she did take care of herself and her calf out on the open ranges of Texas.

"When it did not rain on her range, she, without benefit of weather and crop reports, just got up of her own accord and walked off to where it had. When the water-holes dried in drouth, she prowled the gullies to the head-springs, and when they failed she did not lie down in despair and die because nobody hauled a supply, but pointed her nose into the breeze and walked until she found some. When snows and blizzards came, she headed for the breaks and thickets, and browsed on brush long before cotton seed was ever pressed into cake.

"She did not depend on government trappers for protection, but with sharp horns and sharper senses she fought it out on the ground with packs of coyotes and powerful 'loafer' wolves. She scorned legal quarantine lines and lived happily without them, sloughed off her own ticks before vats were conceived, rubbed the warbles out of her back on the rough bark of the mesquites before rotenone was discovered and self-oilers were built for profit, and raised her calves without the benefit of vaccine. She knew no shipping fever for she took herself up the trail a thousand miles to market.

"She adjusted her own increase to what the range would honestly carry, and followed an 'efficient program of range improvement' just by drinking water and eating grass and walking all over creation while nature had her way.

"Already I can hear the carping critics [ask], 'What positive "program" of improvement did she bring?

"She produced the millions of Longhorn steers that marched up the Texas Trail to distant markets and revived this state economically after the Civil War. She quickly converted the Great Plains from a land of unused grass to a productive industry in twenty years time.

"She took . . . imaginative and daring boys out of the cotton patches without public expense, and converted them into genuine adventurers in life and business. . . . She inducted more boys into the fascinating mysteries and processes of nature than the public schools, converted more hands to the fine art of working cattle than the rodeos ever will, and prematurely took more reckless . . . boys away from home to healthy life and adventure on the trail than have been reformed by the state's corrective schools since.

"In spite of the fluctuations of the business barometer, she kept more cowmen from going broke . . . while furnishing . . . people with buyable beef . . . than any breed on record. And at last she stimulated more good stories, and stirred the minds of old men with more exciting memories, than all the radios combined. . . . And so there should be a scheme—not a 'project' or a 'plan'—but an underground intrigue if necessary, on the part of the few remaining believers in self-reliance and sturdy independence, to erect a monument to this courageous individualist, the Longhorn Texas cow."

115

CHAPTER 11

Padres, Hides, and Tallow

THAT WAS A GREAT CENTURY for Spain—the sixteenth. At its threshold, Christopher Columbus, proclaiming the rotundity of the earth, drove his clumsy caravels into a putative "western hemisphere," allotted to Spain by Pope Alexander, and discovered America of the North. Thereafter Columbus, Ojeda, and Vespucci sought and identified another continent—South America.

In the early decades of the century, Vicente Pinzón made landfall at Brazil; Cortés burned his ships on the tidelands of Mexico and remained to conquer; old Ponce de León, seeking a Fountain of Youth eight years before he died, penetrated Florida; De Soto explored the new land for three years, covering 3,100 miles, and reached the Mississippi; Balboa sighted and claimed for his sovereign the world's largest ocean; Magellan named it the Pacific and, with half-starved crews manning his three antiquated vessels, crossed its vast expanse; before the natives killed him in battle, he had annexed the Philippines; in one worm-eaten craft his ragged survivors made shift to reach Spain, the first seafarers to circumnavigate the globe, vindicate Columbus, and prove that this planet of ours is round—and rugged.

Sebastian Cabot, commissioned by Spain to explore the Río de la Plata, spent three years poking along its banks and cruising up the Paraná, forthwith appropriating for the Crown all of modern Argentina, Uruguay, Paraguay, and Bolivia. Pizarro plundered the Incas and seized Peru and Ecuador. Cabeza de Vaca and three other derelicts of Pánfilo de Narváez' ill-starred Florida expedition headed for Mexico on foot. With the cruising speed of a herd of turtles, it took them eight years to cross Texas,

116

including melancholy spells of servitude to the Indians—the first Americans to employ slave labor. Glamorous Coronado, leading mounted *hidalgos* brandishing spears and foot-soldiers toting arquebuses, enlarged the boundaries of New Spain by scouting an area covered by present-day Arizona, New Mexico, Colorado, Kansas, and Oklahoma.

These and other conquests brought Spain to the peak of her glory. Dominion over South and Central America, southern North America, and across the Pacific to the Philippines was established by her explorers. Enriched by their stolen loot and supported by a fleet that sailed the seven seas, this little kingdom—scarcely bigger than the state of California—in less than one hundred years burgeoned into the greatest empire on earth, with Charles V ruling over more territory than any other living monarch and shaping the political, economic, and religious trends of all Europe. Who could have foretold that within the next two centuries, in a large sector of her domain, the Stars and Stripes would supplant the imperial colors of Castile and Aragon and that the Spanish Main would yield pride of place to Main Street, U.S.A.?

But in the meantime, Spain had bequeathed to us an incalculable and self-perpetuating treasure—livestock. It was De Soto who brought to Florida the three hundred swine that farrowed those tough and self-reliant "razorback" hogs. It was Cortés, Coronado, and Oñate who populated the river valleys, barren deserts, and mountain meadows with horses, cattle, sheep, and goats. Before their coming, North America knew no domestic animal save the dog, which had crossed Siberia to Alaska with the migrating Mongoloids. The tough, light-boned, clean-limbed *jaca jineta* of Andalusia gave us the mustang; the coarse-wooled *churro* begat the shaggy Navajo ewe; the agile, fighting *toro* of Seville sired the half-wild Longhorn of Texas. It is to Spain that we owe the "horse culture" of the Americas and the cattle and sheep "empires" of the open range, a debt seldom recognized in our schoolbooks or the minds of our countrymen.

117

Yes, the sixteenth was a great century for Spain—and for our own Southwest, legatee of a limitless realm of free grass, inheritor of the practical gear of working *vaqueros,* and heir to the quaint stock-breeding traditions of indolent Dons.

The "founding fathers" of New Spain were missionaries, both Franciscan and Jesuit, and the missions they established were economic as well as spiritual institutions. Here thousands of Indians, enrolled as neophytes, were indoctrinated with the faith and taught to cultivate gardens and vineyards, tan hides, and handle cattle on the choice lands owned by the *padres.*

First to penetrate the Southwest with "beef on the hoof" was Francisco Vásquez de Coronado, who in 1540 crossed into what is now Arizona with five hundred cattle, part of a livestock total of 6,500 head of horses, cattle, sheep, and goats, to provide mounts and meat for his fellow *conquistadores.* Some animals escaped, others fell prey to the Indians, and those that remained were slaughtered to feed the army.

Not until 1598, when Juan de Oñate, one of the four richest men in New Spain, founded San Juan at the junction of the Chama and Río Grande in New Mexico, did stock breeding begin in this area. Seven thousand head of livestock and a million dollars of Oñate's money helped mightily in establishing this, the first self-supporting colony in the United States. Fort St. Augustine in Florida, founded by Menéndez, a Spanish naval officer, in 1565, was more of a barracks for forces engaged in driving out the French Huguenots than a civilian settlement.

Actually, for a real "first" in New World cattle culture we have to go back to Christopher Columbus, who on his second voyage, commanding an imposing aggregation of seventeen ships and 1,500 adventurers, landed horses, cattle, sheep, goats, and hogs at Santo Domingo in 1493.

Among the earliest to bring cattle directly from Spain to the mainland was Hernando Cortés, conqueror of Mexico, who was not only a soldier but a rancher de luxe—recognized as such by King Charles, who assigned him vast estates and conferred upon him the unique title of Marquis of the Valley of Oaxaca. About the same time, or perhaps a little earlier, a certain Gregorio de Villalobos shipped into Mexico from Santo Domingo half a dozen heifers and a young bull, some of them descendants of those landed by Columbus.

Incidentally Cortés introduced a novel practice to the range cattle business. After conquering the Aztecs, he branded his Indian prisoners on the cheek with the letter "G," for *guerra*, or "war." Many of them were impressed into service as herdsmen for Cortés and other ranchers. And so it came about that the first "critter" to be branded in the New World was neither calf nor cow, but cowboy.

Another circumstance: the first white man ever to get a look at the American buffalo—that look while crossing Texas in 1528 —was Cabeza de Vaca, "head of a cow." This was pure coincidence, but deliberately purposeful was Cortés' choice of a name for the splendid palace which he built in the Oaxaca valley. He called it "Cuernavaca," or "Cow's Horn," and it is now a picturesque little town south of Mexico City and a favorite resort for United States visitors.

Although it was the *conquistador* who trailed the first herds into the Southwest, it was the *padre* who insured their survival in a hostile environment. At the early missions established along our southern borders from Texas to California, Indians were trained to herd, pasture, breed, and improve this foundation stock under the devoted supervision of their spiritual fathers. Against the raids of predatory savages, the ravages of wild beasts, and the invasion of their terrain by rival nationals these soldiers of the Cross were often the only group available to save for Spain her New World possessions. To the natives they brought practical Christianity and skill in husbandry, to the Crown a consolidation of its temporal power.

For more than two hundred years, in spite of Indian raids, droughts, wild beasts, and insubordinate neophytes, these Spanish missions managed to survive and found a number of similar establishments—totaling, in New Mexico, forty-eight; in California, twenty-one; in Texas, twenty; and in Arizona, eighteen. Whether Franciscan or Jesuit, they became the primary factor in the conquest of the Southwest. Lacking Spanish settlers, the *padres* had to recruit and train the natives in useful pursuits. Thus from these Indian tribes came the first *vaqueros* who in turn taught the American cowboy the tricks of his trade.

Of all the pioneering missionaries, the one to which the livestock industry of the Southwest probably owes the most was Eusebio Francisco Kino of the Company of Jesus. Born in the Austrian Tyrol in 1644, he came to Old Mexico in 1681. After returning from Antillon's abortive attempt to colonize Lower California, he went to Pimería Alta (northern Sonora and southern Arizona), where he labored prodigiously as missionary, explorer, colonizer, and cattleman until his death in 1711.

During twenty-four years, Kino the priest carried the story of the Cross to 30,000 Pima and Yuma Indians, established many missions, and baptized more than 4,000 converts. As explorer and cartographer, he made more than forty journeys, some a hundred, others a thousand, miles in length, penetrating remote areas in Old Mexico, Arizona, and California never before visited by white men. His map of Pimería Alta, published in 1705, made on the basis of actual exploration, was so authentic that it remained the only reliable guide to the region until the beginning of the nineteenth century.

As a rancher, he founded and managed a breeding establishment at his first mission, Dolores in Old Mexico, and from here sent hundreds of cattle and sheep to his Arizona missions as well as to those of Sonora and Lower California. Kino first crossed the present-day Sonora-Arizona boundary in 1691 and thereafter made fourteen *entradas*, assisting and encouraging his Indian converts in the arts of agriculture and animal husbandry. He once covered 467 miles in twenty days, on muleback or afoot, an average of 23 miles a day, a respectable pace in any desert pedestrian's book.

Stock raising was either started or supervised by Kino at nineteen places in Sonora and Arizona, all of them antedating the earliest California mission by more than half a century—Dolores, Caborca, Tubutama, San Ignacio, Imuris, Magdalena, Quiburi, Tumacacori, Cocospera, San Xavier del Bac, Bacuancos, Guevavi, Siboda, Busanic, Sonoita, San Lázaro, Saric, Santa Barbara, and Santa Eulalia. In Arizona some of the ranches started by Kino in the valleys of the Santa Cruz, San Pedro, Sonoita, and Gila are now the pleasant pastures of prize-winning Herefords. At San Xavier, founded near Tucson in 1700, stock raising is still the chief support of the Papagos.

A gentle ascetic, devoted and modest, Kino himself never owned a herd of livestock and never profited personally from the flocks and herds he freely gave to the Indians. His career is succinctly summarized by historian Bolton: "The work which Father Kino did as ranchman, or stockman, would alone stamp him as an unusual businessman and make him worthy of remembrance. He was easily the cattle king of his day and region. . . . The stock-raising industry of nearly twenty places on the modern map owes its beginning on a considerable scale to this indefatigable man."[1]

When Portolá's overland expedition to Upper California reached the Bay of San Diego in July, 1769, spiritual leadership was entrusted to Father Junípero Serra, who founded nine missions in the Golden State, where his name is as revered today as is that of Kino in Arizona. On this first *entrada* Serra brought four hundred head of livestock, realizing that if the natives were to be civilized, they should be taught agriculture, animal husbandry, and simple handicrafts.

The missions were blessed with an equable climate, plenty of water, unlimited pastures, and an abundant labor supply—the Indians, who were trained to care for the stock and made such a good job of it that at herding, roping, and riding, they soon surpassed the Spanish *vaqueros*. And their priestly task-

[1] Herbert E. Bolton, *The Padre on Horseback*, 64.

masters saw to it that they had plenty of raw material to practice on. The first report of their work published in 1773, disclosed that "Each Mission has received 18 head of horned cattle and has now from 38 to 47 head, or 204 in the aggregate; with 63 horses, 79 mules, 102 swine, and 161 sheep and goats at San Diego and San Gabriel alone."[2]

By letting nature take its course, the additional increase in eleven years at nine of the twenty-one missions produced this census: 5,384 cattle, 5,629 sheep, and 4,294 goats. That was in 1784. By 1800 the estimate of all California livestock totaled "74,000 cattle, 24,000 horses, and 88,000 sheep of which a large proportion belonged to the Missions."[3] When the missions reached the zenith of their prosperity in 1833, their own cattle numbered 424,000; sheep, 321,500 (including a few goats and hogs); besides 62,500 horses and mules. These figures indicate a remarkable recovery from the disastrous droughts of 1826 to 1830, when the wells and springs of Monterey dried up, 40,000 head of livestock perished, and immense herds of horses and mules were driven over the cliffs to save a little pasture for the cattle and sheep. Again, in 1840–41, there was no rain for fourteen consecutive months, with comparable losses.

But the severest blow to missionary enterprise came with the enforcement of secularization in 1834. This policy of the recently established Mexican Republic purported to emancipate the natives and divide the mission lands among their neophytes, who, argued the authorities, were "disgusted at having to support by their labor themselves, the *padres*, the government, and the troops."[4] Unfortunately this release from bondage was barren of the intended results, the Indians being no more fitted for self-government and self-support than were the unhappy Negroes of the Reconstruction era following the Civil War. Most of them drank and gambled away their inheritance, many end-

---

[2] H. H. Bancroft, *History of California*, I, 205–206.
[3] *Ibid.*, VII, 54.
[4] *Ibid.*, III, 21.

ing as beggars and thieves. The missions suffered further under avaricious and incompetent officials, and when war with the United States was impending, their property was openly confiscated on the excuse that it was needed to provide means for resisting the invaders.

To neutralize the effect of these harsh measures, the *padres* retaliated. Notable was their wholesale slaughter of cattle in 1834, designed to bring them money from the sale of hides and tallow. All the missions participated in this holocaust, specifically those at San Luis Rey, San Gabriel, and Purísima, where outside contractors, known as *porcioneros,* were hired on a fifty-fifty basis to liquidate the livestock. From May to July there were 5,700 cattle killed at Purísima, yielding 2,850 hides for the mission and an equal number for the butchers. Other contemporary reports mention 5,000 hides shipped from San Gabriel to San Pedro; at another mission 2,000 cattle were killed in a single day, the meat and fat being left in the fields; also 20,000 at the San Jacinto ranch of San Luis Rey, besides unrecorded totals at other missions. One contemporary reported that after a time nothing but the hides was saved. With a final total of 30,000 reported from the hecatomb at San Gabriel, there was alarm expressed at the possibility of a pestilence from the rotting carcasses.[5] When the gold rush of 1849 began, this incredible waste must have been keenly regretted, for stock had to be driven from New Mexico and Texas to provide beef for the miners.

The losses following this wholesale butchery are indicated in the official census of livestock holdings before and after. In 1834, the total number of cattle at the twenty-one missions was 396,-400;[6] in 1842 it had shrunk to a pitiful 29,020—some of this loss admittedly due to the severe drought of 1840–41 and some to confiscation by the authorities enforcing secularization.

The gruesome task of turning living flesh into tons of hides

[5] *Ibid.,* III, 349.
[6] Bancroft, *California Pastoral,* 339.

and tallow was well organized, as thus described: "Six men rode at full speed over the fields, armed with knives. Passing near an animal, one gave it a blow with the knife in the nerve at the nape of the neck, and it fell dead. These *nuqueadores* (killers) passed on, and were followed as by a flock of hungry vultures, by dozens of *peladores* (skinners), who took off the hides. Next came the *tasajeros*, who cut up the meat into *tasajo* and *pulpa* (jerked beef and solid beef); and the funeral procession was closed by a swarm of Indian women, who gathered the tallow and lard in leather hampers. The fat was afterward tried out in large iron or copper kettles, and after cooling somewhat was put in skin *botas*, containing on an average 20 *arrobas*, or 500 pounds."[7]

During colonial days and up to the mid-forties, hides and tallow were the chief, almost the only, source of revenue for missions and *rancheros*. There being a great scarcity of coined money in California, hides were also the principal medium of exchange. It was not long before a cowhide was known all over the Southwest as a "California banknote."

Among the "hide-droghers" along the California coast in the 1830's was twenty-year-old Richard Dana of Boston, who spent fifteen months on shore handling cowhides during the long apprentice seamanship which inspired his classic *Two Years Before the Mast*. He thus describes the job:

"When the hides are taken from the animals, they have holes cut in the ends, and are staked out, and thus dried in the sun without shrinking. They are then doubled once, lengthwise, with the hair side usually in, and sent down, upon mules or in carts, and piled above high-water mark, and then we take them up on our heads, one, or two at a time if they are small, and wade out with them and throw them into the boat . . . [from which] we were to collect all the hides we could and deposit them [at the depot] at San Diego."[8]

[7] *Ibid.*, 340.
[8] *Two Years before the Mast*, 93, 156.

It should be explained that after a Boston trading ship arrived in California—following a four- or five-month voyage via Cape Horn from the home port—it had to spend from one to two or more years rounding up a cargo. This meant endless labor calling at various ports or roadsteads along the coast, collecting and paying for small lots of hides. A Boston vessel on one voyage made calls as follows: seven at San Francisco; thirteen at Monterey; three at Santa Cruz; four at San Luis Rey; seventeen at Santa Barbara; seventeen at San Pedro; five at Refugio; and returned to the depot ten times, frequently anchoring at other places along shore.[9] The bow anchor was hoved up 301 times and the crew killed and consumed 203 bullocks while on the coast. From collecting at a coastal port to curing at the San Diego depot, a hide had to be handled twenty-two times. A vivid word picture is Dana's, whose ship, anchored three miles off Santa Barbara, was loading a lot of hides in 1835, about the time the missions were doing their wholesale slaughtering.

"We all provided ourselves with thick Scotch caps, which would be soft to the head, and at the same time protect it; for we soon . . . found that 'head-work' was the only system. . . . The seas, breaking high, often obliged us to carry the hides so, in order to keep them dry [and] as they were very large and heavy, and nearly as stiff as boards, it was the only way. . . . After we had got our heads used to the weight . . . we could carry off two or three hundred in a short time . . . but it was always wet work; and if the beach was stony, bad for our feet; for we, of course, always went barefooted on this duty, as no shoes could stand such constant wetting with salt water. Then, too, we had a long pull of three miles, with a loaded boat, which often took a couple of hours."[10]

After the collecting came the curing. At the San Diego depot which, boasting a maximum amount of the widely advertised California sunshine, could speed the processing, hides were

[9] Bancroft, *California Pastoral*, 475.
[10] *Two Years before the Mast*, 93, 94.

soaked for some days in sea water to soften them. They were then stretched on the ground and fastened with small stakes. All particles of flesh and fat, which might corrupt and infect the whole if stowed away on a vessel for many months, had to be carefully cut away with a knife, as well as the ears and other parts which would prevent close stowage. After the sun had done its job of drying for a few hours, scrapers removed whatever grease had oozed out. Following a couple of days of sunning and scraping, the hides were beaten with flails to remove dust and then stored in the hide-house, to remain there until the vessel was finally loaded for the home voyage. Aboard ship, the stowage was a mighty task in itself, every last inch of space being crammed with hides through the combined efforts of human muscles and jack-screws. A small brig of 160 tons could carry 14,000 hides. Dana's ship, the *Alert,* of 320 tons, sailed loaded to the Plimsoll line with 40,000 hides and 30,000 horns. For in addition to shoes of leather, Boston's belles craved horn combs and barrettes for their hair.

The *Alert's* hides were all destined to the tanner and currier. Apparently the ship's manifest showed no *botas* of tallow, although candles, or "tallow dips," were still the chief means of illumination in that pre-kerosene era, and an *arroba* (twenty-five pounds) of tallow was locally worth two dollars—which was currently the value of one cowhide. If the melted tallow was not poured into guts or bladders, it found a satisfactory receptacle in a green hide, which was stretched on the ground until sufficiently aired, then folded and sewed with an awl, with an opening left in the neck, through which the tallow was poured. This container, holding five hundred pounds, was a *bota,* and when the shipmaster signed bills of lading, they acknowledged receiving so many *botas* of fat.

To pay for hides and tallow, the trading vessels—most of them from Boston—brought to the Coast merchandise of an infinite variety, including agricultural implements, household utensils, hardware, cutlery, cotton, and women's boots, shoes, and other clothing, marine stores, tea, coffee, sugar, and assorted groceries. The universal practice of barter and exchange imposed on the unhappy "hide droghers" an added burden, that of toting the trade goods ashore and stowing them in the customer's vehicles. Dana had a taste of this at San Pedro, which he reported as "the hardest and most disagreeable day's work that we had yet experienced." Here is a paraphrase of his story:

LARGE OX-CARTS, and droves of mules loaded with hides were seen coming over the flat country. We loaded our long-boat with goods of all kinds, light and heavy, and pulled ashore. After landing and rolling them over the stones upon the beach, we stopped waiting for the carts to come down the hill and take them. But the captain ordered us to carry them all up to the top. . . . So what the oxen would not do, we were obliged to do. The hill was low but steep, and the earth, being clayey and wet with the recent rains, was but bad holding-ground for our feet. The heavy barrels and casks we rolled up with some difficulty, getting behind and putting our shoulders to them; now and then our feet kept slipping, which added to the danger of the casks rolling back upon us.

But the greatest trouble was with the large boxes of sugar. These we had to place upon oars, and lifting them up, rest the oars on our shoulders and creep slowly up the hill with the gait of a funeral procession. After an hour or two of hard work, we got them all up, and found the carts standing full of hides which we had to unload, and also to load again with our own goods; the lazy Indians, who came down with them, squatting down on their hams, looking on, doing nothing, and when we asked them to help us, only shaking their heads, or drawling out *"no quiero."* Having loaded the carts, we started up the Indians, who went off, one on each side of the oxen, with long sticks sharpened at the end to punch them with. This is one of the means of saving labor in California—two Indians to two oxen. . . . For several days we were employed in this manner, until we had landed forty or fifty tons of goods and brought on board about two thousand hides.[11]

THERE IS no available record for the year's shipments at all the missions, but San Pedro, then as now the port for Los Angeles, in 1834 received from missions and *ranchos* 100,000 hides and 2,500 *centals* (one hundred pounds to the *cental*) of tallow and several cargoes of locally made soap.[12] For several years hide and tallow transactions averaged 70 per cent of all of California's foreign trade, which earned for the natives processing the raw material the unlovely name of "greasers."

The decline of the missions following secularization was succeeded by the rise of the *ranchero*. In 1823, California had only twenty-three private ranches. In 1840, more than five hundred. On the limitless, unfenced terrain, cattle and sheep lived, bred, and died without the slightest attention being paid to stock improvement. Their care-free owners, the *ricos* of the Spanish-Mexican aristocracy, ushered in California's Golden Age, which lasted for twenty years, or until it was blotted out by the Age of Gold, heralded by the stampeding forty-niners, and summoning, among others, miners, merchants, gamblers, and prostitutes, human flotsam and jetsam, from the shores of the seven seas.

In striking contrast were those brave figures, the *Dons* and *Doñas* of the Golden Age. The menfolk wore low, broad-brimmed hats, rich waistcoats, knee breeches, and white stockings, or gilt-laced slashed trousers, *serapes,* and red sashes; the women were attired in short-sleeved frocks of silk, crepe, or calico, satin or kid shoes, necklaces and earrings, the unmarried wearing long braids, the married high combs; out-of-doors a *mantilla,* indoors a *rebozo*. Indians, taught by the priests, did all the work. They milked cows and made cheese; they dressed and tanned sheep and calf skins for clothing, wove blankets, made wine,

11 *Ibid.,* 102, 103.
12 Bancroft, *History of California,* III, 641.

raised and ground enough grain for bread, herded livestock, preserved the cattle hides, and prepared the tallow for the Boston ships.[13]

The Golden Age began to wane after the state was admitted to the Union in 1850. By 1870, the 15,000 easy-going Spanish-Californians had succumbed to the harsh commercialism of 750,000 go-getters of alien birth and breeding. Nor were their flocks and herds sufficient to feed for any length of time the invading *gringos*. All too soon the toilers of the placers and the pueblos were reduced to eating the flesh of cattle and sheep trailed in from New Mexico and Texas. These the local butchers, unhampered by price controls, doled out in steaks and chops carved from twenty-five-dollar sheep and two-hundred-dollar steers with the grimy miner's evening meal lighted by a seventy-five-cent candle fashioned from five-cents' worth of tallow.

For the Spanish *padre, ranchero,* and *politico,* it was the end of the trail.

CHAPTER 12

Colonial Cow Keepers

THIRTY MINUTES AFTER SUN-UP, on the meeting-house green of a small New England village, a stoop-shouldered rustic in shirt, jerkin, hosen, shoon, and breeches raised to his lips a conch-shell and blew a mighty blast. At the trumpeted signal, from byre and penfold there began to issue cattle of various ages, sizes, and colors—brindled, banded, spotted, striated—a motley bunch, but comprising the greater part of all the livestock owned by the townsfolk. Propelled by hunger and the herder's shouts, the hurrying kine soon left the village behind and within minutes had reached a near-by unfenced neck of land, bordered by river and bay, and were eagerly munching the lush grass of the town's common pasture. Thus did Haniel Bosworth, on the first day of May, 1661, begin service as official cowherd of the town of Ipswich, in the Colony of Massachusetts Bay.

New Spain and Texas might boast of dashing *vaqueros* and tough trail drivers. Known only to early English colonists along the Atlantic seaboard was the cow keeper, drab guardian of their bovine possessions, somber cicerone of their scrubby stock. As for herdsman Haniel, he had begun the day's chore in full content with the terms of his employment. For the town fathers only yesterday had covenanted with him to "keep the herds of cows on the north side of the river, from the 1st of May to the 20th of October. He is to go out with them half an hour after sun-rise and to bring them home a little before sun-set, at 13 s. a week, 'a peck of corn a head at their going out, one pound of butter or half a peck of wheat in June and the rest of his pay at the end of his time, whereof half to be paid in wheat or malt.' "[1] No mention here of the five-day week or "fringe" benefits.

In Cambridge, which was not only the seat of Harvard College but the home of more cattle than its neighbors (568 head, divided into a "milch" and a "dry" herd), the town's cow keeper was a converted Indian named Waban. On April 12, 1647, he had been engaged "for to keepe about *six score heade* of dry cattle on the south side of Charles River, and he is to have the full sum of eight pound, to be paid as followeth, viz: 30 s. to James Cutler, and the rest in Indian corne at 3 sh. bushel, after micheltide next.—He is to bargain to take care of them the 21 day of the present month, and to keepe them until 3 weeks after michelmas; and if any be lost or ill, he is to send word unto the towne, and if any shall be lost through his carelessness, he is to pay according to the value of the beast for his defect."[2] A contract requiring more familiarity with a Church of England calendar than with a Yankee sun-dial!

In the kind of mixed husbandry practiced in seventeenth-century New England, cow keepers such as Haniel and Waban were indispensable. Where every yeoman was busy from dawn to dusk clearing the land, putting in crops, and providing shelter, there was no time for building pasture fences. Hence not only neat cattle, but sheep, swine, and goats had to be kept off the planted fields—and occasionally defended against wolves and Indians by community herders. These were generally boys or adults incapable of hard labor in the fields. Milch stock, working oxen, and horses were pastured fairly near the town and driven back and forth daily, young cattle and sheep in more remote locations, swine as far away as possible—in New Haven the law prescribed five miles from the plantation. Swine unattended by a herder had to be ringed and wear a wooden yoke to prevent rooting during crop-growing seasons. Ownership of livestock

---

[1] Joseph B. Felt, *History of Ipswich, Essex, and Hamilton,* 44.

[2] Abiel Holmes, "The History of Cambridge," Massachusetts Historical Society *Collections,* VII (1801), 26.

was determined by brands and earmarks, which had to be registered with town officials. A penalty of five shillings a head was collected when cattle were found unmarked after the first of May. In Puritan New England, mavericking was not an activity.

In the fall, after harvest, barriers to the plantings were taken down and the livestock allowed to feed on the stubble. This "opening of the meadows" was an important event in the life of the village. Town authorities fixed the number of animals which might be admitted, each owner's allotment varying according to the acreage he had tilled or the value of the feed remaining on his land. These "proprietors' " rights were jealously guarded, as such pasturage put the stock in better condition for enduring the long winters.

Boston Common is generally conceded to be an outstanding memorial of the primitive conditions that prevailed during early colonial days. Not too well known is the fact that when laid out in 1634 it was definitely intended "for a trayning field and for the feeding of cattell."[3] Since then its fifty acres of turf and trees have never ceased to contribute to the enjoyment of its people and the world-wide fame of "the Hub of the Universe." And for two centuries it did officially function as pasture for livestock and an arena for soldiering.

As early as 1646 it is recorded that only seventy milch kine were allowed to graze on the Common, with young cattle, dry cattle, and horses barred. No person was entitled to the right of pasturage for more than one cow or four sheep. In May, 1701, Deacon John Marion "was appointed to give out tickets for Cows going to the Common, to such persons as have Propriety therein. . . . Such Cows as are found on the Common, other than those whose owners shall show forth a ticket from Deacon Marryon, are to be pounded by the Cow Keepers." Fourteen years

---

[3] Deposition of John Odin and others concerning the sale of William Blackstone's land, known as Boston Common, quoted by Robert Means Lawrence, M.D., in *New England Colonial Life,* 106; Dr. Lawrence's book is also the source of the stories of Boston Common in the three succeeding paragraphs, pp. 11, 96, and 98.

later John Tuckerman, being appointed cow keeper, was ordered to procure sufficient assistance for "looking after and keeping the Cows committed to his charge. And he is to take care about watering the Bulls belonging to the Heard, and to put them up by night." Up to the year 1830, when public grazing on the Common was discontinued, the town records show few references to this activity. One development was the raising of the two-dollar grazing fee, first to five dollars and eventually to ten dollars per head.

In 1675, according to William Wood's *New England's Prospect*, "The inhabitants of Boston for their enlargement have taken to themselves farm-houses in a place called Muddy River, two miles from this town.... In this place they keep their swine and other cattle in the summer (whilst corn is on the ground in Boston) and bring them to town in the winter." Thirty years later, "Muddy River" was incorporated as Brookline, eventually Boston's wealthiest suburb.

As twin activities, pasturing and soldiering on the Common sometimes clashed. Just before the Revolution, when on one occasion the British red-coats stacked their arms after dress parade, some of the cattle collided with these weapons with painful results. At least one cow was seen running around in circles, bellowing with pain, a bayonet sticking in her rump and a musket trailing behind. But in the matter of communal herding, Boston's worthy burghers were only following an ancient precedent established by English law, where, from the fifth to the eleventh centuries, "all the cattle of a village, though belonging to different owners, were pastured together in one herd, under the direction of one person."[4]

The year that Boston Common was laid out, 1634, there were twenty villages in Massachusetts in which lived four thousand people who owned, besides innumerable swine and goats, fifteen hundred head of neat cattle. Quite an increase in the scant ten years since Captain Edward Winslow, on his second voyage

[4] Fessenden, *The Complete Farmer and Rural Economist, iii.*

from England in 1624, "brought three heifers and a bull, the first beginning of any cattle of that kind in the land," as recorded by Governor Bradford of Plymouth Colony. Demand for cattle was so insistent by 1627 that shares in individual animals were allotted. Calvings were satisfactory, and Bradford could report from a court decision the determination to assign "a cowe to 6 persons or shars, and 2 goats to the same, . . . and swine, though more in number, yet by the same rule." In 1625, the next year after Winslow's imports, three ships "which carried kine" brought the first livestock to the Massachusetts Bay "adventurers." To each of these the governing body allotted two hundred acres of land "as well to build them houses as to inclose and manure, & to feede their cattle on."

Massachusetts Puritans paid much more attention to supplying settlers with cattle than did Plymouth. For this colony included many persons of wealth, culture, and influence at Court, by comparison with the Pilgrims of Plymouth, and could easily equip not one vessel but whole fleets containing not merely scores but hundreds of colonists, with all necessary equipment and livestock. Consequently the younger colony soon outstripped the older in numbers and affluence. Jeremiah Dummer, whose *Defense of the New England Charters* was published in London in 1721, estimated that in 1633 the value of Massachusetts livestock amounted to 12,000 pounds sterling (or $240,000 in terms of modern United States money).

In its first year, 1630, the Bay colony imported thirty cows, plus mares, swine, and goats. From then until 1633, cattle arrived on almost every ship. Early emigrants, sailing from the ports of Plymouth or Bristol in southwestern England, undoubtedly selected choice specimens from breeds raised locally, in this instance Devons. These red cows were predominant in seventeenth-century Massachusetts. However, in the early 1630's, when John Mason, founder of New Hampshire, started a colony of Danes on the Piscataqua River in New Hampshire, he made several importations of large, yellow Danish cattle for draft

134

stock in connection with his lumbering and sawmill operations. Their descendants multiplied prodigiously, so that when at Mason's death his widow's attorney, Francis Norton, drove one hundred oxen to Boston, he was proud to get twenty-five pounds sterling a head for them.

The Dutch settled New York in 1614, and by 1625 had brought over from the mother country large numbers of the coarse, Flemish-type bulls and cows. When ten years later two Dutch schooners sailed into Massachusetts Bay, they had no difficulty in disposing of sixty-three heifers to their Puritan customers at twelve pounds a head, besides some mares, horses, and sheep. The next year Samuel Maverick brought eighty goats and fourteen heifers from Virginia and found a home for them on New England's rocky terrain. Even earlier, in 1633, a Captain Stowe of Virginia had sailed from Chesapeake Bay to Massachusetts with a cargo of cattle and salt.

The gradual intermingling of the big, yellow Danish stock, the red-and-white and black-and-white Dutch cattle, and the dubious imports from Virginia with the bright red Devons— sometimes called "Rubies"—resulted in some cross-bred curiosities, it being well-nigh impossible for the early pioneers to pay any attention to selective breeding. They were far too busy subduing the wilderness with ax and mattock, planting, cultivating, and harvesting the crops, building shelters for man and beast, and defending themselves and their possessions from predators, animal and human, to find time for herd improvement. However, after getting well settled and being assured of community safety and personal solvency, these Yankees cared for their herds well, and by the early years of the eighteenth century their livestock was something to be proud of. They had taken pains to control breeding by having experts select the male calves which were to be raised as town bulls, whose service fees were fixed by law.

In the first years of their struggle with nature, the colonists faced the problem of adequate feed. No pasture plants such as timothy, bluegrass, or clover grew in the New World. The cattle had to subsist on "browse" and "swamp grass" for the first few winters, with "leeks" in the spring and coarse grass in summer and autumn for pasturage. The common grasses included small stands of wild rye and broom straw. As long as they had to rely solely on the native forage plants, cattle ran the risk of starvation; drought also often resulted in the loss of whole herds.

Relief came when, largely by accident, from the English hays stored on board ship to feed the stock, seeds of bluegrass and white clover were wafted ashore. By the 1660's these varieties had been fairly well established in New England and the Middle Colonies. But much of the later planting was due to selective importations.

Meanwhile, in less favored communities there was high regard for the coarse reeds and sedges of the fresh and salt water marshes. Although these fattened the cattle in summer, when they were cured into hay their nourishing qualities disappeared, and the stock lost so much flesh in winter that they had to be fed corn to keep them alive. Yet in many instances it was not considered safe or desirable to form a plantation without "fresh marsh" available for feed, or what in present-day language is known as "open swamp."

The need for more and better land for pasturage was a primary reason for founding many, if not most, of the new settlements. Within two years of the landing of the Pilgrims at Plymouth, one had been started at Wessagusset (Weymouth). That was in 1622; by 1635 there were settlements in twenty locations in Massachusetts, with many others in New Hampshire, Rhode Island, and Connecticut. Hartford, Saybrook, Windsor, and Wethersfield in Connecticut were founded because in 1635 the enterprising yeomanry of Cambridge, long on cows and short on pasture, acted upon an impulse thus described by the seventeenth-century historian: "This yeare the servants of Christ, who peopled the Towne of Cambridge, were put upon thoughts of removing, hearing of a very fertill place upon the River of

Conectico, low Land, and well stored with Meddow, which is greatly in esteeme with the people of New England, by reason the Winters are very long. This people seeing that Tillage went but little on, Resolved to remove, and breed up store of Cattell, which were then at eight and twenty pound a Cow, or neare upon."[5]

Emigrants from Dorchester, unwisely starting for Connecticut at the beginning of winter, lost the greater part of their stock. With better judgment, the Cambridge group departed the following spring, led by their pastor, Thomas Hooker. They drove 160 head before them, "and fed of their milk by the way." The journey was not particularly arduous. The herd moved single-file, following an old Indian path, with native villages along the way where food and shelter could be had. That was in 1636, the year Harvard College was founded. But none of these migrants, in whom the love of beeves outweighed the lure of books, remained to enroll.

[5] *Edward Johnson's Wonder-Working Providence, 1626–1651* (ed. by J. Franklin Jameson), 105–106.

Carolina Cowpens

IN THE Middle Colonies, the Dutch received their first cattle from Peter Evertsen Hulft, who in 1625 sent over from the old country 103 head, including typical Holland cattle. These were the roughly-formed, short-coupled, brown-and-white or black-and-white "critters" which the Dutch West India Company allotted to their tenants. Rich patroons, having leased enormous tracts of land in perpetuity on the Hudson and along Long Island Sound, and operating on a semi-feudal basis, also imported and bred Holland cattle with which they supplied their tenant farmers. When the English seized New Amsterdam and renamed it New York in 1664, the agricultural economy changed but little; only in ordering all cattle to be branded with the mark of the town to which they belonged, and in the obligatory fencing of cornfields against strays was their rule more stringent than that of the Dutch.

New Jersey fell to the English along with New Amsterdam, the land lying between the Hudson and Delaware rivers being granted to Lord Berkeley and Sir George Carteret. In 1676 this was divided into East and West Jersey, the line running diagonally from northwest to southeast, actually producing a north and south division. East Jersey seemed destined to become a region of corn and cattle when the Dutch influence faded and many New Englanders settled on small holdings in the hills. West Jersey was flat, favoring a plantation economy and including more slaves than any other place in the North. Off the southeast coast, islands and sandy beaches furnished the free-ranging cattle coarse grass in summer and hay in winter. Scows ferried them across the inlets in the spring and returned them to the mainland in the fall.

Swedes settled at the Capes of the Delaware in 1638, to be ousted by the Dutch in 1655, who yielded to the English ten years later. Like the Pilgrims at Plymouth, the Swedes suffered for some years from lack of livestock. At last a few head were obtained from Virginia and Maryland, and in 1643 they bought from the Dutch 7 oxen for 124 beaver skins and 1 cow, for which they paid 22 beaver skins. The 200 head they finally owned in 1663 were reported to be "of a middling sort."

Maryland, settled in 1634, got its first livestock from Virginia and later some West Indian cattle from the accommodating governor of Barbados. These were turned loose in the woods to shift for themselves, a practice continued long after New England and other regions had begun to fence them in. Marylanders were indifferent to stock raising, being obsessed with the planters' passion for growing tobacco. They did, however, inaugurate a system of wood rangers, who were supposed to prevent the theft of branded stock and to pick up unbranded animals. Unfortunately, some of the rangers were quite as adept as the Indians at cattle thievery.

Of all the colonies, the fastest growing and the thriftiest in farming and stock raising—although the last to be established north of the Potomac—was that of William Penn. When the Swedes settled along the Delaware in 1638, they looked across the river at the dense, unpeopled woods, where forty-four years later stout axemen were felling trees and clearing land for a settlement destined to expand into the great city of Philadelphia. Pennsylvania's early prosperity was due to its excellent soil and the enterprise of its English Quaker farmers, who were followed in the second decade of the eighteenth century by the equally industrious Germans. Within two years after his arrival, Penn was writing to London that "the Weeds of our Woods feed our Cattle to the Market. . . . I have seen fat Bullocks brought thence to Market before Mid-Summer. Our Swamps or Marshes yeeld us course hay for the Winter."

But the wise founder was not content to have his cattle

forage at large in the woods, nor was he satisfied with the marsh hay, which failed to interlard their ribs in winter. So he sowed the lowlands with English grass seed, with clover in the wheat stubble and on upland pastures. Rigorous practices were enforced about branding, fencing, and sheltering stock. Near Philadelphia hay and straw stacks with roofs gave protection from the weather. Eventually it was the Germans who built the finest type of barns, spacious, substantial structures of stone and wood. Unlike the colonists of other sections, Pennsylvania's yeomanry housed and fed their stock, preferring fewer and better cattle to larger numbers of the inferior sort. They were not handicapped by the greed of great trading companies as in New York, nor the arrogance of a landed gentry such as in Virginia and Maryland. Rather, their enterprise, freedom, and independence paralleled the corresponding virtues of the colonial New Englander.

Cattle brought to Virginia in the *Susan Constant* and set ashore at Jamestown in 1607 helped to found the first English colony in America. But they, along with the hogs, sheep, and even the horses, were eventually eaten during the ensuing famine. Sir Thomas Dale brought over another supply in 1611 and insured their survival by decreeing that "no man shall dare to kill or destroy" any of the domestic animals "without leave." Hence in a short time the colonists had two hundred cattle, the same number of goats, many hogs, and a few horses. To supplement natural increase, the parent company in London proposed in 1619 that twenty heifers be sent out with every one hundred settlers. As a result, two ships sailed from England, one with sixty, and the other with fifty-two head of cattle, besides four mares. Although ten of the cows died on the voyage, ten newly-born calves balanced the loss. By 1620, before the first Pilgrim set foot on Plymouth Rock, Virginia could boast of five hundred head, by 1627 from two to five thousand, and by 1633 was provisioning ships for return passages to England and seeking a market for live cattle in Massachusetts and Connecticut. After driving out the Indians, the colonists fenced off a peninsula on the Eastern Shore for their expanding herds.

Beyond Tidewater Virginia lay the Shenandoah Valley, which enterprising Germans from easily accessible Pennsylvania began to infiltrate in the early 1700's. Here there came a boom in cattle raising because of the easy land laws. Jacob Stover, a pioneer carpetbagger who invaded the valley in 1733, is said to have patented five thousand acres by giving as heads of colonizing families human names to every cow, horse, hog, and dog he owned. By 1750 there were two distinct strata in Virginia society. In the Tidewater region, tobacco planters; in the Piedmont and in the valley west of the Blue Ridge, farmers and cattle raisers. Braddock's defeat by the Indians in 1755 sent many of these scurrying back east, but at the end of the French and Indian War there was a new influx into what afterward became the state of West Virginia; soon herds of four hundred and five hundred head found ready markets at frontier forts and in the mushrooming towns to the east.

Less affluent settlers from Virginia drifted into the Carolinas, seeking larger and better ranges for their stock. North Carolina was then only the "back country" of South Carolina, which was founded in 1663. Here the smug and wealthy rice and indigo planters stuck to their plantations along the coast, ignoring the commercial potentials of livestock and naval stores in the "Tarheel" area, which became North Carolina in 1729. When the indigent Virginians entered the Carolina Piedmont, their town trail herds encountered numbers of wild Spanish cattle, descendants of those brought over to Florida from the West Indies. Many were rounded up, and through interbreeding a flourishing stock-raising era was initiated. Other immigrants who had been unable to acquire cheap land near the coast broke away and moved to the rich pea-vine pasturages of the Piedmont. By the middle of the eighteenth century this was *the* cattle country of the American colonies. As one observer wrote: it was "not an uncommon thing to see one man master of from

300 to 1,200, and even 2,000 cows, bulls, oxen, and young cattle."[1] Regularly, great beef herds were driven to Charleston, Norfolk, Baltimore, and Philadelphia. All this prosperity must have reddened the faces of the arrogant planters of the coast, who not only had refused to sell these settlers land, but through legislation had tried to prevent colonists from moving to the up-country, hoping to force them into rice and indigo culture along the seaboard.

Georgia, last of the thirteen colonies to be settled, was founded in 1733 by James Oglethorpe as a refuge for debtors and persecuted Protestants. Here, as in the Carolina Piedmont, was another great potential cattle range, lying between the Savannah and Ogeechee rivers. Farther south, conditions were not so favorable. The low, swampy lands were infested with flies and leeches. Cows wading into the water for their favorite forage, a water grass, were attacked by these pests, which sucked enough blood to cause horrid ulcerations. Aggravated by flies and other insects, the raw and bleeding wounds often resulted in death from what was called "water-rot" or "scald." In the uplands and forest savannahs of Georgia such afflictions were unknown. Incidentally, the back-country white folks bequeathed to posterity one priceless literary gem, the Georgia "cracker," so-called from the noise he made with his bull whip when driving his herds to town. The Indians of this region actually showed as much skill in cattle raising as the "crackers."

The Piedmont and upper coastal plains were the only seventeenth-century regions of the South in which cattle raising attained impressive proportions. Along the shores of the Old Dominion, New England, and the Middle Colonies, cattle raising was but a segment of subsistence farming. On the other hand, to the plateaus and foothills of Virginia, Georgia, and the Carolinas were attracted bold, cattle-conscious pioneers in search of free range for livestock. That their quest was not in vain is

[1] James Westfall Thompson, in *History of Livestock Raising in the United States, 1607–1860*, 63, quotes from *American Husbandry* (London, 1775), 350.

shown by the fact that by the middle of the eighteenth century, the available ranges of South Carolina had become so over-stocked that herds of from 300 to 1,500 head were being shoved across the line into Georgia. Many herds numbering from 1,500 to 6,000 head were driven on the open range from ranches lying between the upper Ogeechee and the Savannah. In the late Co-lonial period and during the Revolution, surplus stock was regu-larly driven to northern markets from the back country of Georgia, the Carolinas, and Virginia.

All this was possible because the stock raisers had supple-mented the practice of letting their cattle run loose with a syste-matic method of herding. This, in turn, depended upon the unique institution known as "stock-penning"—which was noth-ing more or less than driving livestock into an enclosure known as a "cowpen." As early as 1634 the term appears in a court record of eastern Virginia, is mentioned in Maryland in 1661, and frequently thereafter in other southern frontier regions.

Sometimes a cowpen was a small corral incidental to a plan-tation; sometimes the forks of a stream, fenced or ditched across, with an opening for the "drive," the headquarters of a wandering herdsman; frequently merely a temporary enclosure in the woods for holding cattle during the calf-branding season. The cowpen which represented large-scale operations was of a more permanent character, was manned by several keepers known even then as "cowboys," who were housed in adjoining cabins and who "took up the slack" of their idle hours by tend-ing small patches of corn and other crops—an indignity which would hardly have been tolerated by a Texas trail driver.

These large cowpens were the same as ranches, set down in the midst of the Long Canes and the Big Glades of the Pied-mont. In pre-Revolutionary days, "a cow-pen was quite an im-portant institution," according to one writer. "It was usually officered with a superintendent, and a corps of sub-agents, all active men, experienced woodsmen, and unfailing shots at long or short sight with the rifle. For these a hamlet of cabins were erected, besides the large enclosures for the stock; all of which, with a considerable plat of cleared land in the vicinity for the cultivation of corn, made quite an opening in the woods."[2]

One of General Braddock's officers reported in 1750: "The Keepers . . . drive up their Herds on Horseback, and they had need to do so, for their Cattle are near as wild as deer. A Cowpen generally consists of a large cottage . . . in the Woods, with about fourscore or 100 Acres, inclosed with high Rails and divided; a small Inclosure they keep for Corn, for the family, the rest is a Pasture in which they keep their calves; but the Manner is far different from any Thing you ever saw; they may perhaps have a Stock of four or five hundred to a thousand Head of Cattle. . . . These run as they please in the Great Woods, where there are no Inclosures to stop them. In the Month of March, the Cows begin to drop their Calves; they being weak . . . are easily drove up, and the Bulls and other Cattle follow them; and they put these Calves into the Pasture, and every morning and evening suffer the Cows to come and suckle them, which done they let the Cows out into the Great Woods to shift for their food as well as they can; whilst the Calf is sucking one Tit of the Cow, the Woman of the Cow-pen is milking one of the other Tits, so that she steals some milk from the Cow, who thinks she is giving it to the Calf.

"Soon as the Cow begins to go dry, and the Calf grows strong they mark them, if they are Males they cut them, and let them go into the Wood. Every Year in September and October they drive up the Market Steers, that are fat in October, but I am sure they are not so in May, June and July; they reckon that out of 100 Head of Cattle thay can kill about 10 or 12 steers, and four or five Cows a year; so that they reckon that a Cowpen for every 100 Head of Cattle brings about 40 pounds sterling per year. . . . They eat the old Cows and lean Calves that are like to die. The Cow-pen Men are hardy People, and are almost con-

[2] John H. Logan, *A History of the Upper Country of South Carolina,* I, 151–52.

144

tinually on Horseback, being obliged to know the Haunts of their Cattle."[3]

Abilene and Dodge City in the boom trail-driving days had nothing on one of these cowpen communities. Horse thieves and cattle rustlers mingled with honest yokels. The tin dipper of the moonshiner was never idle. Wrestling matches and foot races were the healthiest of the boisterous activities of the camp. However, a cowpen community was more apt to "stay put" than a rail shipping point for Longhorns. If the pasturage held up, the cow keepers might remain for years. If it thinned out, or civilization and farmers crowded in, they would push farther into the wilderness. In 1733 Governor Burrington of North Carolina stated that plantations with buildings, fences, cleared land, and orchards could be purchased for much less than the cost of the improvements, because the owners had removed "into fresh Places, for the benefit of their Cattle, and Hogs."[4]

In order to stock a cowpen in the early days, it was only necessary to round up the wild cattle of the country, drive them in, brand them with the owner's mark, and turn them loose to forage in the woods. The keepers usually placed salt in the neighborhood of the cowpen to attract the stock and take the edge off their natural wildness by seeing men at work. Milk was obtained by placing calves in an enclosure partitioned off from the main stockade. When the mothers appeared in the late afternoon, they were partly milked in the main pen, then turned in with the calves, who had to make shift with half-portions of the richer part of the total milk flow.

In addition to the large herds of the Piedmont, some of considerable size ranged the islands off the southern coast. On the great barrier reef off the shore of North Carolina, cattle still roamed at will as late as the opening years of the nineteenth century. Although the land was privately owned, individuals were

[3] *The Colonial Records of North Carolina* (ed. by W. L. Saunders), III, 430.
[4] Lewis Cecil Gray, *History of Agriculture in the Southern United States to 1860*, I, 151.

permitted to hunt the wild stock and to hold semiannual branding roundups. Another large grazing area—lying outside the English settlements, however—was southern Louisiana, settled by the Acadians in 1765. Here, for example, a Captain Dauterive undertook to provide each family with five cows, plus their calves and one bull. The arrangement must have been successful, because by the end of the century it was estimated that 300,000 head of cattle were feeding on grass as high as a horse's back and on cane fifteen to twenty feet high. But cattle had been introduced to this general region even earlier, when in 1699 the Frenchman Sieur d'Iberville brought livestock to Biloxi in Mississippi. Earlier than that by a hundred years Spanish cattle had been brought to Florida from the West Indies.

In the thirteen English colonies of the Atlantic seaboard, cattle raising on any considerable scale was a distinctly frontier enterprise. In the coastal communities, New England's economy was one of fisheries and lumbering; in the Middle Colonies, miscellaneous trade; in the South, the plantation specialties of tobacco, cotton, rice, and indigo. Stock raisers, all the way from the Berkshires to the Blue Ridge, actually operated on a common frontier of inland foothills and uplands, just as the Atlantic settlements shared a common coast line. This cowman's frontier, a physical thing, can only be visualized by forgetting all about the political boundaries of the colonies. And it was a movable thing. In the mid-seventeenth century, it was the so-called fall line, or the head of navigation of the rivers—in New England, the foothills of the Berkshire and White Mountains; in New York, beyond Albany and the German Flats of the Mohawk Valley; in Pennsylvania, in the Philadelphia region; in Virginia, at the edge of the Tidewater, until Shenandoah Valley was discovered; in the Carolinas, only eighty or ninety miles from the coast.

At the close of the French and Indian War in 1763, the frontier, according to Frederick Jackson Turner, "included the back country of New England, the Mohawk Valley, the Great Valley of Pennsylvania, the Shenandoah Valley, and the Piedmont— that is, the interior or upland portion of the South, lying between the Alleghenies and the head of navigation of the Atlantic rivers marked by the fall line."[5]

For the full length of this inland frontier, from Mason's New Hampshire to Oglethorpe's Georgia, cattle raising and small farming were the chief enterprises. A comparison of their unique stockgrowing operations with those in the Spanish Southwest reveals many contrasts, some resemblances. The Spanish stock and their successors, the Texas Longhorns, were of interest to their owners only as sources of hides, tallow, and beef. In the English colonies, cattle served as dual-, even triple-purpose animals—for plowing, for milking, and for meat. In the Southwest, there was no problem of fodder—the grass that supported vast herds of buffalo was equally nourishing for beef cattle; in the North, marsh grass and browse were poor substitutes. The *vaquero* and the trail driver "rode herd" from the back of a bronco, while the cow keepers of New England were hoofing it around the tiny circuit of a village commons, and Georgia crackers detonated their bull whips in the cowpens of the Blue Ridge.

These are contrasts. T. N. Carver suggests some similarities. In his *Historical Sketch of American Agriculture* he argues that the technique of the colonial operations paralleled that of Texas, and that both owed their origin to the migration of settlers from the Spanish-pioneered West Indies to the eastern colonies.[6] For example, in Jamaica and other islands there were hundreds of "cowpens" long before they first appeared on the Piedmont. And much of the legislation affecting stock raising, including the fence law, toll system, and range regulations, originated in the West Indies, where they dated back to the customs prevailing in the great ranges of old Spain.

[5] Frederick Jackson Turner, "The Old West," Wisconsin State Historical Society *Proceedings*, XIV (1908), 185.

[6] Gray, *History of Agriculture in the Southern United States to 1860*, I, 151.

CHAPTER 14

North Star Guides the Herds

T HE GRASS that fattens a buffalo will nourish a steer. This
naked fact must have occurred to Cabeza de Vaca, the
first white man to cross Texas, and to others from cattle-
conscious Spain, such as Coronado, first to penetrate what are
now New Mexico, Oklahoma, and Kansas; Antonio de Espejo,
rich cattleman from Queretaro; and Don Juan de Oñate, the
colonizer. Also to Zebulon M. Pike, United States Army lieutenant, and Josiah Gregg, observant Santa Fé trader, both of
whom predicted that stock raising would succeed in the high
plains of the Southwest.

In his long trek across Texas in the 1630's, the prophetically
named Cabeza de Vaca, having escaped half-clad from his Indian captors on the East Coast, was probably more delighted to
receive from friendly natives in the buffalo country those "cowhide blankets" than subsequent gifts of a copper hawk-bell and
a fistful of turquoise and emeralds. And on the banks of the Río
Grande del Norte he was equally happy to meet a tribe of the
Cow Nation—so called because of their annual slaughter of immense numbers of buffalo farther up the river—who entertained
him in what he called the "first fixed dwellings of civilization."[1]

Ten years later, when Coronado tarried at Zuñi, he was
visited by Indians from the east, headed by a chief whom the
Spaniards dubbed "Bigotes" because of his immense mous-
tachios, and who talked so much about the "cows" of his part
of the country that Coronado dispatched Alvarado and twenty
men to investigate. The expedition returned with tales of Indian
villages where the natives lived in tents made of skins and sub-

[1] H. H. Bancroft, *North Mexican States and Texas,* I, 65.

sisted on buffalo meat. Incidentally, they encountered a wrinkled patriarch who had seen Cabeza de Vaca and his companions farther to the south ten years before.

In 1583, while on a rescue mission in behalf of the priests Rodríguez and López, supposed to be held by the Indians, the Espejo party traveled 120 leagues along a river they called *Río de las Vacas* because of the vast buffalo herds. This was the celebrated Pecos of today.

Fifteen years later, the restless Oñate—founder of San Juan, where he had already introduced cattle—sent Vicente de Zaldivar with fifty men to explore the buffalo plains to the east. The only recorded result of this junket was the killing of his first bull by the valiant leader, a big buffalo hunt by all hands, and a sorry attempt to capture alive some of the young stock, which the improvised corrals had failed to hold.

Pikes Peak in Colorado memorializes the courageous young United States Army officer, Zebulon Montgomery Pike, who immediately recognized the possibilities of stock raising on these primeval prairies. Under date of February 5, 1807, he made this entry in his journal: "From the Arkansaw to the Río del Norte [Río Grande] . . . the inhabitants would find it most to their advantage to pay attention to the rearing of cattle, horses, sheep, and goats: all of which they can raise in abundance, the earth producing spontaneously sufficient for their support, both in winter and summer, by which means their herds might become immensely numerous."[2]

A quarter of a century later Josiah Gregg added his observations. On the first of his eight expeditions across the great Western prairies, this literate Missourian wrote: "By far the most important indigenous product of New Mexico is its pasturage. Most of the high table-plains afford the finest grazing in the world. . . . The extensive herds of the country, not only of cattle and sheep, but of mules and horses, generally maintain themselves in excellent condition upon the dry pasturage alone

2 *Exploratory Travels in North America*, 229.

through the cold season, and until the rains start up the green grass again the following summer."[3]

On his last trading trip in 1839, Gregg wrote this illuminating paragraph about stock-raising possibilities: "Like the table-plains of Northern Mexico, these high prairies could at present only be made available for grazing purposes, and that in the vicinity of the water courses. The grass with which they are mostly clothed is of a superior quality. . . . Of this unequalled pasturage the great western prairies afford a sufficiency to graze cattle for the supply of all the United States."[4]

Gregg's summary of natural resources embraced a lot of territory. He took pains to point out that the region he described lay between the spurs of the Rocky Mountains on the north and the rivers of Texas on the south, some 700 or 800 miles in that direction, and from the frontiers of Missouri and Arkansas on the east to the foothills of the Rockies on the west, a span of 600 miles. The whole area contained about 400,000 square miles, 30,000 of them in the original limits of Texas, 70,000 in New Mexico and eastward to the 1839 "boundaries of the United States," leaving to the "States" the remaining 300,000 square miles. Had he drawn a map of this region, Gregg might aptly have lettered it *Bovinaria suprema,* for within its boundaries today can be found two-thirds of the range cattle of the nation.

As in New Mexico and California, the first cattle to hoof-mark the soil of Texas were introduced and handled by Spanish missions, near the Louisiana line, in the 1690's. As the mission flocks and herds continued to multiply, their 50,000 to 60,000 head of cattle laid the foundation for the state's later nation-wide leadership in stock raising, which inspired one versifier to sing, "Other states were carved or born; Texas grew from hide and horn."

Incidentally, the first cross-state drive in Texas was made

---

[3] Josiah Gregg, *Commerce of the Prairies,* I, 160–61.
[4] *Ibid.,* 192.

in 1721 when troops of the Marquis of Aguayo, arriving at Los Adaes near the Louisiana boundary woefully short of supplies, were saved from starvation by the timely arrival of two hundred loads of flour transported by muleback from San Antonio, with "four hundred sheep and three hundred head of cattle . . . from the frontier of New Leon, about 340 leagues distant from Los Adaes," a difficult and dangerous drive of more than 1,000 miles.[5] This is the first record of a herd of cattle being trailed across Texas, precursor of the historic drives of the 1870's and 1880's.

One hundred years of Spain's military, missionary, and cattle-raising colonization of Texas were followed by Pike's exciting 1806–1807 exploration and imprisonment in Mexico, and in 1819 by official determination of the frontier between Spanish and United States territory. This line ran from Pikes Peak in Colorado eastward along the upper Arkansas River to the one-hundredth degree longitude, thence south, crossing the Canadian, to the Red River, and down that stream and the Sabine to the Gulf of Mexico.

Two years later Mexico wrested independence from Spain. Forthwith more Americans succumbed to "Texas fever," precipitating a rush of settlers from Illinois, Kentucky, Missouri, Tennessee, and the Gulf states. The alarm of the newly-born Republic of Mexico did not prevail against the successful revolt and establishment of the Republic of Texas in 1836.

Among the grievances of the rebellious Americans, those affecting the stock raiser were preponderant. Their special complaint concerned the conduct of the Mexican soldiery, who requisitioned cattle and mules and never paid for them, and, furthermore, failed to give the stockmen any protection against Indian raiders. Another kind of skullduggery was made possible by the peculiar laws governing the ownership of animals. Every time a "critter" changed hands it had to bear two brands, one

[5] Juan A. Morfi, *History of Texas, 1673–1779* (tr. by Carlos Eduardo Castañeda), Part I, 220.

151

the *fierro* or owner's brand, the other the *venta* or sale brand, until finally the beast carried as many figures and letters as a United States government agency during the days of the Roosevelt New Deal. If a foreigner entered a town with stock, every beast was subject to scrutiny by hawk-eyed bystanders. If a single animal seemed to be *unvented,* it could be seized. Again, any unscrupulous "greaser" might stealthily put a new *venta* on an animal and add his own *fierro.* To any Spanish court this was proof enough of ownership.[6]

The woes of the settlers, who had established several thriving American colonies in Texas prior to Mexican independence, were further aggravated by a proclamation of dictator Bustamante in 1830, prohibiting further immigration from the States. For the unloved "gringoes" this was the last straw. In swift succession came the organization of a provisional government under General Sam Houston, defeat and massacre at the Alamo on March 6, 1836, and glorious victory at the Battle of San Jacinto six weeks later.

Thus salvation for the young Republic of Texas was assured by a baptism of blood. For nine years the Lone Star flag flew unchallenged until replaced by the Stars and Stripes through annexation to the United States in 1845. Meanwhile, immigration continued at high speed. American farmers and ranchers flocked to the Austin colony, already established in eastern Texas. Others found permanent bed-grounds for their flocks and herds elsewhere in Texas. As a result, most of the eastern, northern, central, and southern sections were eventually cut up into cultivated farms. Here could be found "tame" cattle under control, where previously "wild" Longhorns chewed their cuds in the thickets of the brush country or toughened wind and muscle in marathon races for free meals on the open range. It was almost inevitable that the colonization of Texas throughout a century should be paralleled by a steady increase in cattle culture. Although urged by the government to apply himself to

[6] Gregg, *Commerce of the Prairies,* I, 186.

farming, nearly every newcomer decided he would rather be a cowboy. Land grants offered first by Mexico were continued by the Texas Republic. It is small wonder that the immigrants from the States preferred stock raising to farming.

If a married man declared himself a farmer, he received 177 acres—one "labor"—of agricultural land. If he was also engaged in stock raising, a grazing tract sufficient to complete a square league, or 4,440 acres, was added. If unmarried, he received one-fourth of the above amount. And the government could increase these allotments in proportion to the size of the family, with a limit of eleven square leagues for any one family. For the colonist, the over-all cost of a square league was only $180.

Migratory hordes of Texas-bound home seekers were not slow to see that all kinds of livestock could be raised there with far less trouble and expense than farther north. There was an abundance of fodder for horses, sheep, and cattle in the cane-brakes and on the broad grasslands; and for hogs, mast and native peas from the woods. Cattle could be brought in from the States, or purchased in Texas, or from the Mexicans below the Río Grande. Stock matured and multiplied more rapidly, generally doubling within two years. Cows often calved when only eighteen months old, and a pair of sows would increase to forty in a year. Cattle, horses, and mules could be driven inexpensively to New Orleans, or to the coast, where they could be shipped by vessel to that city, or to the markets in Cuba and the West Indies.

No one was more alert to these advantages than the Connecticut Yankee, Moses Austin, whose colony in eastern Texas, started in 1821 and developed by his son Stephen, numbered 20,000 by 1828, with stock raising the principal activity and Spanish cattle the basis for success, in spite of raiding Indians and thieving Mexican soldiers.

Of course, Texas, like other frontiers, had its ups and downs, but population never ceased to grow. From 3,500 Anglo-Texans in 1821, it zoomed to 54,000 in 1841 and to 400,000 in 1860.

Correspondingly, cattle increased from a few score of thousands in the 1820's to an estimated four million in 1860—making a ten-to-one majority for *Bos taurus* over *Homo sapiens*.[7]

By then, the range-cattle business overshadowed the raising of cattle on farms. Without legal title as owners or renters, scores of ranchers took possession of vast areas of unfenced, state-owned lands. Often the stockman held title to less than 160 acres, but as this small holding was always located on running water—springs, creeks, or rivers—he was enabled to range his cattle over immense portions of the Texas domain.

The stockgrower's immediate problem was to find a market for his lean and leggy Longhorns. Along the Gulf Coast some relief was afforded by a growing demand for hides, tallow, hoofs, and horns. As in California, buyers from New England sought hides for leather and tallow for candle and soap making. Texas itself set up a few small "hide and tallow factories," one of the earliest being that of Captain Richard King, founder of the famous King Ranch in southern Texas. Hoofs and horns of slaughtered cattle went to glue and comb manufacturers, hair being utilized for plaster and padding. Carcasses were left to rot or to feed ever-present scavengers. There seemed to be a demand for everything about a steer except his beef.

Still there was some droving as early as the middle 1830's, when herds of unbranded cattle—the "mavericks" of later days —roamed the prairies between the Río Grande and the Nueces rivers. Enterprising men from New England, Tennessee, and Missouri rounded up many of these and drove them to burgeoning frontier towns in droves of 300 to 1,000 head.[8] Here they were bought by ambitious newcomers interested in work oxen and in building foundation herds.

A few herds may have been driven overland to New Orleans previous to the Mexican revolt against Spain in 1821.[9] But drives

[7] Bancroft, *North Mexican States and Texas*, II, 530, 560.

[8] *Tenth U. S. Census, 1880* (Agriculture), III, 965.

[9] Joseph A. McCoy, *Cattle Trade of the West and Southwest* (ed. by Ralph P. Bieber), 20.

were really in full swing by 1842, when small herds were trailed to Shreveport, Louisiana, and loaded on flatboats to be ferried down the Red and Mississippi rivers to New Orleans, which for a dozen years offered the most reliable market for Texas cattle. While the Texas drover gained scant profit, real money was made by "middlemen" such as James Foster, who handled the transaction from Shreveport to New Orleans. Lamar County steers, bought for $10 a head, are said to have brought $45 in the Crescent City.

The primary movement was overland, but there were shipments by boat across the Gulf from Indianola, Texas, at the entrance of Lavaca Bay, as early as 1849. Later, marine shipments went from Galveston, Corpus Christi, Port Lavaca, and Sabine Pass.[10] Shipments from Galveston to New Orleans during the period 1850–56 varied from 2,900 to 10,000 head annually.[11]

The main overland route from western and southern Texas was to Liberty on the Trinity River, thence to Beaumont on the Neches, across the Sabine into Louisiana, and then over the Calcasieu and Mississippi to New Orleans. There were few bridges en route, and most streams were crossed by fording, ferrying, or swimming.

Solon Robinson mentioned the coarse, sedgelike prairie grass on which the cattle were pastured and noted that the fields were so wet that "the cattle were almost amphibious. . . . None but the native, or Spanish, cattle, which are really a very fine breed, can stand such fare, particularly with ten mosquitoes to every spear of grass they fish up from its watery bed," he commented. "They are fat in summer, and *live* through winter."[12]

A three-year record of shipments in the 1850's reveals that 40,000 head crossed the Neches; nearly 13,000, Trinity Ferry; and more than 32,000, the Sabine River—all en route to New

---

[10] *Tenth U. S. Census, 1880* (Agriculture), III, 976.
[11] McCoy, *Cattle Trade of the West and Southwest,* 24.
[12] Herbert A. Kellar (ed.), *Solon Robinson: Pioneer Agriculturist,* II, 180.

Orleans for local slaughter and consumption, or for reshipment to other parts of Louisiana, Alabama, or the West Indies.

While a few Texas cattle went to California with a segment of the Gold Rush,[13] the main movement did not start until four or five years later. The trail used in general coincided with the route followed earlier by Lieutenants William H. C. Whiting and William F. Smith from San Antonio to El Paso del Norte, and thence north of Doña Ana, New Mexico, Guadalupe Pass, the Santa Cruz valley, Tucson, the Pima Indian villages, Yuma, Warner's Ranch, and San Diego or Los Angeles.

In the spring of 1856, Frederick Law Olmsted saw several "California cattle-trains" encamped west of San Antonio, loading a few government stores for the frontier posts, and "awaiting herds of cattle which they were to convey to California." Such a "cattle-train" consisted of four hundred head of oxen "generally in fine, moderately-fat condition."[14] Twenty-five men were assigned to guarding them and driving them. Only a few were paid wages—drovers and experienced frontiersmen. The rest were young fellows, California-bound, who worked for expenses only. All rode mules and were supplied with short government rifles and "Colt's repeaters." Two large wagons and a cart, loaded with stores, cooking utensils, and ammunition, followed the herd. Four men were assigned to each hundred head, and five to six months were spent on the road. If California prices for cattle were unsatisfactory, it cost only cowboys' wages to hold the herds on grass, where they could fatten and thus command higher prices. In 1856 cattle cost $14 a head in Texas, while the year previous they had brought $100 a head in California. They once reached $150, but the price subsequently broke to $60. The Christmas issue of the *Daily Alta California* in 1854 reported that nine thousand cattle came in by the southern route that year, while seven months earlier a Texas paper

13 James A. Bell, *A Log of the Texas-California Cattle Trail, 1854* (ed. by J. Evetts Haley), 4.

14 Frederick Law Olmsted, *A Journey Through Texas; or, A Saddle Trip on the Southwestern Frontier*, 273–74.

claimed that between seven and eight thousand were already on their way.[15]

Outlets for Texas cattle to the north were known as early as 1842, when a herd of 1,500 is reputed to have reached Missouri. Four years later another thousand head were driven by Edward Piper to Ohio, this being the first authentic drive, according to Clarence Gordon.[16] This herd was fattened there, and the finished animals sold for slaughter. As the number of trail cattle increased, the greatest sensation was caused by a drive by Joseph Mallory of Piatt County, Illinois, who in 1853 purchased a herd in Indian Territory, fattened them on his Illinois farm, and then shipped them on to New York.

The main trail crossed the Red River at Colbert's Ferry, north of modern Denison but in Grayson County, Texas, and led northeast some twenty-five to thirty miles through or near Boggy Depot, Indian Territory, and thence to Fort Gibson, continuing to the western boundaries of Arkansas or Missouri. At first the principal markets were near St. Louis, but afterwards many cattle were sold at Booneville, or at Independence and Westport, and just before the Civil War at Kansas City. A few seem to have been driven there before and during the Mexican War, after which stock began to arrive in this state in important numbers. Beginning about 1849 and continuing up to the Civil War, the trade grew significantly.

Another almost legendary Illinois character, Tom Ponting, in 1853 wintered a drove of Texas steers he had trailed from Texas himself and later drove and shipped them east, where they were eventually sold in Albany and New York City.[17] Illinois soon became an active feeding center for Texas and Indian Territory cattle, with Independence, Westport, and Kansas City, Missouri, the biggest markets. In two years 100,000 Southwestern beef cattle reached the latter market, in addition to nearly

[15] *San Antonio Western Texan,* June 1, 1854.
[16] *Tenth U. S. Census, 1880* (Agriculture), III, 965.
[17] Herbert O. Brayer, *Life of Tom Candy Ponting: An Autobiography,* 19–42.
[18] Westport long ago became a part of Kansas City.

32,000 work oxen, mules, and horses of more local origin. A market paper in Kansas City estimated that two-thirds of all the cattle reaching there came from Texas. Evidently the Texans did not let their Southern partisanship interfere with business, for the *Dallas Herald* reported, "Yesterday a drove of two thousand beef cattle went through Dallas, en route for the north, to feed our abolition neighbors. We hope that this southern diet will agree with them."

After Texas joined the Union, St. Louis became a great market, and many Midwestern cattle were fattened, slaughtered, and shipped down the Mississippi to New Orleans. Live cattle from the Cherokee Nation subsequently reached there. George McClure sold twenty-four head, described as "good-for-nothing,"[19] at two cents a pound. An attempt to feed Longhorns with corn at the market was a failure. Not only did they run away from it, but the *Daily St. Louis Intelligencer* of October 30, 1854, related, "Texas cattle are about the nearest to 'wild animals' of any now driven to market. We have seen some Buffaloes that were more civilized."

To this courageous start in marketing Southwestern cattle the Civil War put an abrupt end. Union forces blockaded the Gulf ports, and the Confederate armies drained the state of able-bodied men. But this invaluable experience gave Texans the know-how of cattle trailing and set a marketing pattern for the postwar period.

With no one to herd or drive the cattle during the war, Texas animals ran wild and multiplied at the prodigious rate of 25 per cent each year. By 1865 there were probably six million cattle in the state. This plethora of livestock drove the prices down until even the best cows found no buyers at three to five dollars a head.

In sharp contrast to the surplus in the South was the shortage in the North, where the war had reduced the supply of beef cattle in the East and Middle West to a dangerous minimum.

[19] *Daily Missouri Republican* (St. Louis), August 24, 1854.

Consequently, when combat ceased, a high-grade matured beef animal worth five dollars in the cow country would bring fifty dollars in the North. To the cattle-poor and land-poor Texas ranchman this market looked like a veritable Golconda. But how to reach it? In any attempt at trail driving, the hazards were terrific. There were hundreds of miles of trackless, often water-less, stretches, many infested with hostile Indians, that lay between the source of supply and the terminus of demand. Yet the intrepid Texans never faltered, but pointed their dogies north and northwest. In the next thirty years, over four famous trails, ten million cattle were driven to Kansas railheads or Dakota-Wyoming-Montana pastures for fattening.[20] These trails, as they crossed the Indian country, were known as the Shawnee, the Eastern or Chisholm, the Western, and the Pecos River routes. Each had feeder trails merging into them in Texas, and each had distributive outlets in Colorado, Kansas, Missouri, and the states to the north.

The trail that has seized the imagination of the public, how-ever, is the Chisholm Trail, so much so in the past as now that a woman who traveled the Western Trail two years after the Chisholm Trail was abandoned titled a book of memoirs *A Bride on the Old Chisholm Trail*.[21] In recent years, poets, fiction writers, and playwrights have chosen this trail as their favorite setting for "westerns," and the old cowboy song beginning, "Come along, boys, and listen to my tale; I'll tell you of my troubles on the old Chisholm Trail," is as popular now as in the heyday of the trail. Yet the "honest trader" for whom it was named never pushed his trail into Texas.

It was in 1865 that Jesse Chisholm, hunter and trader, organ-ized a trading expedition to certain Indian tribes dwelling near the Wichita Mountains on the Washita River in the Indian Ter-ritory (now Oklahoma), about the location of present-day Ana-darko. And that is all the "reach" there was to the trail that

---

[20] J. Marvin Hunter (ed.), *The Trail Drivers of Texas* (2nd ed.), 24.
[21] Wayne Gard, *The Chisholm Trail, vi.*

Chisholm traveled. At the mouth of the Little Arkansas he built a trading post, and thereafter until his death in 1868 followed fairly regularly the trail from that point to Kansas, taking buffalo robes, furs, and cattle north, and returning with wagonloads of goods for trading. Soon other whites and Indians were using this trail for various purposes.

Considerable confusion has arisen at times on account of the similarity of the names of Jesse Chisholm and John S. Chisum. Chisholm,the Indian Territory trader, pioneered a wagon trail that lay entirely in Oklahoma and Kansas, that proved to be especially convenient for the northward-pressing cattle drivers. Chisum, a New Mexican cattleman eighteen years younger than Jesse Chisholm, came from Texas up the Pecos to the Hondo, and in 1873 opened a trail from Fort Sumner, New Mexico, to Las Animas, Colorado, over which he trailed 3,500 cattle. He owned successively ranches in Texas and New Mexico, and during the Civil War sent cattle to Confederate armies in Louisiana and Mississippi. At one time Billy the Kid was one of his New Mexico ranch hands, and Chisum was later involved in the historic Lincoln County cattle wars.

Of Jesse Chisholm, T. U. Taylor has said: "For forty years save one, Jesse Chisholm was a factor in the civilization of the Indian Territory. He was a pioneer with the traits of Daniel Boone; he was a patriot of the purest ray serene; he was a peacemaker with the skill of Kit Carson and John C. Frémont. . . . At one time he was adopted into almost a dozen Indian tribes of Oklahoma. . . . Like John S. Chisum of New Mexico, Jesse Chisholm never carried a gun. But while John S. Chisum was forced to hire a feudal army to defend his rights in New Mexico, Jesse Chisholm used the means of peace-making."[22]

Two years after the surrender at Appomattox, jobless Confederate veterans turned trail drivers and began to point their dogies north from the whole Gulf Coast area over pioneer routes of their own to points where they intersected the major trails.

[22] T. U. Taylor, *The Chisholm Trail and Other Routes*, 21–22.

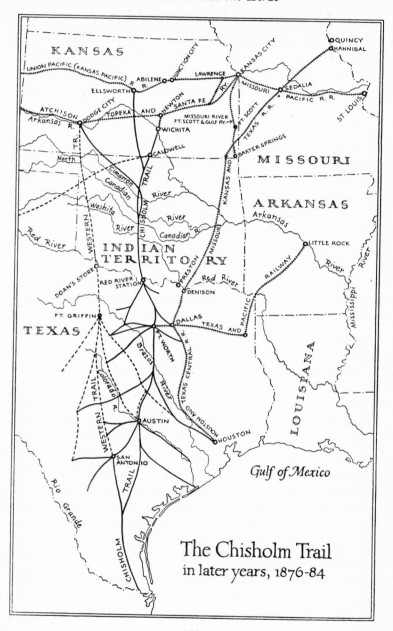

The Chisholm Trail
in later years, 1876-84

The old Shawnee Trail utilized the pre–Civil War route from Colbert's Ferry via Boggy Depot and Fort Gibson; but instead of bearing toward Missouri or Arkansas, it forked to lead into Baxter Springs, Kansas, then the terminus of the Missouri, Kansas and Texas Railroad. This became a celebrated shipping point until guerrillas from the hoodlum days of the Civil War pressed the drovers westward, and Baxter Springs' heyday was over.

Even before 1870 most of the drives were traversing the Eastern Trail, which seemed to originate almost anywhere in South Texas, and by converging paths reached the famed Red River Crossing. Hundreds of old trail drivers have described in detail the particular route in Texas which they happened to follow as the "true route of the Chisholm Trail." The trail traversed by Jesse and made official by the state of Oklahoma[23] was originally merely a segment of the Eastern Trail.

Just when it began to be called the Chisholm Trail is uncertain, says Wayne Gard—whose recently published book, *The Chisholm Trail*,[24] examines thoroughly the questions of route, origin, and nomenclature, and should lay to rest for all time the various controversies surrounding the trail—but he found it so mentioned in a Kansas newspaper as early as 1870. Government maps published in the 1870's called it the Abilene Cattle Trail, although it seldom led to Abilene after 1871, and it was also referred to as the Great Cattle Trail. In Texas, the name "Chisholm" caught on more slowly, but in time became so firmly fixed that in both history and folklore the name now applies to the whole length of the route, including feeder branches in Texas.

Starting in South Texas, wherever a herd was banded together, the feeder trails joined a main trail somewhere along

[23] The Oklahoma Legislature has officially marked as the Chisholm Trail the route from Red River Station on through Enid; as the Western, or Texas, Trail, the route from Doan's Crossing. Red River Station was in the northwestern corner of Cooke County, Texas, where Mud Creek flowed into the Red River from the north. The curve in Red River was known as the Illinois Bend. Doan's Store was on the Red River in Wilbarger County, Texas, about fifteen miles due north of modern Vernon.

[24] Norman, University of Oklahoma Press, 1954.

An Ox-Pull in Yankeeland

New England Homestead

Calf Scramble at the Houston Fat Stock Show

Bill Tipton

The Wild White Cattle of England

Faber & Faber, London

The Newbus Ox
Reproduced from the prints in the collection of Messrs. Walker's
Galleries, Ltd., London.

C. F. Curtiss

Livestock at a California Mission
From a drawing by E. Wyttenback

California hides and tallow being loaded on ships for New England.
From a painting by Carl Oscar Borg.

Texas trail drivers of the early 1880's holding herd just outside Abilene, Kansas.

J. F. Weadock

Fort Gibson, Indian Territory, in 1868

From the Art Collection of Edward Eberstadt & Sons, New York

Seven yoke of oxen used in breaking sod in North Dakota in 1904.

Joseph S. Anderson

Wool from McIntosh and MacGillivray being delivered in Albuquerque, in July, 1900, by Mexicans from Estancia Valley with their own yokes of oxen.

New Mexico Wool Growers' Association

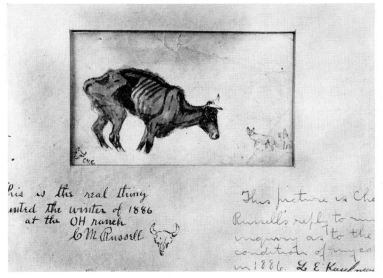

Cowboy Artist Charles M. Russell replies to L. E. Kaufman's inquiry about the condition of his cattle in 1886.

Montana Stock Growers' Association

Slaughtering Scene in France, about 1566

The Celebrated Cattle Market at Brighton, Massachusetts

the route from the Río Grande, through or past San Antonio, Austin, and Fort Worth, and entered the Indian Territory at Red River Station, following roughly a line of cities in present Oklahoma—Duncan, Chickasha, El Reno, Kingfisher, Enid, and Pond Creek—and on to Abilene, Kansas.

It should be remembered that the trail was not a road or highway, but a general direction of travel, wide enough to meet the grass requirements of the hungry herds—narrow for the season's first travelers, broadening as the later drives came on, since trailways had to be feedways, too. Only when homesteaders moved in did the trail narrow to the 500- to 600-yard width described by later writers. Four million cattle traveled this route between 1866 and 1885, though farm settlements, barbed wire, and disease quarantines forced abandonment of much of the upper end of the Chisholm route by 1880.

The great drives up the Chisholm Trail were made possible by the audacious enterprise of Joseph G. McCoy, a native of Sangamon County, Illinois. In 1866 he had noted the mistreatment of Texans, driving more than a quarter of a million head of cattle, who had crossed the Red River that year striving for a northern market. Enlisting the interest of the Kansas Pacific (Union Pacific) Railroad officials, he proposed to build pens, yards, and other equipment necessary for handling obstreperous Longhorn cattle at a Kansas railhead. He stressed the vicissitudes of the Texans, pointing out that Indians assailed the drovers, stealing horses and stampeding cattle; that semi-banditti from western Missouri were hostile and predatory, while bands of "no-count" discharged soldiers ranged the precious grasslands, stealing, pillaging, and murdering. He cited the potential volume of business if such lawlessness could be suppressed.

In search of connecting lines, McCoy also visited the office of the Missouri Pacific, but was rebuffed, whereupon he made arrangements with the Hannibal and St. Joseph Railroad to deliver the carloads of cattle to Quincy and so to Chicago. This move resulted in the rise of the Chicago market and the decline of St. Louis as a cattle center.

On a scouting trip to locate his railhead, McCoy met Colonel John Jacob Myers, of Lockhart, Texas, in Junction City, Kansas, where the two talked the indefinite but purposeful language of cowmen. "They sat and chatted, Myers telling about the herds of wild longhorns ranging over Texas, McCoy revealing his ambition to establish a cattle-buying and shipping depot."[25] McCoy's dream neared realization when Colonel Myers promised him one million cattle from Texas and actually marked the trail from the Red River Crossing to Lockhart. He also spread word in Caldwell, Gonzales, Travis, Bastrop, and Hays counties that McCoy would maintain an honest market in Abilene. Everybody began "throwing together" herds for the long trek to Kansas, but Myers led off with his own trail outfit. Many have laid claim to being the first to arrive in Abilene with Texas stock—McCoy gives the credit to Colonel O. W. Wheeler—but railroad records award the honor to Colonel Myers.

Settlements, cabins, and wire fences eventually made an obstacle race of the Chisholm Trail, and by 1876 the Western Trail, crossing Red River at Doan's Store, was attracting increasing numbers of hooves. This route had been blazed the year before to reach the new Santa Fe railhead at Dodge City. From San Antonio it saved as much as twenty days' drive over the time required in following the Chisholm Trail.

When in 1884 Cherokee Strip cattlemen blocked the trails from the south with barbed wire and in 1885 the Kansas Legislature, fearing infection from ticks, forbade Texas cattle other than Panhandle herds to enter their state, a national trail was proposed, to be made official and permanent by a Congressional act. It started from the Point of Rocks at the southwestern corner of Kansas, leaving a 200-mile gap between there and the Western Trail. This gap the indomitable drovers closed by turn-

[25] Eugene Whitmore, "John Jacob Myers and the Early Cattle Drives," Chicago *Westerners Brand Book,* Vol. IX, No. 8 (May, 1947).

ing west at Camp Supply and, proceeding to a point south of the Kansas-Oklahoma-Colorado boundary intersection, swung northward west of Kansas on what was popularly called the Northern or Texas Trail, a portion of the planned National Trail. Straight north of Kit Carson, Colorado, a branch turned northeast into Nebraska to reach Ogallala, rail shipping point on the Union Pacific. A number of herds of cattle traversed the National Trail, but legislation was never enacted in Congress, and by the 1890's, with railroads pushing farther and farther into the cattle country, the great trail drives were a thing of the past.

One branch of the Western Trail used by drovers from the Panhandle did not originate in Texas, but was first used by two freighters named Jones and Plummer, who hauled supplies from Dodge City to Camp Supply in Oklahoma, and later to Generals Sheridan and Miles on campaign against the Arapaho and Cheyenne Indians. The last routing of the Jones and Plummer Trail ran direct from Dodge City to cross Beaver Creek in Oklahoma, and thence to Adobe Walls on the Canadian River in Hutchinson County, Texas; still later it reached Fort Elliott, Texas, established on McClelland's Creek in the Panhandle in 1876 to protect the cattle drives lying to the west of the older routes.

One such route along the farther west line was claimed as the Potter-Bacon Trail by Jack Potter, trail boss for the New England Cattle Company. When he reached Albany, Texas, over the Western Trail with a bunch of cattle from the south in the spring of 1883, he received route instructions from Alfred T. Bacon, company manager located at Greeley, Colorado, together with a map designating a new trail, which, if followed, would reduce driving time from forty to as little as twenty days. The map showed the locations of the Goodnight Ranch, Tascosa, Buffalo Springs, the OX outfit on the Cimarron, Fort Lyon on the "Arkansaw," and the "South Platt" itself at the mouth of Bijou Creek in northern Colorado.

"I got through all right by having a fuss with the Goodnight people," says Potter, "and having to detour around their range because their cattle, having been driven from the north, were not immune to tick fever. Leigh Dyer, Goodnight's brother-in-law, told me this was the first through herd that had ventured out from the Western Trail, and since I had opened the way, he thought others would follow and cause them a good deal of trouble. I have seen this trail marked on different maps called by different names. I am sure I blazed it, and it should be named the Potter and Bacon Trail. Bacon mapped it and Potter drove it."[26]

Meanwhile, though the rush to California was over, there was still a reasonably strong western movement. Before the Civil War the southern route via El Paso, Guadalupe Pass, Tucson, the Gila River, and Yuma had been most popular; after the war, the herds moved up the Pecos into New Mexico, west through Fort Sumner, and along the thirty-fifth parallel.

When the government advertised for matured beef steers to be delivered to feed the Indians at Fort Sumner in 1866, Charles Goodnight and Oliver Loving blazed a new trail for their cattle, starting from old Fort Belknap on the Brazos, thence by way of the Concho and Horsehead Crossing on the Pecos to their destination. John S. Chisum used this trail in the late 1860's, and his name was sometimes attached to it, making confusion worse confounded concerning the Chisholm Trail. Up to the time the long drives north were abandoned, a quarter of a million Longhorns had traveled the Goodnight and Loving Trail.

Half a million head followed the North Star by other trails, among them being the three already mentioned—the National, the Jones and Plummer, the Potter-Bacon—and the Jim Stinson Trail, which went farthest west in Texas of all the well-known routes. Jim Stinson, manager of the New Mexico Land and Cattle Company, drove 20,000 head from West Central Texas in 1882 to the Estancia Valley in New Mexico, entering the state through the Salt Lakes in the eastern part of modern Hudspeth County, Texas, and Las Portales Springs. Eventually this trail was extended to the Arizona line. In a single season, at Fort

[26] Jack M. Potter and Laura Krehbiel, *Cattle Trails of the Old West*, 7.

Sumner alone, 20,000 head were normally placed on pasture, and additional numbers were grazed around modern Vaughn, Encino, and Willard.

Whether or not historians so title them, these "cut-off" trails, like all the main ones, by any other name would smell as chokingly dusty, reek as strongly of horse lather and cow dollops, and scour quite as deep a hoof-marked trough in the unfenced grasslands reaching from the Río Grande to the Canadian border. The millions of Longhorns and hundreds of cowpokes who hit this long, long trail deserve a chapter of their own.

CHAPTER 15

Rugged Days on the Texas Trails

THE FIRST "cowboy" in the Southwest was a Texas border
raider of the early nineteenth century. And the word
carried about the same stigma as that borne by Rob Roy,
his eighteenth-century prototype—the "Red Robert" of Scott's
novel—whose Highland banditti made a living stealing cattle
from their panicky compatriots of the Scottish lowlands.[1]

In the troubled days preceding the founding of the Republic
of Texas, gangs of young men—transients from the North and
embattled homesteaders seeking a foothold in the disputed terrain—scoured the area between the Nueces and Río Grande
rivers driving off stock owned by Mexican *rancheros*. "Generally timing their forays with moonlight," says J. Frank Dobie,
"a band of ten or fifteen 'cowboys' would rush from two to six
hundred cattle together and head them northeast in a long run,
which they would keep up for 24 hours, after that merely walking or trotting. . . . Some of the cattle thus lifted were driven to
the New Orleans market. The majority were used to stock the
coastal ranges. . . . For forty years the Bloody Border knew no
peace."[2] Only after four decades of raiding and counter-raiding
did this Rob Roy type of cowboy attain respectability. The term
"cowpuncher" came later, when cowhands used metal-tipped
poles to chouse cattle into railroad stock cars.

[1] The origin of the word "cowboy" is a historical mystery. During Revolutionary days, the British guerrillas were sometimes called "cowboys" and the
Americans "skinners." Charles J. Lovell, of the Department of American English at the University of Chicago, reports that the earliest example of the use of
"cowpuncher" which he has unearthed was in Colorado in 1878, although "puncher" appeared in the Virginia City, Nevada, *Territorial Enterprise* in 1870.

[2] J. Frank Dobie, *The Longhorns*, 28–29.

In addition to water and grass, cattle raising has always required a third indispensable, the herder. The first on this hemisphere was the Aztec slave, branded on the cheek by Cortés in the sixteenth century. The last was the carefree Texas trail-driver of the late 1880's. Through the centuries the drudgery of herding, day and night, has remained the same. Only the actors have changed. One of the earliest was the primitive Indian, keeping watch by far-flung water holes. His only shelter was a rude lean-to, open on three sides, with a rear wall and roof made of hides and in front a feeble fire fueled with cow chips. Wearing a big hat, *serape*, shirt, and sandals, he rode his tough little mustang bare-legged, with rowelled Spanish spurs strapped to his heels. His only drink and food were *aqua prieta, atole* made of corn meal, and what game he could bring down with bow and arrow, for he had no firearms. In the lingo of his early mission days there were no such words as "Arbuckle" or "Colt." Hovering over his smouldering fire, half-starved, he hesitated to butcher a steer, for it was the property of his *rico* employer, to whom he was fanatically loyal—a virtue stoutly proclaimed by his successors of the Texas trails.

As skilled and daring a horseman as the wild Comanche, this peaceful cowherd boasted that he could ride any outlaw in the *remuda* and, like his predecessor in ancient Crete, could perform wonders with his rope. Not only could he snare an unruly steer, but his *reata* often brought to earth a fighting stallion or, with some help from his *compadres,* a marauding grizzly. For sport he would sometimes mount and ride a plunging Longhorn, antedating by a century or more the Brahman-bull riding of the modern rodeo. His solitude was cruelly interrupted by frequent raids. Savages from the Staked Plains of Apacheria, once they had acquired horses, stampeded and stole his cattle, and often killed their courageous guardian. Indian or "breed," he was a credit to his calling.

Besides cattle, the high plateaus of the Southwest supported hordes of bison. These were pursued and killed by the *cibolero*

—the Buffalo Bill Cody of his day. Riding a wiry mustang and, according to Gregg, clothed in leather trousers and jacket, wearing a flat straw hat, and armed with a bow and quiver of arrows and a long-handled spear, the New Mexican *cibolero* killed his quarry, dried the meat in the sun, and often followed the Indian practice of kneading the slices with his feet, claiming that this contributed to its preservation. If he was in a hurry or the weather was damp, he sometimes dried his meat over a fire. The result was *carne seco*, or jerked beef. Piling the provender on mule-back or loading it in ox-drawn *carretas*, he headed for home with enough meat to feed his family. He was a good provider.

When the *cibolero* began to trade with the Indians, he became a *Comanchero*. With the Mexicans to the south the Comanche Indians were always at war, but maintained friendly relations with those living in New Mexico, partly because they had few possessions worth stealing, partly because of favorable trade opportunities. It all began when indigent New Mexican villagers, outfitted with twenty dollars' worth of trinkets, first trekked to the Staked Plains and there bartered these trifles for horses, mules, and cattle which the Comanches had stolen in the south. With the passage of time, the *Comanchero*—often backed by unscrupulous Americans—enlarged his trading stock and his volume of business. The poor Indian usually got the worst of the dicker. A good mule went for a barrel of rot-gut whiskey, a pack horse for ten pounds of coffee, a buffalo robe for little or nothing, and cattle for what they could fetch. As a trader, the wily *Comanchero* had it all over David Harum. So successful were these shady transactions that at the end of the Civil War a New Mexican confessed to Charles Goodnight that the loot from Texas stockmen had amounted to 300,000 cattle and 100,000 horses and mules.[3]

With the passing of the buffalo and the subjugation of the Comanches, many a *cibolero* and some of the *Comancheros*, confronted with the alternative of "root hog, or die," became trust-

[3] Paul I. Wellman, *The Trampling Herd*, 211.

worthy *vaqueros—caballeros con vacas,* "horsemen with cows" —they and their descendants earning their keep as trail-herd hands.

The post–Civil War drives from southern Texas, celebrated in song and story, began in the spring of 1866 when 250,000 head crossed the Red River into the Indian Territory bound for Missouri or Kansas. It is estimated that during the next thirty years ten million cattle and one million horses were driven from Texas to the railheads, pastures, and packing plants of the North. The last drives up the long trail were those of 1896—12,500 XIT steers—and of 1897 when "Scandlous John" McCanless pushed a small herd north to write *finis* to the saga of the Texas trails.[4]

At first all were Longhorns—the best breed of bovines for trail-driving the world has ever known. Charles Goodnight claimed they could go farther without water and endure more suffering than the blooded stock of later drives, hold together better in stampedes, were more easily circled in a run, and rarely split off when the front of the herd was turned. Blooded cattle would run over a rider if he didn't get out of the way, but Longhorns would always turn, if possible. Their hoofs were superior, they had less tendency to lose weight, spaced themselves well when being trailed, could be handled at less expense, had twice the endurance of others, and, when circumstances permitted, lived longer, attaining a ripe old age without shedding a tooth.

The organization of a Texas trail drive—with its trail boss, its point, flank, swing and drag riders, its chuck wagon and cook, its horse wrangler and remuda, its routine of daily chores —the story of it all has been so frequently and competently told by others as to need no rehashing here. But a few sample adventures and incidents of a typical hegira from the Río Grande to the Yellowstone may be of interest.

On the long drives north, Longhorns had to swim so many streams that they earned the jocular title of "sea lions." This back-handed compliment was well earned. As early as the fall

[4] J. Evetts Haley, *The XIT Ranch of Texas,* 143.

of 1862, a rawboned Texas lad of seventeen named W. D. H. Saunders and a half-dozen others of his generation headed for New Orleans with 1,100 head of steers. After swimming them across the Colorado, Brazos, Trinity, Neches, and Sabine rivers, they reached the Mississippi, only to learn that New Orleans was no longed held by the Confederacy. Detouring north, they figured they could dispose of their cattle in Mobile. With no craft available to ferry them, "right down to the brink of the rolling Mississippi, a mile wide and forty feet deep at that point, the wild young cowmen took the steers—and then with shrill yells and lashing lariats urged the animals into the water. One boy took to the river on his swimming horse and rode ahead of the herd as a guide. Others flanked the cattle which by now were churning the river into a creamy foam. The rest brought up the drag. It was a manifest impossibility to swim a herd across the lower Mississippi—yet somehow these Texans did it. Of the 1,100 steers, a full thousand took to the water like amphibians and swam the mile-wide torrent, landing far downstream on the other side. The herders—mere children some of them, their milk teeth scarcely shed and their beards ungrown—swam their horses alongside and howled at the cattle like exultant young fiends. . . . The longhorns, their eyes rolling in fear and panic, wallowed in the waves like hippopotami, breasted the muddy tide, struck out boldly, each following the wake of the beast in front of him, and eventually, miraculously, clambered in safety up the opposite bank."[5]

It was from the ranks of such youngsters as Saunders that four years later were recruited many of the volunteer trail drivers of the first big push to the North. They comprised a motley assortment of herring-gutted veterans of the war, experienced stockmen, riff-raff from southern river towns, gamblers, former freighters, and farm boys. Facing unknown hazards ahead— dust, mud, tornadoes, stampedes, Indians, outlaws, nesters,

[5] Wellman, *The Trampling Herd,* 66–67.

quarantines, and high-jackers—they hit the trail in a spirit of joyous adventure.

The next three decades saw a great improvement in the character and efficiency of these organized drives. For one thing, the cowboy learned how to dress properly for the grueling work ahead. And his costume was a far cry from the fancy duds worn by modern dude ranchers and Hollywood screen stars. Salty Jack Weadock of Tucson, writer, old-time cowman, and cavalryman, put it this way: "I was looking at a picture a few days ago which showed a young fellow who was really fancied up. From his white Stetson to his multi-colored boots he was right pretty. I don't know what that outfit cost him, but it didn't come for free. What caught my attention was the caption which said something about an 'outstanding working cowboy.' Well, a fellow might go for that outstanding part, but the working part is something else again. That lad just never did much cow work in those duds. Not and look like that after he was through. I guess he must have had his picture taken on his day off."

To prove his case, Weadock pointed to a picture taken with an old-fashioned plate camera in the early 1880's showing a crew of Texas trail drivers—thirteen cowboys and a cook. "They all look like they were working, or had been right recently," says Weadock, adding, "The way those fellows dressed would never get them a part in a cowboy movie, especially in one where the cowhands sing and play guitars. There isn't a single ten-gallon hat in that whole outfit. Except for the cook, they're all wearing beaten-up, wide-brimmed, low, round-topped hats which look like something discarded by a Mississippi river-boat gambler. The cook is different. His hat looks like an old Homburg, mashed on top. There aren't any fancy vests in that outfit. In fact, most of the vests look like they're worn mainly to tote a tobacco sack and some matches and they all look like fugitives from the old clothes bag. Shirts seem to be light-colored calico, one showing checks. There isn't a pair of fancy boots in sight.

173

Those old boys holding that herd outside of Abilene had duds which would stand the wear and the weather, and horse equipment built for use. A fellow just didn't want his rig coming apart in rough country a long walk from home."[6]

More than thirty years ago that veteran cowboy and famous artist, Charles M. Russell, under the pen name of "Rawhide Rawlins," wrote that the old-time cowboy reminded him of the Eastern girl who asked her mother, "Ma, do cowboys eat grass?" "No, dear," said the old lady, "they're part human." Russell figured maybe the old girl had 'em sized up right, but he believed they, although human, belonged to a separate species.

"I'm talkin' about the old-time ones, before the country's strung with wire 'n nesters had grabbed all the water, 'n cowpuncher's home was big. It wasn't where he took his hat off, but where he spread his blankets. He ranged from Mexico to the Big Bow river of the north, 'n from where the trees get scarce in the east to the old Pacific. He don't need no iron hoss, but covers his country on one that eats grass 'n wears hair. All the tools he needed was saddle, bridle, quirt, hackamore 'n rawhide riatta or seagrass rope. . . . The puncher himself was rigged, startin' at the top, with a good hat—not the floppy kind you see in pictures, with the rim turned up in front. The top cover he wore holds its shape 'n was made to protect his face from the weather; maybe to hold it on, he wore a buckskin string under the chin or back of the head. Round his neck was a big handkerchief; tied loose 'n in the drag of a trail herd it was drawn over the face to the eyes—hold-up fashion—to protect the nose and throat from dust. . . . His feet were covered with good high-heeled boots, finished off with steel spurs of the Spanish pattern."[7]

The first drives knew no such thing as a chuck wagon. Every cowhand carried his own grub and tin utensils and cooked his meals over his own cow-chip fire. This didn't last long after the

[6] Interview with J. F. Weadock, May 18, 1953.
[7] Charles M. Russell, *Rawhide Rawlins Stories*, 41–43.

pokes heard of a contraption put together out in the Panhandle by the versatile Charlie Goodnight, which had a hinged lid which let down on a swinging leg to form the cook's work-table. Inside was a jar of sourdough. This chuck-box was attached to the back of a government wagon which the inventor had rebuilt with tough, seasoned bois d'arc. It had iron axles in place of wooden and carried a can of tallow for axle grease.[8] It first was set in motion by yokes of oxen, later by harnessed mules or horses. Shortly all Texas trail herds had chuck wagons.

That first drive in 1866 ran into trouble. The five civilized tribes—the Cherokees, Choctaws, Creeks, Chickasaws, and Seminoles—were themselves cattle raisers. When a quarter of a million hungry bovines suddenly invaded their terrain, eating all the grass in sight, they demanded a toll of ten cents a head. Some of the drovers paid it; others gave cattle in lieu of money; a few drew their six-shooters and bulled or bluffed their way through. Still others detoured east and into Arkansas, risking attack and thievery by Ozark Hills outlaws.

More ominous were the threats to life and limb by the Comanches. Before he was old enough to vote, young Jimmy Cook —descendant of the famous English navigator Captain James Cook—hired out to Charlie Slaughter in the early 1870's, before there was a strand of wire fence between the Gulf of Mexico and the Canadian border. His job was to help drive a mixed herd of 2,500 head from central Texas to Kansas. He had acquired considerable skill as a marksman and "brush popper"—gathering cattle in the mesquite, chaparral, and prickly pear jungles. When he reported to Joe Roberts, the trail boss, this was his briefing: "They tell us you can catch a cow, and can shoot a rabbit's eye out at every pop. Now if you can ride for the next four months without a whole night's sleep, and turn your gun loose on any damned Injun that tries to get our horses, well, get ready. We roll out tomorrow."

It was not long before young Cook and his Henry rifle had

[8] J. Evetts Haley, *Charles Goodnight: Cowman and Plainsman,* 121–22.

175

a chance to prove their competency. After they had suffered the loss of five hundred head in a stampede, Allen Harris, another of Slaughter's foremen, arrived with more cattle to make up the deficiency. The two herds were split, riding a few miles apart. One night the Indians tried to stampede the Harris herd by running into it with their ponies, dragging a buffalo robe at the end of a rope. Cattle and horses broke for freedom, but the men stayed with the stock and held them.

The Comanches did not give up. They would slip up to the herd in the night and bring down a Longhorn or two with their arrows. The wounded beasts would plunge about, bellowing and often starting another stampede. It got so that night herders had little enthusiasm for their job, expecting to get a Comanche arrow in the ribs every time they rode out to sing a "Texas Lullaby" to their drowsy-eyed dogies. One night, after the savages had acquired firearms, Cook rode into camp from the cedar break where the cattle had been bedded down. Suddenly he heard a dozen shots. As he dismounted, his horse turned its head, got an Indian bullet squarely in the forehead and fell dead. Every man sleeping round the campfire ran for the thicket, among them Cook and Frank Dennis, an old-school cowboy. Crawling under the low-hanging branches of a big cedar tree, Cook was nearly overrun by the stampeding horses, who in turn panicked the cattle. "The crashing and crackling of brush and branches under the hoofs of that crazed mass of animals made about as great an uproar as any cowboy ever heard." In the midst of the hubbub, Roberts, the foreman, yelled, "Don't let 'em get away with the horses, boys! Stay with 'em!" One by one the men answered him. "I didn't like to get out from beneath that tree," says Cook, "but neither did I care to be called a coward, so I joined him. It was so dark an Indian could have slipped up within three feet without being seen."

As Dennis failed to appear, Cook and Roberts wandered about until daylight looking for him, without success. Meanwhile the men with the cattle had managed to hold the herd half a mile from camp. About sunrise Dennis rode in, pale but cheerful. There was blood on his clothes and on the handkerchief that bound his left hand. A bunch of Indians had crawled up to within fifteen feet of the circle Dennis was riding and blazed away, sending a bullet through the center of the cowboy's hand, several through his blanket and saddle. One arrow lodged between his saddle and blanket, another shot off the saddle horn. The savages got away with about one-fourth of the cowboys' horses.

In the afternoon, a couple of buffalo hunters trudged into camp saying that the Indians had stolen all of their ten horses. They wanted to borrow ponies to follow the thieves and recover their stock. Roberts let them have two from his decimated *remuda,* and said that anyone who wanted to could join the avengers. Cook and two others volunteered. Surprising the Indians in camp—where the stolen stock was picketed in a willow thicket—the buffalo hunters opened fire at daybreak. As Cook lay concealed in a buffalo wallow, one Indian, leaping on a pony, charged up the hill straight to where he was lying. Flattened out, the redskin kept belaboring his mount at every leap. One of the hunters began firing at him, telling Cook to lie low as the bullets were striking nearer to him than to the fleeting target. "Not daring to rise up to a proper shooting position," says Cook, "I merely took a pot shot at him as he passed. My bullet broke his pony's back just behind the rider's seat. The pony went down, but the Indian went over its head, landed on his feet, and continued his flight. He dashed into a bunch of willows in a little valley behind me, causing me extreme mental discomfort, for he had a gun in his hand when he passed." The Indian camp now being abandoned, the cowboys recovered not only all their own horses but those stolen from the buffalo hunters, besides fifteen head of Indian ponies, squaw saddles, and blankets.[9]

Not all stampedes were caused by raiders. Lightning, tornadoes, a wind-blown blanket—any one of these could start a

[9] James H. Cook, *Longhorn Cowboy,* 101, 116–17, 120ff.

Longhorn panic. Indeed, young Cook himself caused a stampede the first time he went on night herd. The cattle had not yet lain down, but were quiet and motionless, with the exception of one old black cow which had probably once served as a milch cow to a Mexican family, and which insisted on feeding all through the evening. Riders repeatedly turned her into the herd, but soon she would be wandering off again to feed. Finally, about thirty yards from the herd, she lay down to rest. The men detoured to include her in the circle they were riding. She would let them pass within a few feet and never stir. "Every time I came around," says Cook, "I would see how close I could come. . . . Finally she allowed me to ride within two feet without moving. The next time around I decided to see if the old longhorn bossy would let me touch her. . . . I leaned over one side and touched her neck with my foot. She must have been asleep, for she gave a snort and a bound, and plunged into the herd—or rather the place where the herd had been; for the instant she snorted, there came a roar and a crash such as I had never heard before, and the earth seemed fairly to tremble. . . . The herd had stampeded." When a Mexican rode up, Cook innocently asked, "What's the matter?" "The herd has stampeded," he replied, "We won't have one of them by morning."

"What stampeded them?" Cook asked.

"*Dios sabe.*" (God knows!) Cook hoped that no one else did! The scared Longhorns stayed pretty well together—all but 500 head—and were trailed back to camp by morning. The missing stock was later replaced by the cattle brought up by Allen Harris. "My employer's loss was my gain," concluded Cook, "for I had learned my lesson and I never again tried such an experiment."[10]

Riders lost their lives in stampedes. Fifteen-year-old Teddy Blue Abbott and others were holding a herd of 500 cows near the Blue River in Nebraska one night in 1876, when a fearful storm arose, scattering the herd and sending their four guardians

[10] *Ibid.,* 113–15.

after them. When morning came, one rider was missing. They found his body among the prairie-dog holes beside his horse. Abbott says: "The horse's ribs were scraped bare of hide, and all the rest of horse and man was mashed into the ground as flat as a pancake. The only thing you could recognize was the handle of his six-shooter. We tried to think the lightning hit him, and that was what we wrote his folks down in Henrietta, Texas. But we couldn't really believe it ourselves. . . . I'm afraid his horse stepped into one of them holes and they both went down before the stampede. We got a shovel—I remember it had a broken handle—and we buried him nearby, on a hillside covered with round, smooth rocks that we called niggerheads. We dug away a little of the ground under him and slipped his saddle blanket under him and piled niggerheads on top. That was the best we could do. . . . The awful part of it was that we had milled them cattle over him all night, not knowing he was there. . . . After that orders were given to sing when you were running with a stampede, so others would know where you were; if they didn't hear you, they'd figure that something had happened. After a while this came to be a custom on the range."[11]

[11] E. C. Abbott and Helena Huntington Smith, *We Pointed Them North,* 43–44.

CHAPTER 16

"The Thund'ring Hoofs of Cattle"

QUEER THINGS caused stampedes. When trail driver Anderson bedded down a big herd of beeves on a small slope in Indian Territory between Cache Creek and the Washita River, he did not know that it was the roosting place of every prairie chicken in that part of the country. The next morning, when those chickens took to the air, the noise they made frightened 3,000 cattle into a disastrous stampede. Several were killed and a hundred got away.

When four thousand big Texas steers from the famous King Ranch started a jump off the bed ground near Fort Laramie, Wyoming, the foreman, Tom Moore, figured that they had gotten a whiff of the Negro cook recently hired to replace the Mexican who had served the crew ever since leaving the home pasture in South Texas months before. This same herd stampeded a short time later when a big black wolf got too close. The men had an all-night job heading the leaders, starting a mill, and holding them until daylight; fifty-five head got away but were recovered.

Another time a careless foreman bedded his herd down right in the middle of a big prairie-dog town. The ensuing stampede and recovery of 635 steers caused a considerable delay, though the net loss was only five head. Another time, when the herd was passing a settler's cabin, an old setting hen flew cackling across another herd, which promptly panicked. Those in the lead kept right on while the cattle in the middle doubled back, stormed pell-mell in the opposite direction, ran over the cook's ox team, and upset the wagon.

In 1881, within ten miles of Dodge City, Kansas, lightning once stampeded no less than fifty different trail herds. George Brock of Lockhart, Texas, caught in a severe Kansas storm near the Platte River, said that "the lightning would strike the ground and set the grass on fire, then the rain would put it out." Brock was riding one horse and leading two. Dismounting, he tied the three together, took off his spurs, six-shooter, and pocket knife, laid them on the ground, and moved away. All cowboys believed it was fatal to be wearing anything metal during an electrical storm.[1]

Teddy Blue (E. C. Abbott) thought the worst hardship on the trail was loss of sleep. The cowboy's day would end about nine o'clock, when he grazed the herd to the bed ground. Then every man in the outfit except the boss, the horse wrangler, and the cook would have to stand two hours' night guard. If a man's guard was from 12:00 to 2:00, he would stake his night horse, pull off his boots, and crawl in at nine, get three hours' sleep, and then ride two hours. Coming off guard, he would sleep an hour and a half, or until the cook yelled, "Roll out," at 3:30. That was when the weather was fine, with no stampedes to keep him up all night. "Sometimes we would rub tobacco juice in our eyes to keep awake. . . . I have often sat in my saddle sound asleep for just a few minutes," says Abbott. "In '79, when we hit the Platte River with that Olive herd, a strong north wind was blowing waves two feet high in their faces, and they [the cattle] bulled on us, which means they won't do nothing, only stand and look at you. So since they wouldn't take the water we had to hold them, and we had one of those bad electric storms and they run nearly all night. We got them across the river the next day, and that night on guard my partner, Joe Buckner, says: 'Teddy, I am going to Greenland where the nights are six months long, and I ain't agoing to get up until ten o'clock next day.' "[2]

When he went up the trail in 1876 young Jimmy Cook found sleeping arrangements even more primitive. "At night,"

[1] These incidents are described at length in *The Trail Drivers of Texas,* ed. by J. Marvin Hunter.
[2] Abbott and Smith, *We Pointed Them North,* 80–81.

he reported, "we camped in the open and after supper simply curled up on the ground and went to sleep. . . . A 'Tucson bed' was quite a common thing on that trip and on many a trip thereafter. For those who may not understand, I will explain that the Tucson bed is made by lying on your stomach and covering that with your back. It was allowable to put your saddle and saddle blanket over your head, should you happen to have such articles with you, as protection from any hailstones larger than hen's eggs."[3]

Mention of hailstones recalls the experience of a Texas woman trail driver who made a three months' trek from the coastal county of Nueces to Newton, Kansas, with her husband and a score of cowhands, mostly Mexicans. In April, 1871, ranchman W. F. Burks of Banquette topped out a thousand head of his best steers, had them road-branded at Pinatas, and started north, accompanied by a neighbor with another thousand head.

In a light buggy, drawn by two brown ponies, rode Mrs. Amanda Burks. All went well until the herd reached Bosque County in central Texas. Here an early evening electrical storm, with violent rain and hail, forced her husband to picket her team in the woods while he and the crew rode away to try to hold the frightened cattle. Mrs. Burks, sitting alone in the buggy, cold, wet, and hungry, for the first and only time on the long trip ardently wished she were back on the old home ranch. Some time after midnight she heard the chuck wagon rolling and her husband's voice calling her name; they finally made camp at one in the morning and enjoyed the first meal since breakfast the day before. Mr. Burks and the others started eating. Mrs. Burks noticed that their hands were covered with big blood blisters caused by the hail. One of the boys said, "the beat of the hail on my head made me crazy. I would have run, but didn't know which way to go."

Fire was another hazard which seemed to pursue the Burkses.

[3] Cook, *Longhorn Cowboy*, 21.

In the Indian Territory one night when sleeping in their tent, the couple was awakened by a flaming box of trinkets which had been set afire by a lighted candle. At another time a prairie fire drove them out of camp before breakfast to a part of the plain previously burned, known locally as a "burn." Two days later Mrs. Burks herself caused one. "I thought I would build a fire in a gulley," she says, "while the cook had gone for water. Not later than when I struck a match, the grass all around was in a blaze, which spread so quickly that the men could not stop it. They succeeded in beating out the flanks of the fire so that it did not spread out at the sides at the beginning. The fire blazed higher than a house and went straight ahead for fifty miles or more. Investigators came next day to find out who the culprit was, and when they learned it was a woman, nothing was said, except for a remark one of the men made that he was glad that he didn't strike that match." Finally, when they were camped on Emmet Creek, twenty-two miles from Newton, a prairie fire crept up so quickly that the crew barely had time to break camp and get the cattle to safety. There wasn't time to harness the ponies to Mrs. Burks' buggy, so the mounted men tied their ropes to it, told her to jump in, and away they went on a dead run for the nearest "burn," birds and animals fleeing with them.

Many of these prairie fires were started by squatters who wanted to keep strangers off their land. They would plow a boundary around their stake and set fire to the grass outside. While the Burkses were wintering their stock in Kansas, their ordeal of fire was succeeded by that of snow and ice. Nine horses perished in one storm, many young cattle lost their horns, and ice had to be chopped from the streams so the cattle could drink. For all of the hardships, Mrs. Burks arrived at her Texas home "in much better health than when I left it nine months before."[4]

Some sixteen years later another female made her contribution to Texas trail-driving lore. In the spring of 1888, Samuel Dunn Houston found himself short-handed with a steer herd of

[4] Hunter, *Trail Drivers of Texas*, 296–305.

2,500 not far from Clayton, New Mexico. Riding into town to see if he could hire two or three trail men, he was told that there were no men to be had, but "a kid of a boy" who wanted to go up the trail could be found at the livery barn. Houston hired the lad and put him in charge of the horses, finding him altogether satisfactory. "The kid would get up on the stormiest nights and stay with the cattle until the storm was over. He was good-natured, very modest, didn't use any cuss words or tobacco, and always pleasant." When the herd was halted just outside Hugo, Colorado, the kid came to Houston right after the noon dinner and told him he wanted to quit, saying he was homesick. Reluctantly the boss let him go. "About sundown" says Houston, "we were all sitting around camp and the old herd was coming in on the bed ground. I looked up toward town and saw a lady all dressed up coming toward camp, walking. I told the boys we were going to have company. . . . When within fifty feet of camp I got up to be ready to receive my guest. Our eyes were all set on her, and every man holding his breath. When she got within twenty feet of me, she began to laugh and said, 'Mr. Houston, you don't know me, do you?'

"Well, for one minute I couldn't speak. She reached her hand out to me, to shake hands, and I said, 'Kid, is it possible that you are a lady?' That was one time that I could not think of anything to say, for everything that had been said on the old cow trail in the last three or four days entered my mind at that moment.

"I told the cook to get one of the tomato boxes for a chair. The kid sat down and I said, 'Now I want you to explain yourself.'

" 'Well,' " she said, " 'I will tell you. My papa is an old-time trail driver from southern Texas. He drove from Texas to Caldwell, Kansas, in the '70's. He liked the country . . . so on the last trip he went to work on a ranch up there and never returned to Texas. . . . In two or three years he and my mother were married. After I was ten or twelve years old, I used to hear papa

184

talk so much about the old cow trail I made up my mind that when I was grown I was going up the trail if I had to run off. I had a pony of my own [and] not being far from Clayton I saddled up [one day] and told my brother I was going out in the country and I might be gone for a week ... and not to worry, I would be back. I had on a suit of brother's clothes and a pair of his boots. . . . Now Mr. Houston, I am glad I found you to make the trip with, for I have enjoyed it. I am going just as straight home as I can and that old train can't run too fast to suit me, when I get on it.' "

Houston and most all of the crew were in Hugo that night to see the little girl off on the 11:20 train. "I suppose she was the only girl that ever made such a trip as that," says Houston, adding, "She was a perfect lady." In after years, at his ranch on the Pecos, he received many letters from the girl and her father, thanking him for his kindness.[5]

Another woman incident: Old-timer L. B. Anderson of Seguin, Texas, remembers the time in the 1870's when he and a crew were camped near John Tom's ranch in Atascosa County. While they were driving a herd of old Mexican beeves down a long lane, the animals stampeded and started back up the lane. A man and woman had just passed them riding horseback. When they heard the noise and saw the herd coming, the couple turned and rode for their lives. It seemed as if the herd was surely going to overtake the woman, riding side-saddle. Suddenly she swung herself astride her horse and pulled off a race that beat anything Anderson ever saw, for she outdistanced every critter in the herd and rode safely away.[6] The speed of her mount was probably accelerated by fright caused by the strange antics of this female "switch rider."

Drudgery gave way to horseplay whenever the weary waddy had a chance. In August of 1883, E. C. Abbott was trailing a herd near Union Pacific railroad trains which were carrying emigrants going West. Once, as a train slowed down at a station,

[5] *Ibid.*, 75–77.   [6] *Ibid.*, 204.

185

the boys threw over a telegraph pole a straw-stuffed dummy with a rope around its neck. The whole outfit began to shoot at it as it was swinging in the air. The shots severed the rope, down came the dummy, and away went Abbott on a dead run across the flat, dragging the "corpse" with his rope, the rest shooting at it. "Women fainted and children screamed. They begged the conductor to pull out before we held up the train. Someone telegraphed to Lincoln saying the FUF cowboys had hung a horse thief. Hell began to pop. The boss, the sheriff, and the coroner arrived. They demanded the corpse at once. We pointed to it. Marion Olive, who was driving the team which brought them, got the biggest laugh. But our boss told us to get busy and hit the trail for Montana."[7]

Even fighting the Comanches sometimes had its lighter side. Line riding one day along the Clear Fork of the Brazos, a cowboy found a cow with an unbranded calf and did what every enterprising waddy should do. He built a fire, heated an iron, and placed his boss's brand on the calf. "At this juncture, a solitary Indian lurking in the brush near at hand took a pot shot at him. Without an instant's hesitation the cowboy vaulted into his saddle, swung his rope and went at the savage with a yell. Vainly the Comanche tried to load his old-fashioned gun, saw vengeance bearing down on him, and turned to run just as the noose whistled through the air, whipped about his legs, and brought him to the ground. The well-trained cow horse immediately began to walk sedately toward the branding fire, which was still blazing, dragging behind, as if he had been any ordinary maverick, a very glum and sullen captive.

"At the fire the cowboy dismounted, reheated his iron, and grimly placed his brand on a prominent portion of the Comanche's anatomy left bare by the dangling breech clout. Then, snatching the Indian's own knife from its sheath, he bent over the prostrate and bedraggled savage and added the ranch earmarks as corroborative proof of the authenticity of the brand.

[7] Abbott and Smith, *We Pointed Them North*, 84–85.

Having completed all this, he loosed his rope and kicked his captive to his feet.

" 'Git now,' growled the cowboy, 'an' the next time some feller calls ye a maverick, tell him that he's a liar. An' tell yore folks, when ye next see 'em, that I'm comin' no'th, come next grass, to round up and brand the hull damned tribe.' "[8]

One of the best and oldest saddlery firms in Arizona is Porter's, with stores in Phoenix and Tucson. Its humble beginnings in Abilene some eighty years ago endured the pot shots of playful cowboys. As Jack Weadock tells it, Abilene was "an uncurried town in those early days, and the cowhands delivering cattle didn't make it any quieter. After being months on the trail, they would collect their pay, get cleaned up, and start out to do the town. Old man Porter, founder of the business, had set up shop in a tent. Working at night, he made an inviting shadow-target, and the punchers would shoot holes in the tent just to see the saddle-maker jump. Porter's ingenuity was equal to the need. He dug a pit inside of the tent, moved his stuff back in and worked below ground level. The shooting didn't bother him after that, except that the tent was kind of leaky."[9]

Ever since that eighteenth-century *caballero* banged the tails of horses tethered outside a California *baile*, or the nineteenth-century "Virginian" of Owen Wister's novel changed the babies at a Wyoming ranchers' dance, cowpokes have been frolicking high, wide, and handsome. Some folks seem to think that is all there was to the old-time cowboy's life. When an Eastern school ma'am asked a grizzled Texas puncher, "Didn't the boys used to have a lot of fun riding their ponies?" he came back at her: "Madam, there wasn't any boys or ponies. They was all men and horses."

Men and horses, indeed; durable horses and daring men, who feared only two things in all the world—a decent woman and being set afoot.

[8] Wellman, *The Trampling Herd*, 51–52.
[9] Interview, May 18, 1953.

CHAPTER 17

Neck Yokes and Wagon Wheels

IN A SPIRITED SPEECH at Plymouth in 1802, John Quincy
Adams, then thirty-five years old, solemnly trumpeted:
"Westward the star of empire takes its way!" Although it
is doubtful that Adams' "west" extended so far, within five years
Captain Zebulon Pike and his fifteen seedy dragoons, accused
of trespass, were languishing in a Santa Fé jail in Spanish New
Mexico; in ten years three unabashed traders had reached the
same city unchallenged; and in 1824, eighty more, piloting
twenty-five wheeled vehicles loaded with $35,000 worth of mer-
chandise, had inaugurated the historic Santa Fé trade, which,
during fifty-six years, sometimes grossed half a million dollars
annually.

Although trespassers and hucksters were the first to demon-
state the truth of imperialist Adams' statement, others with different objectives were soon following their particular "stars"
over more northerly trails. The Cross beckoned missionaries to
the Indians; gold lured fortune-hunters to California; persecu-
tion drove Mormons to the Great Salt Lake; land hunger enticed
the landless to any spot with enough water and grass to support
a squatter, his crops, and his cattle.

This westward movement covered half a dozen routes. Chief
of these were the California-Overland and the Oregon trails,
their alternative cut-offs and tributaries having what one writer
called "as many loose ends as a horse's tail in a high wind."
There was the Bozeman Trail, battleground of the fighting
Sioux; the Overland, shuttling mail and express to and from
Sacramento; the Salt Lake, pioneered by Brigham Young and
his Latter-day Saints; the Gila and the Old Spanish trails, guid-

ing miners and trappers to southern California. These were the "Great Medicine Roads of the Whites," as the Indians called them—Santa Fé, road of commerce; California, route of the gold-seeker; Salt Lake, path to the Land of Deseret; Oregon, highway of missionary and homeseeker.

All these were predominantly ox trails, handling a prodigious number of emigrants and enormous tonnages of supplies. Between 1859 and 1869, an estimated 250,000 west-bound pilgrims traveled the California-Overland Trail; 51,000 used it in the one year of 1852. More than one-half of the Santa Fé traffic was moved by oxen. As early as 1834 their hooves had furrowed an 800-mile trough between Independence, Missouri, and the New Mexican capital. On the 2,000-mile trail linking Independence and Fort Vancouver, Washington, a stage passenger in one day counted 888 west-bound covered wagons, nearly all drawn by six- and eight-yoke teams of oxen.[1] On August 14, during the 1850 gold rush, the register at Fort Laramie recorded the presence of 39,506 men, and more than 3,000 women and children, 36,000 oxen, 7,300 cows and 9,000 wagons, besides hordes of horses, mules, and sheep. As not more than four-fifths of the travelers registered, the number probably totaled 55,000.[2]

An observant pilgrim on the Oregon Trail in 1845 pointed out that cattle stood the trip better than mules or horses, that they were less trouble and less liable to be run off by the Indians. Stock raised in Illinois or Missouri, being accustomed to prairie grass, fared better than those from Indiana or Ohio. They could be turned out at night to graze, whereas horses and mules, coveted by the Indians, had to be picketed. Each family usually had a few cows for milking, some of them yoked and put to the wagon whenever it was necessary to relieve any of the oxen.

[1] Grace R. Hebard and E. A. Brininstool, *The Bozeman Trail,* I, 69, quoting Root and Connelly's *The Overland Stage to California.*

[2] LeRoy R. Hafen and Francis Marion Young, *Fort Laramie and the Pageant of the West,* 164n., quoting from *Publications* of the Nebraska Historical Society, XX, 230.

In one traveler's journal, it was noted that "over two thousand head of cattle were scattered over the prairie," when let out to graze, "at a distance of four or five miles from camp."[3] When the company reached Oregon, all surplus cattle were sold at a handsome profit.

A migrating body which numbered more than 1,000 persons, 120 wagons, and several thousand loose horses and cattle, which negotiated the Oregon Trail in 1843, inspired one of the emigrants, Jesse Applegate, to chronicle some of the high lights, ox-wise, of the journey. In order to achieve discipline and orderly progress, those with less than four or five cows were brigaded in one column, those with sizable bands were alloted to another, slower-moving "cow column," of which Applegate was the chosen captain—and volunteer narrator. Describing the scene at daybreak, when the far-roving cattle and horses are being gathered to resume the day's journey, he notes: "Sixty men start [for] the vast herd . . . that form a distant semi-circle around the encampment, the most distant perhaps two miles away. . . . The well-trained animals move slowly toward camp, clipping here and there a thistle or tempting bunch of grass on the way. In about an hour 5,000 animals are close up to the encampment, and the teamsters are busy selecting their teams and driving them inside the 'corral' to be yoked."

That was the morning scene. Toward the end of the day, formation of the so-called "corral" is thus described (the "pilot" being the guide, the "captain" the boss of the column): "The sun is setting low in the west and at length the painstaking pilot is standing ready to conduct the train in the circle which he has previously measured and marked out, which is to form the invariable fortification for the night. The leading wagons follow him so nearly around the circle, that but a wagon length separates them. Each wagon follows in its track, the rear closing on

3 Joel Palmer, *Journal of Travels over the Rocky Mountains . . . 1845, 1846*, 142.

the front, until its tongue and ox-chains will perfectly reach
from one to the other; and so accurate the measurement and perfect the practice, that the hindmost wagon of the train always
precisely closes the gateway. As each wagon is brought into position, it is dropped from its team (the teams being inside the
circle), the team unyoked, and the yokes and chains used to
connect the wagon strongly with that in its front. Within ten
minutes from the time the leading wagon halted, the barricade
is formed, the teams unyoked and driven out to pasture. . . .
The corral is a circle 100 yards deep . . . a strong barrier that
the most vicious ox cannot break, and in case of the Sioux would
be no contemptible entrenchment."[4]

At the crossing of the Platte, the water was so deep in places
that it ran into the wagon boxes. As a single team and wagon
would have been swept away, the entire train was formed in
a single file and a chain was run through the train to which
teams and wagons were attached. Men waded the river alongside
their oxen, at times clinging to the ox yokes, and swimming. In
the deep places the oxen seemed to swim and the wagons to float,
being held up and in line by the chain to which they were attached.

One warm day when an ox had been slaughtered near Fort
Hall, some of the boys in the party discovered the swollen stomach and invented a somewhat unsavory sport. The stunt was to
take a running start, dive to butt one's head against the distended
paunch as hard as possible, and bounce back, the recoil being
in proportion to the force of the contact. One boy, Andy Baker,
tall and slender, with close-cropped hair, was determined to
beat all the rest. He went way, way back, lowered his small
head, charged at top speed, and, with the others yelling, "Give
her goss, Andy!," leaped high and came down on the paunch
like a pile-driver. But he did not bounce back. The rest rushed
up and found that Andy's head had punctured the paunch,
which had closed so tightly that he could not remove it. The

[4] Jesse Applegate, *A Day with the Cow Column in 1843,* 17, 6.

gang grasped his legs and pulled him out. And the slogan, "Give her goss, Andy," became a winning political rallying cry for Baker for public office in Oregon.[5]

Among the transients who stopped at Fort Laramie were many Mormons, bound for Zion at the rate of three to ten thousand a season, motivated either by religious zeal or canny opportunism. For among Brigham Young's promises to candidates for sainthood were wagons at the point of departure for $75; oxen, with yokes and chains, $75 to $80 a yoke; and cows from $16 to $25. Subsequently the Prophet conceived the unhappy idea of the handcart. For poor European proselytes, unable to buy wagons and livestock, he proposed to "make hand-carts and let the emigrant foot it and draw upon them the necessary supplies, having a cow or two for every ten. They can come just as quick, if not quicker, and much cheaper."[6] By early autumn, 1,500 pilgrims—and an equal number in the next three years—were pushing, pulling, and cursing these two-wheeled nuisances over the 1,300 weary miles from Iowa City to Salt Lake. The rigors of the road and early snows brought death to scores of the footsore Saints before the scheme met its own demise in 1860.

In sharp contrast to the sober-minded Mormon, the frenetic fortune hunter burst in on the Oregon Trail way-stations like a human tornado. Writing from Fort Kearny on the Platte, one observer reported: "The ice is at last broken, and the inundation of gold diggers is upon us. The first specimen, with a large pick-axe over his shoulder, a long rifle in his hand, and two revolvers and a bowie knife stuck in his belt, made his appearance here a week ago last Sunday. He only had time to ask for a drink of buttermilk, a piece of ginger-bread and how 'fur' it was to 'Californy' and then hallooing to his long-legged, slab-sided cattle drawing a diminutive yellow-top Yankee wagon, he disappeared on the trail toward the gold 'diggins.' "[7]

5 *Ibid.*, 59–60.
6 Hafen and Young, *Fort Laramie and the Pageant of the West*, 248.
7 *Ibid.*, 146.

Even more impressive than the wagons of the emigrants were the enormous freight caravans that dominated the trails. Among dozens of smaller concerns, the oustanding contractors were Ben Holladay and the firm of Russell, Majors and Waddell. Between 1861 and 1866 it cost Holladay one million dollars a year to feed his stock—approximately two and one-half million more to run his lines the first year. His stage-coaches operated daily over 5,000 miles, and his 500 freight wagons were hauled by thousands of oxen.[8] As for Alexander Majors' operations, when Horace Greeley visited company headquarters at Leavenworth in 1859, he ejaculated: "Such acres of wagons! Such pyramids of extra axletrees! Such herds of oxen! Such regiments of drivers and other employes! No one who does not see can realize how vast a business this is, nor how immense are its outlays as well as its income. I presume this great firm has at this hour two millions of dollars invested in stock, mainly oxen, mules, and wagons. (They last year employed six thousand teamsters, and worked forty-five thousand oxen)."[9]

What Greeley saw at Leavenworth was but a small fraction of the total equipment—including 6,250 oversized wagons, each of three-ton capacity, with 75,000 oxen for motive power—needed to handle all their far-flung operations. Charles F. Lummis doubted that in all the United States there were at that time as many oxen working as this firm owned and used. Yet they did not have a monopoly. In 1858 other outfits left Atchison, Kansas, bound for the far West, with 775 wagons, 1,114 men, 7,963 oxen, 1,428 mules and horses and 3,730,905 pounds of merchandise. [10]

What did set the Majors firm apart from all others was its insistence on moral and religious practices. When the government awarded it a contract to supply the United States Army, then maneuvering against the Mormons, the firm inserted this

[8] Hebard and Brininstool, *The Bozeman Trail,* I, 67, 68.
[9] Hafen and Young, *Fort Laramie and the Pageant of the West,* 260.
[10] *Ibid.*

advertisement in the *Nebraska Advertiser* of March 2, 1858:

ARMY OF THE WEST!

10,000 yoke good working cattle, from four to seven years of age wanted at Nebraska City, N.T., for hauling freight from that point to Utah, for which SEVENTY-FIVE dollars per yoke will be paid.... FIFTEEN HUNDRED TEAMSTERS also wanted, to commence April 15, 1858. They will be paid twenty-five dollars per month, there and back, unless otherwise agreed, for eight months or thereabouts. None but men of good health need apply. The use of intoxicating liquors as a beverage, card playing, and profane language are prohibited. Each man will be presented with a Bible and a hymn book. Early application had better be made.

RUSSELL, MAJORS & WADDELL

Alexander Majors followed this up by requiring every man he hired to take an oath never to swear, drink whiskey, play cards, or treat animals cruelly. If he broke his oath, he was fined five dollars. Among others who worked for Alex that year was teen-aged Billy Cody. As the noted Buffalo Bill of later years Cody told the following story of his experiences.

On one occasion teamster Charley Martin broke his oath— and with Alex Majors' permission. Charley was with a train that was trying to get into the government lane in Salt Creek Valley. It was bad weather, and the first they knew the whole wagon train was stuck. For hours they tried to coax the oxen to pull out, to no avail. Then, as one spectator reported it, Alex Majors came up.

" 'What's the matter, boys? Can't you make it?'

" 'Make it,—hell,' shouted Charley. 'How the h—'

" 'Tut-tut-tut,' broke in the old man. 'No swearing, Charley, no swearing. Remember your oath!'

" 'Yes, and if you'd just take that damn—'

" 'Tut-tut now—'

" 'Well, these here oxen are used to cussing. They won't do

anything unless they're cussed. They ain't no church oxen, these here. For God's sake, Mr. Majors—'

" 'Now, now, Charley. No swearing, please! Remember your—'

" 'Mr. Majors,' said Charley, squaring himself around, 'if you'll just take that da—, that confounded oath off, I'll show you how to get up this hill. Won't you please—?'

" 'But it won't do any good, Charley.'

" 'But please, Mr. Majors, take the oath off for two hours and let us cuss them oxen outen that hole!'

" 'I'll give you an hour.'

" 'Make it two, please!'

" 'Two it is.'

"Well, sir, of all the cussing that was ever done, it was done in those next two hours. Those drivers cussed in English, they cussed in Indian, they cussed in Mexican, and still they didn't cuss enough to let it all out of their systems. They threw their Bibles at the oxen, they jumped up in the air and cussed while they were jumping. They got out of the wagons just to see how it felt to stand on the ground and cuss. They cussed every way that cussing was possible—and you ought to have seen those oxen pull! That was what they'd been waiting for. They respected a man with a good line of cuss words in those days. And the way they pulled out of that hole was a caution. And all the time it was happening, there was old Alex Majors standing there looking on, just a-grieving. Even getting that wagon train out of a hole hurt him when it took cussing to do it."[11]

But oxen—cussed or uncussed—were the only beasts who could pull the trick; only the bovine, patient and unhurried, rather than the high-strung equine, could make old Farmer Virgil's prediction, written in 35 B.C., that "the solid beech-wood's unmusical axle and the metal-plated crossbeam shall strain them in earnest." The worthy Dutch burgher Van Tienhoven also appreciated the superior steadiness of the ox when

[11] *South Dakota Historical Collections,* XIV (1928), 277–78.

in 1650 he advised his fellow colonists of New Netherlands to "Yoke oxen for the plough, inasmuch as in new lands full of roots, oxen go forward steadily under the plough, and horses stand still, or with a start break the harness in pieces."

Some freight oxen, especially the older ones, were pretty smart. According to J. Frank Dobie, one of the smartest must have been a muley steer named Old Brindle, belonging to an outfit that used to trek to a railhead with wagons empty, returning with heavy loads of merchandise. One evening, preparing to start on the long journey for freight, the wagon boss told the night herder to bring in the oxen before daylight the next morning. By the time the animals arrived, bed rolls were on the wagons and breakfast was ready. Hurriedly wolfing his food, each bullwhacker began to hook up his team.

Strangely enough, Old Brindle, of Joe Goodbread's team, was missing. The night herder swore he'd brought him in, and the boss remembered seeing him walk over toward his proper wagon. All the wagons, including the trailers, were covered with wagon sheets, and Brindle, being a muley, was noticeably conspicuous. With the light of day the boss and night herder mounted their horses and began scouring the surrounding country, which was as bare and level as a billiard table. Finally the boss told Joe to turn Brindle's mate into the "cavayard," yoke up another pair of oxen for wheelers, and pull out.

Eight miles along the trail the train stopped for a late dinner. While the men were eating, they continued to speculate on the disappearance of Old Brindle. Joe Goodbread remarked that he was going to have to grease his wagons. Said he, "From the way my trailer is pulling, you'd think it was loaded."

Suddenly Joe jumped to his feet as though a thought had struck him. He went around behind the ox-drawn vehicle and looked into the trailer. The wagon sheet at the rear was closed with the puckering string. The one at the front was open. Joe grinned.

"Come here, fellers," he shouted.

In a couple of minutes he had enough eyewitnesses to prove what some skeptics might not believe. In the trail wagon, hidden by the sheet, was the missing ox, sleeping. He was even using Joe's bed roll for a pillow. Joe couldn't be mad. He was proud of having such a smart ox. He crawled in and delivered a few well placed kicks. Old Brindle opened his eyes, yawned, scrambled to his feet and jumped out.[12]

In spite of the oxen's reputation for "slow motion," some wagon masters insisted that they could outlast mules on a long haul. Among such was Lew Simpson, one-time boss of young Billy Cody, whose *Autobiography* contributes the following incident.

"That spring [1859] Simpson was busily organizing a 'lightning bull team' for his employers, Russell, Majors & Waddell. Albert Sidney Johnston's soldiers, then moving West, needed supplies, and needed them in a hurry. Thus far the mule was the reindeer of draft animals, and mule trains were forming to hurry the needful supplies to the soldiers.

"But Simpson had great faith in the 'bull.' A picked bull train, he allowed, could beat a mule train all hollow on a long haul. All he wanted was a chance to prove it. His employers gave him the chance. For several weeks he had been picking his animals for the outfit. . . .

"A mule train was to start a week after Simpson's lightning bulls began their westward course. Whichever outfit first got to Fort Laramie [750 miles from Fort Leavenworth] would be the winner. No more excitement could have been occasioned had the contestants been a reindeer and a jack-rabbit. To my infinite delight, Simpson let me join his party. . . .

"We made the first 150 miles easily. . . . The ordinary bull team could do about 15 miles a day. Under Simpson's command his specially selected bulls were doing 25, and doing it right

12 Dobie, *The Longhorns,* 243–44.

along. . . . Presently Stewart's train came shambling up, and a joyful lot the 'mule skinners' were at what they believed their victory.

"But it was a short-lived victory. At the end of the next 300 miles we found them, trying to cross the Platte, and making heavy work of it. The grass fodder had told on the mules. Supplies from other sources were now exhausted. There were no farms, no traders, no grain to be had. The race had become a race of endurance, and the strongest stomachs were destined to be the winners.

"Stewart made a bad job of the crossing. The river was high, and his mules quickly mired down in the quicksand. The more they pawed the deeper they went.

"Simpson picked a place for crossing below the ford Stewart had chosen. He put enough bulls on a wagon to insure its easy progress, and the bulls wallowed through the sand on their round bellies, using their legs as paddles.

"Stewart pulled ahead again after he had crossed the river, but soon his mules grew too feeble to make anything like their normal speed. We passed them for good and all a few days farther on, and were far ahead when we reached the North Platte. Thus ended a race which I shall never forget."[13]

Majors reported that in fulfilling his 1858 government contract he employed 3,500 wagons, 40,000 oxen, 1,000 mules, and more than 4,000 men, trailer wagons not having yet come into use and each wagon requiring one driver.

Forty years later, on August 31, 1898, "Cody Day" at the Trans-Mississippi Exposition in Omaha, drew thousands to pay tribute to Nebraska's famous citizen, their own "Buffalo Bill." Following Senator Thurston's eulogy, a hush fell upon the crowd as old Alexander Majors, the man who gave the fourteen-year-old Cody his first job, that of a bullwhacker, rose to pay his respects.

"I gave Cody a man's pay because he could ride like a man,"

[13] *An Autobiography of Buffalo Bill,* 25–28.

198

said Majors. "His salary was twenty-five dollars a month. I paid his first month's salary to him in half-dollars, fifty of them. He tied them up in his handkerchief, took them home, and spread them out over the kitchen table."

Whereupon Cody interjected, "And I've been spreading them ever since."

This got a great laugh, for Bill was famous for his lavishness and generosity; but few knew that among the places he was spreading his money was an allowance to the man who first employed him.[14]

Another noted scout, James B. (Wild Bill) Hickok, drove freight oxen and stagecoaches over the Santa Fé Trail in 1859–60. One winter day he was driving three spans of mules harnessed to the stage over the Raton Mountains in southern Colorado. He had come south through the Pass and was heading down the New Mexican slope when, at the head of a narrow defile, on an icy stretch he met an ox-drawn freight wagon loaded with barrels of whiskey. The five yokes were keeping their feet with difficulty and their driver was obviously worried. Hickok told him chains should have been wrapped around the hind wheels of the wagon, just as they were around his own vehicle. After passing the freighter, Wild Bill had gone about two hundred yards when he heard a commotion. Looking back, he saw that some of the oxen had fallen. The heavy wagon was rolling rapidly down the trail, dragging all the animals and throwing some of them into the air. Hickok realized that it would soon overtake and wreck the stage. His passengers were screaming and trying to climb out of the coach. He yelled to them to stay in, this being their only chance for safety. In spite of the danger in doing so, he put the mules into a rapid trot. By magnificent horsemanship he held the bouncing stage on the icy trail and kept the skidding, frightened team on their feet. As the runaway wagon bore down on him, he lashed them into an even faster pace.

[14] Dexter W. Fellows, *This Way to the Big Show,* 158–59.

199

The stage had just swayed, slipping dangerously, around a broad turn in the road when the wagon crashed into a protruding rock and was smashed to smithereens. One barrel of whiskey was hurled forward against the ledge overhanging the coach; splintered, its contents cascaded over stage and passengers. Another loaded barrel, hurtling down the trail, was gaining dangerous headway. Should it strike the stage it would demolish it. Hickok flogged the mules to still greater speed. Leaping over an intervening boulder, the barrel seemed bound to hit the vehicle. But at that instant, it struck a particularly rocky spot right under the hind wheels, burst open, and the coach was saved. All ten oxen were killed, the wrecked wagon and the carcasses plunging over the precipice.[15]

The dependence of the military, the miner, the merchant, and every segment of a frontier community upon the freighter was summarized in a tribute written thirty years ago and published at Rapid City, in the Black Hills of South Dakota, in which it was pointed out that "No man bore a more important part in opening up for settlement and occupation of the Black Hills than the Freighter. Indeed upon him all others of necessity depended. What was true of the pioneering of this section was equally true of every military post, every frontier settlement, and every isolated mining camp of the west. All depended upon him for the supplies necessary for their sustenance. He worked hard, often under wretched conditions. . . .

"Attacked by Indians and compelled to fight, he had to fight in the open. The hunter or prospector or pony express rider might have some chance of dodging, running, or exercising some choice of ground on which to make a stand. The freighter had to 'corral' the wagons in a circle with the stock inside and try to stand off the attackers as well as possible from such shelter as the wagons afforded. Considerable time was required to prepare even this meager protection, while men and animals were exposed to the Indian bullets without a possibility of returning the fire.

15 William Elsey Connelley, *Wild Bill and His Era*, 27–29.

"Time was ever of the essence of the freighter's contract. Whatever the difficulties encountered, whether by reason of high water, bad weather, bottomless gumbo, or Indian depredations, the freight must be delivered and even at this day the exhortation to 'pull your freight' is understood by the old-timer as a command to be obeyed, not questioned."

The efficiency of the service was attested by the fact that before the big freighting outfits were organized in the spring of seventy-six, flour cost sixty dollars a hundred weight in Deadwood Gulch but, with the coming of summer and the freighter, the price dropped, and in the fall of that year it was plentiful at nine dollars.[16]

[16] Jesse Brown and A. M. Willard, *The Freighter* (ed. by John T. Milek), 68–70.

CHAPTER 18

Argonauts in Sunbonnets

SOMEONE HAS FIGURED that if they were strung out in single file, those 75,000 oxen and 6,250 wagons owned by Russell, Majors and Waddell would form a procession forty miles long—which is as far as from Boston to Providence, or halfway from Chicago to Milwaukee.

Now we wonder how high all the books, pamphlets, and magazine and newspaper stories about "How I Crossed the Plains in a Covered Wagon" would reach if they were piled one on top of another. Chances are they'd rear a pylon equaling the stature of the Washington Monument, with the narrators approximating the number of persons whose ancestors came over in the Mayflower.

However, at the risk of piling Pelion on Ossa, the authors are adding a few layers to the already top-heavy structure precisely because in the most stupendous migration of recorded history the great inseparables were the emigrant and the ox. The picture in the large has been painted by one writer in these words:

"Here the Americans come out of the woods to the great rendezvous at Independence, yoke their six and eight ox teams or hitch up their kicking, biting, bawling Spanish mules, pop their 20-foot rawhide lashes over bottomless bogs of rain-soaked prairie, ford or ferry the bankfull streams, shiver in rains and steam in the sun. They meet the trains from St. Joseph in central Kansas, converge on the Mormon pushcarts and wagons in central Nebraska, and together follow the wanderings of the Platte thru weary miles. They run buffalo, agonize over children lost or killed in stampedes or stolen by Indians, die of cholera, drown in swollen streams, make love, marry, are born, die, and are buried in unmarked graves along or under the trail. They stand night guards in blizzards, throw away precious heirlooms to lighten the wagons, hack their way over thick forested mountains, heave their wagons up impossible cliffs, drink alkali water and burn in the desert, watch their stock die, and stumble on on foot. But most of them get thru and they are carrying America to the Pacific in their rumbling tepees on wheels."[1]

The vignettes have been sketched by many a nostalgic and voluble veteran of the great hegira. Bewildered by the search among hundreds of these for source material, one is tempted to apply the law of the sea for imperiled passengers, "Women and children first"—after all, they crossed in prairie "schooners" —and limit the storytelling to two members of the pioneering sisterhood.

In a sprightly narrative told half a century ago, Elizabeth Laughlin Lord of The Dalles, Oregon, described her journey as a little girl across the continent, with brothers, sisters, and parents, who started for California in 1850 but changed their minds en route and headed for Oregon.[2]

Soon after Elizabeth's parents were married, they left Illinois hoping to better their lot at a new home site in Missouri. Early in March, 1841, "these two poor but proud young people packed all their belongings which they could possibly get in, or pile on, or hang under a two-wheeled cart and hitched it to a yoke of oxen which they had taken in part payment for their place. They stayed their last night in Illinois at Grandpa Laughlin's. Here they made an addition to their load, stowing away two young pigs. . . . Behind the cart was tied their cow." When they reached the Mississippi bottom near Alexandria, they had to tug, dig, and pry the cart out of one hole after another.

[1] Kenneth C. Kaufman, "Research Charts Nation's Great Western Trek," *Chicago Sunday Tribune* Book Review Section (October 24, 1943), 11.

[2] Mrs. Elizabeth Lord, *Reminiscences of Eastern Oregon.*

"Father was completely discouraged, and nothing but mother's helpful reassurance and quiet determination to overcome difficulties . . . enabled them to get through."

Mr. Laughlin built up a substantial farm property in Missouri, but after nine years succumbed to the gold fever, sold the farm, and on April 12, 1850, he and his family "pulled their freight." Their one wagon and team of oxen made just eight miles the first day.

"Driving six yoke of half broke cattle was a feat," wrote Elizabeth. "Father and the man walked, one on each side, when they could keep up with them, and tried to hold them in the road by ropes on the horns of the leaders. Next to the wheel was a fine Durham bull and a big ox, then two pairs of cows and three yoke of oxen ahead of these. Those untamed creatures would have terrified mother, only that for days she and her three children were so seasick that she did not care what became of her. . . . The wagon had been fitted up by a carpenter, with lockers or compartments in the wagon box, in which the supplies were stored. Everything, both clothing and provisions, were put in sacks and packed in these lockers, which formed a deck, leaving a space in front. The bedding was placed on this deck and made a comfortable daytime resting place for women and children. In the last compartment at the back was the camp outfit, cooking vessels, provisions for the day, and a tent. The family slept on this deck and the driver had his bed in the tent, but in fine weather slept in the open "where the ground looked softest and smoothest."

If the oxen ran away in open, prairie country, nothing serious happened; but in timber, when they went crashing through trees and over stumps and logs, it was terrifying. Mr. Laughlin became so discouraged at the friskiness of his team that he allowed himself to be persuaded by a stranger into swapping two yoke of fine young steers for four little old stags, not worth half what his own were, since he thought only forests lay ahead. But after being ferried across the Missouri, the family found themselves on a boundless prairie, where the cattle might have run all day long without upsetting anyone or anything.

As these prairies yielded little or no wood, Mrs. Laughlin's only fuel was buffalo chips, white from age and exposure to the weather. "Mother thought at first that she could not stand that, but she found that by making a fire and letting it burn for some time until it was all aglow, the objectionable features were, to a great extent, destroyed, so she got along after a fashion; but she was never reconciled to that kind of fire, and never liked to think of those experiences afterwards."

When it came to crossing the North Fork of the Platte, each family made a ferryboat of a wagon box, with ropes attached from each end to draw it back and forth. The ropes were carried over by a man swimming his horse and holding the rope's end. The best places were plainly indicated by the posts to which previous caravans had tied their ropes. The cattle were crossed by swimming them. A man would lead a gentle cow or ox and swim his horse, while the others would be driven into the stream, following as closely as possible. One drove stampeded and tried to return to the side from which they had gone in. When driven back, they swam to where the Laughlins were crossing in a boat. "After aimlessly milling around in the water, and terrifying all of us," says Mrs. Lord, "mother rose to the emergency and began calling her cows by name, when they soon quieted down, fell into line and swam after the boat."

Twenty miles beyond South Pass, where the routes divide, Mr. Laughlin decided to shift to Oregon rather than join the stampede for California. Forty miles farther on, what with scanty grass and rocky going, one of the little stags gave out and had to be left. Mr. Laughlin had already shod some of the cattle with sole leather, their hoofs being so worn down they had gone lame. At Green River the outfit was ferried across and camped a few miles away where the grass looked fine. But here the stock got into alkali water and were badly poisoned. They were so bloated they looked as if they would burst. Therefore "mother got out the fattest bacon she could find and sliced it thin but the cattle refused to swallow it. Father then tied them one after another with their heads as high as he could get them, caught their tongues in his hand, and thrust the slices down their throats. One or two cows were stubborn and wouldn't let him get hold of their tongues." Exhausted and disgusted, he lost his temper, got the ax and vowed he would brain them.

His wife rushed up and said: "Mr. Laughlin, stop and think what you are doing. Don't be foolish. Here we are not half way across, with a poor team at best. These cows have been our hardiest and best animals. They don't know what they're doing. We should have been more careful, and not let them get this alkali water. Now we must make the best of it. You rest awhile and I will try."

Mrs. Laughlin soon had the cows under control, and they were saved. The grease in the bacon neutralized the alkali in their stomachs, but they were a long time getting over the effects of the poison.

In a fertile valley on Bear River, a Frenchman had a ranch and small trading post. Here, writes Mrs. Lord, "father felt he must strengthen his team, so he rode our pony down to the house and came back walking and driving the largest cow I ever saw. He had traded the pony and twenty-five dollars for her. We called her Old Pied and kept her for many years."

Later on we read: "I remember one day we were driving along in a plodding, listless way when, crossing a tiny rivulet, the lead oxen poked their noses down, gave out a bellow, and jumped right up off the ground. Each succeeding yoke did the same thing. Before the last ones were over, father had solved the mystery. The water was nearly boiling hot. The spring was only a few steps away and the weather was warm."

The Laughlins traveled for days through alkali regions where the soil was cut into fine dust from three to six inches deep. One day their eight-year-old daughter—the future Mrs. Lord—jumped from the moving wagon in which the family was riding.

"My skirt caught on the king-pin," she reports, "and this threw me under the wheels. The first one ran across my face, taking all the skin off that side. The next one, across my abdomen. The wagon was going down a little pitch, so the wheels had both passed over me before the oxen were stopped. Father and mother were both out in a moment, expecting to find a dead child. I was badly hurt, but the dust was so deep that it softened the weight and lightened the load, all of which were in my favor. In a week or ten days I was out again, but my face showed the scar for a year or two."

Six months after leaving Missouri, the family arrived at The Dalles, Oregon, where they subsequently made their home. Mrs. Lord's comment is significant: "When the rest of the company took what was then called Sublette's cut-off for California, it was pretty hard for father to decide, but Oregon won and we never regretted it."

Another member of the sunbonnet brigade was Miss Sarah Raymond, afterwards Mrs. Herndon, whose jottings in her daily journal betrayed the customary interest of a marriageable female in matters domestic—and romantic. Her covered wagon experiences began in Missouri on May 1, 1865, and ended with her arrival at Virginia City, Montana, four months later. Thirty-seven years afterward, her diary, written on the trip, blossomed out as a book entitled *Days on the Road*.[3] Besides Sarah, two other girls, "Cash" and "Neelie," shared the journey's sweet and bitter amalgam. One of the first entries in Sarah's journal indicates their interest in "boys."

A broken tire on one of their ox-wagon wheels sent Sarah and one of the men to a blacksmith shop for repairs; the rest of the party moved on. While waiting, Sarah was surprised by having a young friend ride up and greet her. He was awaiting the arrival of a wagon train a few miles back. Rejoining her girl companions, Sarah was asked, "Did you see any one we know?"

[3] Sarah Raymond Herndon, *Days on the Road: Crossing the Plains in 1865,* 11–260.

"Yes, an especial friend of yours, Cash—Bob Smith, of Liberty."

"Oh dear, I wish I had seen him. Was Thad Harper with him? Are they going back home?"

"No, they are waiting for better roads and good company. I did not see Thad Harper. Bob said they will overtake us in a few days."

"I hope they will. They would be quite an addition to our party."

"Yes, but they won't. Do you suppose they are going to let us see them cooking and washing dishes? Then they would have to play the agreeable once in a while, and that is not what they are going to do on a trip of this kind. . . . They would rather stay where they are another week than join our party."

And that's just what happened. However, the three girls had a pretty good time without "beaux." For instance, Sarah's description of her daily round of work and play reveals that "Mother prepares breakfast, while I roll up the beds and cover closely to protect them from the dust; one of the boys milks the cows, while I assist mother, and when breakfast is over—hot biscuit, breakfast food, ham and eggs, applesauce, coffee—I strain the milk into an old-fashioned churn that is big at the bottom and little at the top, cover closely and fix it in the front of the freight wagon, where it will be churned by the motion of the wagon, and when we stop in the evening we have a pat of the sweetest, most delicious butter any one ever tasted.

"Mother washes the dishes, we prepare lunch for our noon meal, I stow it in the grub-box under the seat in the spring wagon, the boys take the pipe off the little sheet-iron stove, empty the fire out, leave it to cool, while I am putting things away in the places where they belong. It is wonderful how soon we have learned to live in a wagon, and we seem to have an abundance of room.

"When horses are harnessed, oxen yoked, and everything ready to start, we girls proceed to saddle our ponies; some of

the boys usually come and offer assistance, which is politely de-
clined, as we are going to wait on ourselves on this trip. The
wagons start, leaving us to follow at leisure. We don our riding-
habits, made of dark brown denim, that completely cover and
protect us from mud and dust, tie on our sun-bonnets, mount
our ponies unassisted, and soon overtake and pass the wagons.
. . . It is delightful riding horseback in the early morning."

Six weeks later, the journal recorded a somber scene: "We
stood by the graves of eleven men that were killed last August
by the Indians. There was a sort of a bulletin-board . . . stating
the circumstances of the tragedy. They were a party of fourteen, twelve men and two women, wives of two of the men.
While camped at Plum Creek, a short distance from where the
graves are, all were at breakfast except one man who had gone
to the creek for water. He hid in the brush, or there would have
been none to tell the tale of the massacre.

"There had been no depredations on this road all summer
and emigrants had become careless and travelled in small parties.
They did not suspect that an Indian was near until they were
surrounded, and the slaughter had commenced. All the men
were killed and scalped and the women taken prisoners. They
took what they wanted of the provisions, burned the wagons
and ran off with the horses. The one man that escaped went
with all haste to the nearest station for help. The soldiers pursued the Indians, had a fight with them and rescued the women.
One of them had seen her husband killed and scalped and was
insane when rescued. She was taken to the station, where she
died. The other woman was the wife of the man that escaped.
They were from St. Joe, Missouri."

Two weeks later, Sarah's journal noted: "Among the men
who are driving for the Walkers is an eccentric old bachelor
named Fogy. He is very bashful when in the presence of ladies.
. . . He admires Neelie very much (at a distance, of course). We
often hear the extravagant compliments he pays her. . . . I have
often heard it said that men cannot drive oxen without swearing.

209

It is a mistake. I have seen a whole lot of ox-driving on this trip, and today I heard the first profane oath since we left the Missouri River. It would have been funny had it not been so shocking.

"Soon after the start this morning, Neelie and I rode to the front to escape the dust and sand that were flying. As we came near the front wagon we were startled by hearing a terrific oath. The wagon had stuck in the mud and this would, of course, stop the entire train. Mr. Fogy was the driver. He was greatly embarrassed and distressed when he knew we had heard him swear. He stopped stock still and let the wheels sink into the mud so that they had to double teams to get them out. He afterward told some of the boys he was effectually cured of swearing; that he never felt so cheap in his life, and that if he is ever tempted to swear the remembrance of that moment will check him."

When her friend Neelie fell sick, Sarah wrote some frank words about the Kerfoot family's cooking: "I fear they are destined to have considerable sickness before this trip is ended, they have such a sameness of diet, and it is so poorly cooked. When we started on this trip not one member of the family had ever prepared an entire meal. They had always had a houseful of servants to cook and do everything else for them. The first two or three weeks Neelie and her mother tried to learn to cook and mother and I tried to teach them. It takes great patience to learn to bake in stoves out of doors, they heat red-hot so quickly and cool just as suddenly. They must have careful attention all the time.

"They made several failures baking light bread and, giving it up in disgust, settled down to biscuit, that are as hard as brick-bats when cold, bacon, coffee and beans—when we stop long enough to cook them. They were well supplied with fruit at first; the canned fruit was so easily served that now it is all gone. They have dried fruit, but think it is too much trouble to cook. Neelie does the cooking, with some assistance from her father, such as getting wood, making fires, bringing water, grinding the coffee, etc. Henrietta and Emma, the next younger sisters, wash the dishes. It is no small undertaking to cook for a family of twelve. I do not blame Neelie for getting tired, she says they have such appetites it is not worth while to tempt them with extras. She is the sweetest, most unselfish daughter and sister."

At the crossing of the South Platte, under date of July 1, Sarah's journal tells us: "While we were getting breakfast the men were raising the wagon-beds and fixing them upon blocks as high as the wheels, and binding them tight with ropes to the coupling poles and lower parts of the wagons, ready to ford the river. They had a top-heavy appearance, as if the least jolt would topple them over. Some of the women were very nervous, about riding in wagons set upon stilts, and felt quite certain somebody would be drowned. . . . Some enterprising young men have the blocks and ropes there to rent, at a very reasonable hire. . . . The river is half a mile or more wide; about half way over there is a large freight wagon stuck in the quicksand . . . it has been there since yesterday; it is slowly, slowly sinking, and cannot be gotten out. It has been unloaded and left to its fate."

Having crossed safely, the Raymonds joined the huge, bustling caravans on the north bank, where 1,000 pilgrims and 200 wagons presented a scene in the early hours of the morning of July 3 which the journal called "hard to describe. . . . Corrals and camps here, there and everywhere. Cattle and horses being driven into corrals to be harnessed and yoked, men and women cooking by camp-fires and on stoves. Everybody seemed to be in a great hurry, all was animation and life, men riding after horses, oxen and mules; yelling, hallooing and calling; but not a profane oath did I hear. Among so many children, we rarely ever hear a child cry, and never hear a woman scold."

There is a hint of nostalgia in Sarah's comment on the breaking up of this happy hodge-podge of humanity: "Our train was the third to break camp and file into the road this morning. We have folded our tents and ridden or driven away. Our town of tents and wagons that was teeming with life this morning is this evening deserted, silent, uninhabited. The place that knew us yesterday will know us no more forever."

After they reached their destination, the teeming mining camp of Alder Gulch, Montana, Sarah's cheerful conclusion was, "After four months and four days of living outdoors we are all in the most robust health. Yet we shall be glad to have a roof over our heads once more, even if it is a dirt roof."

From Ghent's *The Road to Oregon* we learn more about the distaff brand of heroism, wherein trials and discomforts fell most heavily on the women. All the diarists affirm that most of them bore their part heroically. Clyman, a poor speller and grammarian but a good reporter, tells of "me[n], women and children dripping in mud and water over Shoe mouth deep" and adds "I Thought I never saw more determined resolution even amongst men than most of the female part of our company exhibited." And a few days later, he writes: "And here let me say there was one young Lady which showed herself worthy of the bravest undaunted poieneer of [the] west for after having kneaded her dough she watched and nursed the fire and held an umbrella over the fire and her skillit, with the greatest composure for near two hours and baked bread enough to give us a plentifull supper."

In the rainy belt, between Independence and the Platte, cooking often had to be suspended entirely. Water was everywhere, and blessed was the family whose thoughtful head had provided a wagon cover of double thickness and of specially prepared fabric. Otherwise the rain came through, drenching every person and thing in the wagon bed. Under such circumstances, to keep her youthful charges dry was a duty that taxed all the resources of the careful mother. To keep them clean and in freshly laundered clothes was a harder task. During the rainy spells there could be little laundering and no drying, and when the higher altitudes were reached, the whirling dust clouds often deposited more dirt on the garments hung up to be sunned than had just been washed from them. The earlier parties made small provision for washing clothes. Narcissa Whitman, at Fort Boise, six months out from her New York home, tells of her third washing day: "Last night I put my clothes in the water, and this morning finished washing before breakfast; this is the third time I have washed since I left home, once at Fort William [on the Laramie] and once at Rendezvous [on the Green]."

Probably the two trapper parties with whom she traveled felt little concern about clean clothes. Later, however, emigrants were more considerate, and clothes-washing day was frequently, if not regularly, observed.

There was courting and marrying on the way—but no divorces. Young John Minto, penniless, but strong, active, and susceptible to romance, started for Oregon in the spring of 1844. Crossing the Missouri at Capler's Ferry, among the tents and wagons of Gilliams' company he sought and found a job with a thrifty farmer named Wilson Morrison, who was selling out to make the journey. On the promise of bed, board, and transportation, Minto engaged to tend stock and make himself generally useful.

He had just seated himself at some petty task when, looking up, he saw a young girl coming from the house. Instantly he thought, "There, Johnny Minto, there goes your wife that is to be." She was his employer's younger daughter. For some reason he seems to have resolved not to reveal his secret until the journey was done. But the keen-eyed and jolly-hearted mother must soon have divined it. One day, in camp on the prairie, she offered him, holding it carefully by the stem, a sprig of foliage, telling him that if ever he treated badly any girl back home it would betray his conduct by wilting. The gulled youth, eager for such a test, grasped at the teasing bait. It was a sprig of the sensitive plant, and of course its leaves shriveled. He stood there abashed and speechless, until the rippling laughter of the mother assured him that all had been done in a spirit of play. It is pleasant to

213

record that in this case the course of true love ran with perfect smoothness and the girl became the bride of John Minto, one-time secretary of the Oregon Historical Society, a pioneer breeder of Shorthorn cattle, and an authority on the sheep industry of the United States.

CHAPTER 19

Valley of the Corn Feds

T HAT EASE IS NO STIMULUS to civilization and that the urge to get ahead grows stronger as the environment grows more difficult was long ago exemplified in the case of the native New Englander. Quitting his rock-bound acres and seeking greener pastures in the hinterland, it was the Yankee who finally wrested the mastery of a continent from successive Spanish, Dutch, and French competitors, and national leadership from his easygoing compatriots south of Mason and Dixon's line.

Early in the nineteenth century, it looked as if the winning of the West would be achieved by Southerners. Virginia backwoodsmen, led by North Carolina's Daniel Boone, had settled Kentucky—the first new state west of the formidable mountains—and were fighting the French, who had barred the path to English settlement; the Southern planter was finding an expanding market for his cotton in the textile mills of Britain; and, to cap the climax, one Yankee had invented a steamboat to speed plantation produce up and down the Mississippi, another a machine to card and clean his cotton bolls. No wonder he gloated over the fact that these "Yankee notions" promised more profit to him than to his Northern cousins. Apparently Dixieland was destined to rule the Union.

But by 1865 the situation was reversed. After unsuccessfully trying to redress economic troubles by taking up arms, the Southerner discovered that he had lost the Civil War before it was fought; that the Easterner, who had given him the river steamer and the cotton gin, had promptly won the heart of the West with the double gift of a locomotive and a reaper-binder,

215

thus solving the vexatious problems of transportation and labor. As a consequence, the country's communication lines had been shifted from the vertical to the horizontal, and railway traffic between Chicago and New York was rapidly eclipsing the total water-borne tonnage moving between New Orleans and St. Louis. Western allegiance to the East had been won by a new pair of "Yankee notions," and New Englanders, product of the toughest terrain in the land, had demonstrated that "the greater the difficulty, the greater the stimulus."[1]

One of the first and richest acquisitions in the winning of the West was the Ohio River basin. This fertile, far-flung area, ultimate location of seven sovereign states, would in due course bring to the nation unchallenged world leadership in the production of tender, corn-fed, yearling beef. Following its bloody conquest near the end of the eighteenth century, there was no immediate stampede from the East, where the happy but exhausted colonists were just beginning to get their breath after winning the war of the Revolution.

But in the year 1794 two events started west-bound emigration and stimulated stock raising. One was the Battle of Fallen Timbers near modern Fort Wayne, which removed the British and Indian menace. The other was the unsuccessful Whiskey Rebellion, in which United States troops convinced the farmer that he could not manufacture corn "likker" without a federal permit, and so forced him to raise cattle and hogs.

The early-day British hunters, trappers, and traders, whose small groups at their peril had traversed some parts of the trans-Allegheny region, were followed by agricultural immigrants, who were also appareled in coonskin caps and fringed buckskins and carried long-barreled rifles. This first class of settlers usually cleared a small patch of ground for raising corn, owned a cow, horse, or mule, and a few hogs and chickens, and pieced out their meager returns from barnyard and garden by hunting and fishing. These were the men who regarded an Indian as nothing

[1] Arnold J. Toynbee, *A Study of History*, 98, 99.

more than a pleasurable target for their weapons. When too many white neighbors moved in, they packed up to seek a new frontier.

In the second class of newcomers were cattlemen from the Carolina cowpens, bringing a number of small, lean animals, and depending less on wild game for nourishment. For their livestock little fodder was cured, but sometimes corn was set aside for winter emergencies. Their cattle had no shelter, and feed was occasionally so short that trees had to be felled for browse. Regardless of quality, all calves were retained, scrub bulls begat inferior stock, four- and five-year-old cattle weighed only 700 to 900 pounds, and a 1,000-pound steer was an exception.[2]

The third class—who finally took over the country—attached themselves to legally patented acreage, raised more cattle, built brick farm homes, substantial wooden barns, out buildings, and fences, cultivated more land, sowed down hay meadows, and improved their livestock which, when profitable, were fattened for market.

Eighteenth-century cattle entered the eastern Mississippi Valley either afloat or afoot. Some emigrants from the upper Allegheny River moved on locally built rafts, selling the logs on arrival at destination. Others bound for Kentucky by way of the Ohio River built wooden shelters on the after-decks of flatboats for their livestock. In a seven-month period 177 of these "Noah's arks" passed Fort Harmer—at the mouth of the Muskingum near modern Marietta—carrying 766 cattle, 1,333 horses, and hundreds of hogs, sheep, and poultry.[3] It was about this time that, in an eleven-month period, 900 boats moved Kentucky-ward with 2,500 cattle and four times that number of horses, swine, and sheep.

The first land route to be used was the Wilderness Road— the 1775 creation of Daniel Boone and thirty companions—from Virginia and North Carolina by way of Cumberland Gap; short-

[2] James Flint, *Letters from America,* 207–208.
[3] *Independent Gazetteer,* Philadelphia, July 10, 1787.

ly thereafter a more southerly trail was blazed, skirting the southern end of the Appalachians to reach Nashville. Cattlewise, however, the important routes led across Pennsylvania. The largest number moved over the Forbes Road, from the eastern part of the state through Harrisburg, Carlisle, and Bedford to the confluence of the Monongahela and Youghiogheny rivers, then Fort Pitt. Joining this road from the south was the older Braddock's Road, leading up the Potomac from Baltimore and vicinity and crossing over the Youghiogheny at its juncture with the Monongahela. Later routes were one across New York via the Mohawk Valley to Lake Erie and southward toward the Ohio Valley, the other up through Virginia by the eastern Roanoke and the Great Kanawha River valleys. This became the most important post road after 1800, with west-bound cattle and hogs moving freely over it up to 1812 and eastward thereafter.

This eastward movement was the result of surplus cattle production in the trans-Allegheny regions, which was hastened, as has been pointed out, by the successful removal of the Indian menace at the Battle of Fallen Timbers, the unsuccessful attempts of the yeomanry to convert their corn into whiskey, and a glut in the New Orleans market caused by the enormous tonnage of salted and barreled meats which producers had been floating down the Ohio. For twenty years following the downfall of Napoleon annual shipments of dried beef, according to United States Treasury reports, had ranged from forty thousand to eighty thousand pounds, and pickled beef from a half million to nearly two million pounds.

Attempts to drive livestock overland date back to 1802 when Michaux noted herds being headed for Philadelphia and Baltimore.[4] But the first Ohioan to win a niche in the drovers' hall of fame was George Renick, who in 1805 trailed a herd from the Scioto Valley to Baltimore via Zane's Trace, Wheeling, Cumber-

[4] François André Michaux, *Travels to the West of the Alleghany Mountains,* 111, 190–91.

land, and Frederick.[5] Thereafter over this route—ultimately U. S. highway 40—moved a lengthening chain of men and beasts, market-bound, stagecoach Jehus and freighters going both ways, and prairie schooners heading west for "Missou" or "Ioway."

On the National Road, which threaded Pennsylvania, Morris Birkbeck wrote in 1817, "We are seldome out of sight, as we travel . . . towards the Ohio, of family groups. . . . A small wagon (so light that you might almost carry it, yet strong enough to bear a good load of bedding, utensils and provisions, and a swarm of young citizens,—and to sustain marvellous shocks in its passage over these rocky heights) with two small horses; sometimes a cow or two, comprises their all; excepting a little store of hard-earned cash for the land office of the district; where they may obtain title for as many acres as they possess half-dollars, being one-fourth of the purchase-money. . . . A cart and single horse frequently affords the means of transfer, sometimes a horse and pack-saddle. Often the back of the poor pilgrim bears all his effects, and his wife follows, naked-footed, bending under the hopes of the family."[6]

Over the crude roads of Kentucky and Tennessee lumbered the heavy, long-bodied wagons of the Southerners, hauled by four- or six-horse teams. The poorer trudged along on foot, often pushing or pulling all their earthly possessions in handcarts. The well-to-do took cattle, horses, and sheep, household equipment being transported either by wagon or by steamboat up the Mississippi.

These were the people who by 1815, through resolute and resourceful attention to business, had achieved such high production as to require outlets for their surplus stock. Up to this date, most of their east-bound animals were either ready for slaughter or would require only a short time on feed. After that, increasing numbers of stock cattle were included—mostly three-year-old

[5] Ohio State Board of Agriculture *Third Annual Report* (1848), 162; *Tenth Census, 1880* (Agriculture), *lxxx*.

[6] Morris Birkbeck, *Notes on a Journey from the Coast of Virginia to the Territory of Illinois*, 25, 26 (quoted by Turner in *Rise of the New West*, 79–80).

219

steers grass-fattened to a certain extent but not enough for butchering. These reached the Potomac Valley or eastern Pennsylvania in the fall, where they were sold for finishing on hay or grain during the winter and marketing in the spring at Baltimore or Philadelphia.

Grain-fed stock fattened in Ohio went directly to the slaughter. Success depended on labor conservation and efficiency. Scioto Valley farmers fed the unhusked corn with the stalks directly from the stacks in the field. Cattle were usually enclosed in eight- to ten-acre lots, followed by hogs to clean up unconsumed ears, scattered kernels, and undigested remnants in the droppings. Elsewhere corn fodder was fed in limited amounts, the leaves and tops being torn off by hand. In contrast, Scioto farmers of the Pickaway Plains favored abundant rations with the least expenditure of human effort. Many herds numbered 200 to 500, and by 1835 some stockmen owned more than 1,000 head.

In June of 1817, New York City welcomed its first consignment of Ohio fat steers. These were publicized by the newspapers as being "as fresh as if just taken off one of our Long Island farms."[7] This after they had been driven nearly one thousand miles! The average traveling pace for fat cattle trailed from Ohio—half a century before the first Texas Longhorns were "pointed north"—was seven miles a day, cattle with hogs somewhat less, and stockers about nine miles.[8] Forty to fifty days were consumed in reaching Baltimore, Philadelphia, or New York from the home pasture. Opinions differed concerning how to handle trail cattle. Some claimed the heavy purebred Durhams suffered more from travel on frozen ground than did the lesser breeds. Others thought certain Illinois cattle driven to the Scioto valley and fattened there stood the transmontane drive better than Ohio-bred animals. Mud and dust were the

[7] Quoted in Thomas F. De Voe, *The Market Book*, II, 411. Mention of the drive also appears in *Niles Register*, Vol. XII (1817), 287.

[8] I. F. King, "The Coming and Going of Ohio Droving," *Ohio Archaeological and Historical Publications*, XVII (1908), 249.

bane of the drovers, but their heartiest "cuss" words were reserved for the macadam-surfaced stretches, whose sharp-edged stones operated like meat-grinders on the hoofs of the herd. Along the way, blacksmiths provided heavy gear for lifting big animals so they could be shod.

Pounds lost on the drive were called "drift." Beeves started on the trail seldom weighed more than 900 to 1,000 pounds, as heavier stock was thought to lose too much flesh en route. As it was, a 1,000-pound bullock suffered at least 150 pounds "drift," a 900-pounder from 100 to 150 pounds. Shrinkage in weight, of course, depended to a large extent on how well the cattle were fed and how judiciously they were driven.

After Ohio, the next center of surplus cattle production was Illinois, although it required about one hundred years for full development. Even during the infancy of the Kentucky settlements, a few habitants owning cattle and other stock had located near the old French forts and trading posts connecting Canada and the Mississippi Valley. When in 1763 the English acquired the strategic sites, most of these Gallic husbandmen and their "lowing kine" moved across the river. However, until well after the Revolution, some continued to vegetate near Fort Vincennes on the Wabash, Fort Chartres on the Ohio, and Kaskaskia and Cahokia on the Illinois bank of the Mississippi. But their livestock never amounted to enough to start a droving business comparable to that which flourished in Ohio after 1812. The 168 French and Spanish people living at Fort Vincennes in 1767 owned only 588 cows and 352 oxen in addition to other livestock, with outside Illinois settlements reporting a total of 342 cows and 295 oxen, along with swine, sheep, and horses.

Originally, farmers and stockmen had clung to the watercourses in settling a new country. To consign livestock and humans to the treeless, almost waterless prairies, was risky business. The bold adventurers who pioneered the movement were not always successful. George Rapp's New Harmony colony in Indiana, hopefully established in 1813, eventually failed. The

English Prairie in Illinois near the mouth of the Wabash likewise produced more frontier color than cattle when a visitor in 1821 wrote: "There are but few cattle-yards and sheds; and the cattle are mostly left abroad in winter, with no shelter but what the leafless trees afford. I have seen no barn in any part of the English settlement. . . . There are no granaries or store-houses except corn-cribs. . . . Oxen and cows are now more plentiful, but hitherto they have been fetched from the states of Indiana and Kentucky. They are of various sorts, but on the whole pretty good; some of them are handsome, and with a little care and expense an excellent breed might be raised. . . . The price of beef . . . is now . . . five cents, but expected soon to be cheaper."[9]

Although production costs at the English Prairie were low, markets were far off and difficult to reach. Once in a while an Ohio drover would come to buy stock cattle, but New Orleans was the chief outlet and livestock destined for that city had to compete with shipments from Kentucky, so that profits vanished in the frequently glutted markets.

Into the unbroken wilderness that was northern Illinois up to 1830 poured hundreds of settlers following the Blackhawk War two years later. Most of these came from New England, New York, and the Western Reserve of Ohio. Their cattle, together with other herds from Illinois, Indiana, and the Missouri River (as far as Booneville for a time), found buyers who drove them to Ohio, where they were fattened and marketed as Ohio stock.[10] With the coming of the railroads the pioneer prairie interlude reached an end. Thereafter the Illinois cattle breeder became a capitalist. With a backing of cash or credit, he traded in stock cattle, trailed them across Indiana to Ohio (especially to the Scioto), bringing back cash money for circulation in his community. Many were enabled to buy more land and expand their operations. Banks in those days frowned on loans secured

[9] John Woods, *Two Years Residence . . . on the English Prairie in the Illinois Country,* 174–80.

[10] King, "The Coming and Going of Ohio Droving," *Ohio Archaeological and Historical Publications,* XVII (1908), 147–53.

by livestock or other personal property, but would accommodate the farmer with varying amounts of money based on a conservative valuation of his mortgaged land. When the panic of 1837 deflated many of the corn and wheat farmers, pioneers and immigrants alike began to look around for some kind of a product for which they could find a market. The answer was livestock. Heretofore the pioneers located along the streams or at the edge of the forests had held the advantage. Now the boldness of those who struck out for the prairies with flocks and herds was destined to make many of them rich.

As "cattle kings in the prairies," Paul Wallace Gates has listed scores of successful operators, whose development of huge properties usually progressed through five stages.[11] First the cattleman bought and grazed, then drove enough cattle east to realize a cash and credit base on which to expand. Next he bought more land, consolidating his holdings so as to promote efficiency. The third step, into which he was forced by disgust with shiftless hired hands, was to divide his land into quarter-sections to be

[11] Paul Wallace Gates, "Cattle Kings in the Prairies," *Mississippi Valley Historical Review*, Vol. XXXV, No. 3 (December, 1948), 379–412. Included in his list are the following: The well-known Isaac Funk, his son Lafayette, and his grandson Eugene. (The great-grandson "Ted"—Theodore Funk—heads the cattle operations for the Funk interests today.) Contemporaries of Isaac were Jacob Strawn and others whose holdings ranged all the way from 2,500 acres in Illinois to 300,000 acres in Texas, and 650,000 in other states and Mexico. Among these "landed gentry" of the American terrain whose names are not forgotten were James N. Brown, B. F. Harris, John Buckles, Titus Suddeth, William A. Scully, Robert Latham, William N. Rankin, Elisha Crane, Leonard N. Scroggin, Samuel W. Allerton, Hiram Sibley, William Hoge, Abraham Holderman, Phillip Collins, John W. Goodwine, William N. Fithian, James Gaines, Terrence Clark, James S. Sconce, John T. Alexander, Abraham Mann, William Fowler, John C. Smith, Thomas Armstrong, Nelson Sumner, and John D. Gillett—all owning in excess of 2,000 acres.

Some with even larger "spreads" included Michael L. Sullivant, who sold off 22,000 acres in 1866 and lost 40,000 more following the panic of 1873; Lemuel Milk, with 65,000 acres; Edward Sumner and Alexander Kent, 30,000 acres each; Adams Earl, with 20,000. Some operated in several states—Samuel Allerton in Illinois, Ohio, Iowa, Nebraska, and Wyoming. William and David Rankin in Illinois and Missouri; Nelson Morris, meat packer, owned farms in Indiana, Nebraska, and a ranch in Texas; John S. Bilby held 26,000 acres in northwestern Missouri and 65,000 more acres in Nebraska, Kansas, Oklahoma, and Texas.

operated by tenant farmers who would grow corn and pasture and fatten cattle brought in from outside. He did this either on a share basis or by direct sale to the landowner at prevailing market prices.

Gates cites the case of John D. Gillett, who, when he began improving his land, at first found it easy, on account of the influx of immigrants, to hire enough hands to do the work, often employing one hundred during the growing season. After the Civil War, however, he had begun to substitute tenants for the less dependable laborers, believing that "a stake in the business would make tenants . . . use their best talents and energy in improving the land." They would assume "a part of the risk involved in grain growing and livestock feeding. . . . In 1877 there were 19 tenant improvements—and funds were provided to enable the tenants to buy and fatten steers." When ready for market, the cattle were to be sold to Gillett, provided he offered a "price as good as any other."[12]

In the fourth stage, the operator increased the growing of grain crops and decreased cattle feeding—partly because of the mounting burden of taxes and partly because the shift to commercial crops required more cash for the tenant in lieu of farm subsistence. In the fifth and last stage came the tenant's demand that the cattleman be forced to sell his holdings, coupled with complaints about an absentee landlordship whose concern was for maximum annual cash returns from the soil with little concern for the future. The situation of Gillett seems a case in point.

"For his land and cattle business Gillett accumulated an estate estimated at one and a half million dollars at the time of his death in 1883," writes Gates. "A life interest in the land was devised to his wife and the seven surviving daughters and one son, and the fee to the third generation. Gillett's love for his land is apparent in his efforts to entail the estate as far as

[12] Quoted by Gates, "Cattle Kings in the Prairies," *Mississippi Valley Historical Review,* Vol. XXXV, No. 3 (December, 1948), 393, from five agreements between tenants and John D. Gillett, I, Miscellaneous Deeds, Logan County (Lincoln), Illinois.

the law would allow, and also in the admonition to his descendants that they follow his example in retaining ownership of the land and restricting the right of alienation."[13]

Gillett's obsession with land ownership merely exemplified one of man's incurable cravings. To own a piece of Mother Earth is the commonest aspiration of mankind the world over. It is significant that even on his death bed this subject was uppermost in the mind of John D. Gillett. When a friend called to offer his sympathy, the sick man confessed that he had made one great mistake in his long and successful career. When the visitor vigorously protested such an admission, the old gentleman said, "Bend down!" Then looking around carefully to see that no one was near, he whispered hoarsely, *"I should have bought more land!"*[14]

Neighbors and businessmen enthusiastically boasted of the great prairie cattle kings and their massive holdings, but deplored their unprogressive attitude toward young and ambitious communities. Most of the land barons opposed bond issues for schools, roads, drainage, and similar projects because they brought heavier taxation. However, this attitude was more characteristic of their descendants than of the pioneers themselves. For example, old-timer Captain James N. Brown, an Illinois legislator and owner of Grove Park Farm west of Springfield, a prize-winning show place in 1856, was so deeply interested in better agriculture that he pressed for passage an appropriation for this cause, adding, "So you will know how I stand for this heart and soul, I will duplicate dollar for dollar any appropriation you may make." This promise he made good with a $3,000 donation, matching a similar sum voted by his fellow legislators.[15] Moreover, he established awards for attractive prairie homes and farmsteads.

A feature of the westerly drift of cattle across the Missis-

[13] Gates, *Ibid.*, 396.

[14] Edward N. Wentworth, *The Portrait Gallery of the Saddle and Sirloin Club*, 260.

[15] *Ibid.*, 256.

sippi Valley was the translocation of the low-cost areas of prime beef production. Up to the mid-1840's Ohio enjoyed a near monopoly, then for ten or more years west central Indiana dominated, and by the mid-1850's Illinois was beginning to take over.

But by the late 1880's Illinois could no longer meet on a cost basis the prairie and cornland production of Iowa—first from the eastern areas, then, after 1900, from the southwestern section, just above the Rankin and Bilby cattle empires around Tarkio and Marysville in Missouri. With the crossing of the Mississippi, the force governing this westward hegira came into clear focus. It was *cheap corn calling for top-grade cattle.* At the end of World War I, the center of this movement hurdled the Missouri to eastern Nebraska. And when the hundredth meridian was reached, this marked the farthest-west barrier for low-cost, cornfed "critters."

While this migration of corn and cattle across the great valley of interior America was never spectacular, the mighty economic force behind it was immeasurable. Although the Mississippi drained the "corn crib" of the world, it also watered the feedlots of its most concentrated beef area. And this area still holds pride of place, despite trade routes from the Southern Hemisphere and minor domestic shifts in competitive costs, railroad tariffs, and consumer markets.

CHAPTER 20

Among the Lop-Ears and the Tar-Heads

THE FIRST COW-PATH in the so-called "Oregon country"—
the half-million square miles now comprising Oregon,
Washington, southern British Columbia, western Montana, and Idaho—was probably blazed by a seafaring Longhorn
from California. To the 1788 settlement which followed Juan
Pérez's earlier discovery of Nootka Sound, on Canada's Pacific
Coast, came vessels bearing cattle and sheep from Monterey—
the first recorded livestock deal between the "Lop-ears" of Oregon and the "Tar-heads" of California.[1]

Presently there arrived Captain George Vancouver, English
explorer, for whom our northern neighbor later named an island
and a city. Taking a look at the well-fed flocks and herds, this
thirty-two-year-old sea-dog, who had already circumnavigated
the globe, made a momentous decision. To improve the condition
of the Kanakas—and start a revictualling supply for British
ships—he would introduce stock raising to the Sandwich Islands,
which Captain James Cook and he had recently visited.

Dropping down to Monterey, Captain Vancouver stowed
aboard a mixed assortment of cattle, sheep, and other stock, and
sailed for the islands. Here he wheedled King Kamehameha into
the livestock business and from 1792 to 1794 kept him supplied
with shipments of cattle from the mainland. On the fertile up-

[1] Californians confused the word "Oregon" with the Spanish *orejón,* meaning
"long ear" or "lop ear." To retaliate, early Oregonians called their neighbors to
the south "Tar-heads" because the Indians of northern California covered their
heads with tar as a sign of mourning. These epithets long remained in use.—
H. H. Bancroft, *History of Oregon,* I, 19–20; II, 46. Incidentally, the origin of
the name "Oregon" is unknown.

lands of the big island of Hawaii, herds multiplied and waxed fat. Shortly the navigators of four nations—Spain, Russia, England, and the United States—whose ships touched at the islands on their trading or exploring voyages were being besieged by Kanaka hucksters crying their wares from canoes filled with beef and small livestock, as well as fruits and vegetables. As cattle surpluses accumulated on Hawaii, settlers began to populate the northwest coast of America; in the ensuing trans-Pacific trade, the islands became a prime source, and Honolulu the chief distributing point, from which Oregon got its first cattle. A small number were also trailed overland at this time at great hazard from the Russian post at Fort Ross on the California coast. There also were reports of overseas shipments of livestock on Astor's ship the *Tonquin* in 1811, on the *Isaac Todd*, Donald McTavish's craft which touched at Monterey in 1813, and casual consignments of cattle from Hawaii in 1817. A little later the Hudson's Bay Company's coastal schooner *Cadboro* brought California cattle to the mouth of the Columbia and from there an "ark," built especially for livestock transport, ferried them upstream to Fort Vancouver.

Somewhat more has been written about another seaborne transaction which occurred in 1835 when the brig *May Dacre*, under charter to Nathaniel J. Wyeth, prosperous Cambridge iceman and visionary colonizer, landed a few Hawaiian cattle, sheep, goats, and hogs on Sauvie's Island, only five miles distant from where 450 cattle, 200 sheep, 100 horses, and 300 hogs were grazing on the 3,000-acre farm of the competing Hudson's Bay post at Vancouver.[2] Wyeth and fifty followers had made their way overland from Boston, en route establishing Fort Hall in present-day Idaho. Before starting, Wyeth had written his agents in Liberty, Missouri: "You can be looking up 2 bulls and 8 cows for driving overland to stock a fort, also one yoke of cattle for provisions fat for eating." This was his third attempt to colonize Oregon since 1832.

[2] H. H. Bancroft, *History of the Northwest Coast*, II, 442.

Although this final venture was a failure, forcing him within two years to sell his Columbia River Fishing and Trading Company to the big fur company, it was Wyeth who more directly than any other man, blazed the trail for the ox teams which were soon to "move an Americanized civilization across the roadless continent." Strange to say, it was calculated kindness, not cruelty, which hastened his exit from the scene. As one writer puts it, the Hudson's Bay people "preceded him, followed him, surrounded him everywhere, and cut the throat of his prosperity with such kindness and politeness that Wyeth was induced to sell his whole interest, existent and prospective, in Oregon to his generous, but too indefatigable, skillful, and powerful, antagonist."[3]

The target of such an accusation could have been none other than the courtly Dr. John McLaughlin, chief factor of the Hudson's Bay Company with headquarters at Fort Vancouver, which he had founded in 1825. Here he was visited by all kinds of people—Americans, Canadians, Scotsmen, Irishmen, Englishmen, Indians, and Sandwich Island Kanakas, to all of whom he dispensed impartial justice and even-handed hospitality. For example, with Wyeth's group had come the Reverends Jason and Daniel Lee, Methodist missionaries; two years later came Dr. Marcus Whitman and the Reverends Spalding and Parker, Presbyterians. To the Lees, McLaughlin loaned seven oxen, one bull, and seven cows with their calves, and gave $130 to their mission. When Dr. Whitman's cattle, overcome by exhaustion on the long trail from the east, had to be abandoned at Fort Boise, it was McLaughlin's agent there who gave the Doctor an order on Fort Walla Walla for others to take their place. Similar favors were later extended to the Catholic missionaries, Fathers De Smet and Demers.

The shrewd but hospitable Chief Factor had started his 1825 herd with twenty-seven cows and steers, later supplemented by three head of British Durhams (Shorthorns), thus

[3] Thomas J. Farnham, *Travels in the Great Western Prairies,* II, 94–95.

increasing the yields of beef, butter, cheese, and milk. Under an ironclad rule that no cattle should be killed—except one bull calf every year for rennet to make cheese—McLaughlin was trying to build up a sufficient stock to meet all demands of the company and to assist settlers. To increase his herds further, he was lending to retired French-Canadian servants in the Willamette Valley two cows each and steers for teams, the increase to revert to the company. If any died, the settler was under no financial obligation to the company for them.

Had McLaughlin sold, instead of lending, the cows, he would have lost the increase and could not have supplied other newcomers. Already would-be extortioners, hoping to sell calves at exorbitant prices, had offered him $200 a head for cows. But this inexorable Scot refused to sell to anyone—not even to the visiting British squadron commander, Sir Edward Belcher, who in vain demanded beef for his crews. That was in 1839; and until 1843 McLaughlin never failed to offer all new arrivals the same terms as those given the Canadians. Nevertheless, some of the Americans complained that he was "trying to maintain a monopoly in cattle." But if that were so, where was the profit in refusing to sell? Meanwhile, the post's officers and employees continued to live on fresh and salted venison and wild fowl. It was not until 1838, when a herd of one thousand had been accumulated, that the first beef was killed.

Fort Vancouver, at the junction of the Columbia and Willamette rivers, was now the most important of all the Hudson's Bay posts west of the Rockies, the "heart and brain" of the entire Oregon Territory. Other posts thrived through the efforts of the Chief Factor. The most western was Fort George, a skeletonized replacement of the defunct Astoria of 1811–14. More flourishing were Forts Nisqually, Cowlitz, Okanogan, Walla Walla, Colville, Hall, and Boise. Those having grazing facilities were stocked with cattle. Colville, which began with two cows and a bull, eventually began to rival Vancouver in its impressive production of beef, butter, and milk.

All this expansion of British interests had not been achieved without some preliminary maneuvering between John Bull and Uncle Sam. Following the treaty of 1818 between Great Britain and the United States and pending the determination of a permanent international boundary, Oregon Territory for thirty years got along as best it could under a dubious arrangement known as "joint occupancy." For this a political cartoonist might have pictured a giant Oregon, the ultimate bridegroom, holding at arm's length two hair-pulling females, Columbia and Britannia, each demanding that he marry her, the struggle ending in 1848 with the designation of the forty-ninth parallel as America's wedding band.

Meantime pressures had been building up between the Hudson's Bay people and the Yankee home-seekers and missionaries. One early cause of friction was McLaughlin's tight control of the cattle situation, as was succinctly stated in 1836 by Purser W. A. Slacum of the United States Navy, who, after investigating the Willamette settlements on orders from President Jackson, reported that he "found nothing was wanting to insure comfort, wealth, and every happiness to the people of this most beautiful country but the possession of neat cattle." To show his good intentions, the officer said that he would transport to California in the brig *Loriot* all persons agreeing to trail back whatever Spanish cattle could be bought there. At the meeting which followed, with both Americans and Canadians in attendance, the Willamette Cattle Company was organized with the old-time trail hand Ewing Young as leader and Philip Edwards as treasurer. Slacum himself handed Jason Lee $500, the Methodists and other settlers raised $1,100, and for the fur company McLaughlin contributed nearly $900, while nine Americans and two Canadians signed up as trail herders.

In California, as Mexican law forbade the export of live animals, Young with difficulty managed to secure a special permit from Governor Alvarado at Monterey. Even then he could buy only by bribing intermediaries, and what he got was the poorest kind of stock. It took these Oregon "cowboys" seven weeks just to collect and deliver 800 animals to the San Francisco and San José missions and reach the San Joaquín River. On the first day's drive, many cattle were so weak from being beaten and starved to make them manageable that they dropped to the ground. The first night out 200 broke from the corral, only 118 of which were recovered. Young complained to the local administrator, who agreed to furnish others for those which were lost. But on reaching the spot designated, the party found no cattle. Another order promised delivery at a *rancho* farther on. Yet when the outfit reached the San Joaquín River, 80 animals were still missing. Thus ended another lesson in bovine barter between the "Lop-ears" and the "Tar-heads."

With such ornery brutes, the river crossing was a cowman's nightmare. First a strong corral was built on the bank and the cattle driven into it. Then a few cows were teased into swimming after their calves, which were being towed across by men in canoes. Next day all hands, some afoot and some on horses, tried to make the remainder take to the water, but halfway across the herd panicked and started to turn back. Seventeen animals were drowned. Next, rafts were made from bullrushes. On each two men were stationed. One grasped a line fastened to a tree on the opposite bank and pulled the raft while the other dragged a beast through the water by a rope looped around its horns. It took seven days to get all the animals across. Meantime the job of night and day herding was doubled, since two camps had to be maintained, one on each side of the stream, while men and beasts were tortured by hordes of mosquitoes.

On the day the last Longhorn was being crossed, a pack mule bearing the ammunition fell into the water. This was the last straw for Edwards, who wrote in his diary: "Powder entirely lost! Horrors! Now we chased cattle till the moon rose, trying to get them across a little water not more than knee-deep. . . . Men ill-natured and quarreling, growling and cursing.

... Another month like the last, God avert!"[4] Yet they were only sixty miles on their way, and five hundred miles from the Willamette Valley.

The succeeding three months were marked by scaling almost impassable mountains, a quarrel between Young and the men about killing a beef for food, the murder of an Indian boy by one of the gang, and skirmishes with the red men, who retaliated by making arrow-filled pincushions of horses and cattle. The column finally reached the Willamette about the middle of October. Of the original 729 head, 630 young cows and bulls survived all misadventures. After figuring expenses and losses, the promoters found that the cattle for which they had paid $3.00 a head in California ultimately cost them $7.67 each. Earnings of the men who went as drivers at one dollar a day were paid in livestock at the same rate. McLaughlin allowed the Willamette settlers to keep the company's broken-in oxen and turn in the wild California stock in their place. This was certainly generous, because locally the prevailing price of Spanish stock was $9 while $100 a head was gladly paid for whatever well-bred stock could be had. McLaughlin also took calves in even exchange for fully grown cattle, since the company wanted mature beef and the young stock would grow up before they were needed.

With their aggregate holdings of 182 head, Young, Edwards, Slacum, Daniel Lee, and Cyrus Shepherd formed a joint-stock company which evidently prospered, although the cattle had little care beyond protection against predators. When Slacum died in the East, at the request of a nephew his share was sold to settle his estate. Of his original twenty-three head, the increase of sixty-three gave the estate eighty-six animals, which were sold to McLaughlin for $860.[5]

With the passing of Ewing Young, who had charge of the

[4] Philip Leget Edwards, Diary (copy of the original in archives of the Oregon State Historical Society, Salem, Oregon).

[5] Bancroft, *History of Oregon,* II, 152.

herd until his death in 1841, some of the cattle escaped to the hills and became so troublesome that the settlers on the edge of the valley began to hunt them with rifles, ostensibly "to make the fields safe for women and children"—but not forgetting they could get two dollars apiece for hides.

This first cattle drive from California accomplished its primary object: viz., freeing the Willamette settlers from the economic domination of the Hudson's Bay Company. It also marked the first modest step toward creating a commonwealth. Finally, in 1842, a slow-moving administration at Washington granted Oregon grudging recognition and dispatched its first representative, an Indian sub-agent, in the person of Elijah White. By dying intestate the previous year, Ewing Young had already helped things along. Since he had no heirs, the settlers had been forced to establish some form of local government in order to administer his estate. For this purpose they elected Oregon's first judge, clerk, and sheriff.

The precedent of importing cattle from the South was followed by McLaughlin's obtaining a permit to drive from California 2,000 head of cattle and 4,000 sheep. As farming and stock raising now promised to outstrip fur trading, the Puget's Sound Agricultural Company, a Hudson's Bay subsidiary, was formed in 1844; its assets included 8,000 beef and dairy cattle and hundreds of draft oxen. Other early followers of Ewing Young's example were Thomas Hubbard, who brought a herd north in 1840, after his agents, on their south-bound journey, had narrowly escaped massacre in the Rogue River region. Another adventurer was Captain Joseph Gale, who, less fearful of stampedes than hurricanes, sold his sailing ship, *Star of Oregon,* in San Francisco to finance and drive 1,250 cattle and 600 horses and mules back to the Willamette, a feat which he accomplished in seventy-five days.

By 1841, the French-Canadian settlers on the Willamette alone were estimated by Duflot de Mofras to have 3,000 cattle and as many swine.[6] In the same year Lieutenant Charles Wilkes of the United States Navy visited the settlement, noting the contentment and general happiness in contrast to the "unnecessary" haste and bustle of the Anglo-Saxons. At the same time, he complimented the Hudson's Bay Company on its fine dairies, herds of cattle, and bands of sheep. Incidentally, McLaughlin was operating at Vancouver a grist mill powered by oxen. At the Whitman Mission at Waiilatpu, near Walla Walla, the 1839 stock of one yoke of oxen, two cows, and an American bull had grown to double that number. By 1841, the Hudson's Bay Company had opened a path and driven cattle from Yakima to Nisqually.

The settlement of Oregon by Americans began hesitantly enough. In 1834 they numbered less than 50, in 1838 only 86, and in 1839 but 151, most of these being included in the missionary groups. An additional hundred followed Indian Agent White westward in 1842. It was the immigration of 1843 which really blazed the famous Oregon Trail and brought from Independence, Missouri, to the Willamette Valley, two thousand miles away, "one thousand persons, with 120 wagons, and 5,000 cattle," according to "Captain" Jesse Applegate, owner of more livestock than anyone else in the train, and author of *A Day with the Cow Column.* Each wagon was hauled by from two to five yokes of oxen. Some of the white-topped prairie schooners bore the slogan, "For Oregon," others repeated Farnham's lugubrious theme, "Oregon or the Grave"

Peter Burnett, leader of the expedition, thought that selfish motives prompted Dr. Whitman at Waiilatpu Mission and Factor McKinley at near-by Walla Walla to advise the immigrants to "leave their animals, either to exchange for California cattle, or to pay one dollar per head for their keeping," claiming that no grass would be found west of there. Applegate reported that the mission gave one fat bullock of Spanish stock for two poor emigrant oxen. Ignorant of the difference between Spanish and

[6] Marguerite Eyer Wilbur (ed.), *Duflot de Mofras' Travels on the Pacific Coast,* I, 111.

American cattle, many consented to pay this high price for fat beef. Thus in the spring the missionaries had two fat American work oxen for their one bullock.

The natives did better. They gave a fat bullock for one lean heifer, for breeding purposes. Burnett adds, "What surprised us most, after the representations that had been made, was the fine pasturage all along the way, and especially at The Dalles, where we had been led to believe the cattle could not subsist at all during the winter." At Walla Walla, Applegate left his stock to be herded at a cost of a dollar a head. But when he reached Vancouver, according to Burnett, McLaughlin protested his making such a bargain, and not only gave back his American cattle but rejected Applegate's offer of compensation for the care they had received during the winter.[7] The following year Burnett added a cheerful note when he wrote to the *Ohio Statesman*: "Cows have calves here when from 15 to 20 months old. . . . The reason is they are always fat and get their growth much sooner."[8]

Adding the 900-odd Americans who arrived that year, the "whole population of Oregon" in 1843 was estimated by Lieutenant Neil Howison of the United States Navy to be, "exclusive of thoroughbred Indians . . . nine thousand souls, of whom two thousand are not natives of the United States, or descendants of natives." Over 1,400 more trickled in the following year, and a tidal wave of 3,000 in 1845 doubled the previous year's roster. The 1,700 who reached the Territory in 1846 brought two hundred head of cattle with them. By 1848 the historian could report that "only a small portion of the land being fenced, almost the whole Willamette Valley is open to travel, and covered with the herds of the settlers, some of whom own between two and three thousand cattle and horses. Though thus pastured, the grass is knee-high on the plains and yet more luxuriant on the low lands. . . . Besides the natural increase of the first im-

[7] Bancroft, *History of Oregon*, II, 4.
[8] Alfred L. Lomax, *Pioneer Woolen Mills in Oregon*, 56.

portations, not a year has passed since the venture of the Willamette Cattle Company in 1837 without the introduction of cattle and horses from California, to which are added those driven from the States annually after 1842."[9]

Among such were some well-bred Durhams (Shorthorns) introduced by David Guthrie in 1846 and more of the same breed from Henry Clay's herd at Blue Grass Grove, Illinois, which John Wilson drove to the Willamette Valley the following year. A fine cow from the same herd was driven to Oregon by Joseph Geer. Up to now most of those trailed from the East had been bulls, usually draft animals, but the larger number of cows in this year's drive promised well for the breeding of improved stock.

About this time a well-known politician, Judge O. C. Pratt, bought a bunch of California Longhorns from a man named Durham. When he sold them, the buyer was led to believe they were genuine "Durham" stock. From that time on, Pratt's political followers were derisively dubbed "Durhamites" by their opponents. To appreciate the cruelty of this jest, it should be remembered that the animals originally introduced into California from Mexico were of deteriorated Spanish breed, definitely "scrub" stock. Roaming in untamed freedom over the interior valleys, they had increased prodigiously. From about 262,000 in 1850, they were estimated at 1,180,000 in 1860 and 3,000,000 in 1862.[10] Light in weight, of all colors, with long, thin legs, widespread horns carried on high, slender heads, they were valued chiefly for strength and endurance, though difficult to drive because of their wildness. Yet they seem to have possessed certain milking traits not found in Texas Longhorns, "when raised in green pasturage," as Duflot de Mofras said, the cows were calving before they were two years old.

Such, too, were the animals which grazed the far-flung hills and valleys of the northern California *ranchos*. And such was

[9] Bancroft, *History of Oregon*, II, 4.
[10] Bancroft, *History of California*, VII, 54n.

the stock which from the 1830's through the 1860's comprised much of the wealth of such well-known pioneers as Captain John Sutter, Dr. John Marsh, John Young, the Vallejos (Don Salvador and General Mariano), Doña María López Carillo, and the Dane, Peter Lassen. Against the forays of hostile Indians, these "buffer" ranches and the Russian fur-trading posts at Fort Ross and Bodega were the only, and quite inadequate, protection. As for the cattle, they were valued only for their hides and tallow by the whites and for intermittent nourishment by raiding red men.

Between the sources of the Sacramento River and the Oregon country, the far-ranging herds of livestock caused many a bloody struggle between settlers and savages. A typical incident occurred when Pit River Indians stole five head from John Weikel near Honey Lake and five men started in pursuit. When overtaken, the Indians immediately slaughtered the cattle as twenty warriors rushed up in support of the thieves. The white men retreated, appealed to old Winnemucca, chief of the Paiutes, who ordered some of his young braves to join Captain Weatherlow and thirty-two white men. The avengers meted out punishment by destroying two Pit River *rancherías*, capturing two women and putting to flight some seventy warriors. These having succeeded in making their escape, the party returned home, only to find that in the meantime they had been plundered by a renegade band of Washoes.

The region over which a dozen tribes of pillaging Indians ranged included some 50,000 square miles in the general area where, on today's maps, the boundaries of northern California and Nevada approach those of southern Oregon and Idaho. This area, thinly populated by whites, could not be protected by soldiery against cattle thieves, with small breeding herds separated by miles of swamp or sagebrush. The regulars did not like the state militiamen and vice-versa. And with the boundary between California and Nevada a subject of continual dispute, the two governors assumed no responsibility beyond the collection of taxes.

About the middle of March in the year 1862, William B. Long, James Briden, Henry Sidorus, A. L. Harper, and others began to gather cattle in a canyon east of Susanville, in Lassen County, California. After the ranchers had rounded up several hundred head, on the morning of March 25, Long went alone on foot to inspect the unguarded herd. With the exception of seven head of Spanish steers belonging to Briden, they were all gone.[11] Getting a horse, Long followed the trail and found several mired down but not hurt, and the footprints of five or six Indians. Returning, he recruited a posse of fifty men from all directions, who elected Dave Blanchard captain and Henry Arnold and Johnson Tutte lieutenants. They had horses enough to pack provisions and blankets and for twelve or fifteen men to ride.

Heading northeast, they were soon bogged down in mud. Where it was driest, the horses sank to their fetlocks, and in the creeks up to their bellies. Mired pack horses had to be unloaded as men sloshed through muck over their ankles. Three miles east of Secret Valley the posse found sixty dead cattle. The leaders having sunk deeply into the mud, the animals following had clambered over and smothered them. Following the first day's trek of twenty miles the men were handicapped on the next by heavy snow. Repeatedly they found mired-down cattle which the Indians had knocked on the head, punctured with arrows, hamstrung, gutted, or otherwise mutilated. Occasionally they had gouged out a heart and a tongue or parts of the meat and tallow. The pursuers camped at Smoke Creek that night. Cold, wet, and hungry after a twenty-mile march, they butchered and ate a young steer which they found there.

The next day, concluding that they could get along better without them, the posse sent the pack train and the mounted

[11] Asa Merrill Fairfield, *Fairfield's Pioneer History of Lassen County, California*, 274ff.

men and their horses by road to Deep Hole. The force now numbered thirty-three, each man packing a blanket and enough food for three or four meals. When Steve White spied an Indian on the ridge three-quarters of a mile ahead, he fell back and notified the others. Carefully sneaking to the top of the ridge, they found no red men, but did spot about forty head of cattle. This was a second band, following another in front. Working their way through these, they succeeded in getting within seventy-five yards of three Indians, one standing, the other two cutting flesh from a felled steer. Others were lurking in the background. When a man named Taylor came up and saw the Indians he yelled to his dog, "There they are, the S.O.B.'s; sic 'em, Bob!" Whereupon the three Indians dropped to the ground and rolled down the steep canyon to safety. The cattle, which they had abandoned, were guarded that night by two of the posse.

Further pursuit resulted in the capture of no Indians, only more animals, many so badly maimed that they had to be killed. It was a victory for the raiders, a defeat for the ranchers. All they had recovered from the Indians were forty-five cattle, five of which died on the drive home. Long's loss amounted to 220 head. His herders later discovered that the Indians had camped for a week at the head of the canyon while cowboys toiled to gather the beeves the thieves planned to steal. Meanwhile, all the unhappy Taylor heard for the next six months was the mockingly maddening cry of "Sic 'em, Bob!"

The whole situation became so bad that in the end General Crook had to make several campaigns against the Rogue River Indians and other tribes of southern Oregon and the Pit River region, while Majors Smith and Mellen wiped out Smoke Creek Sam's Paiute band in the Guano Valley, Nevada. Although minor thefts persisted, the more lethal ravages of Indian cattle raiders were pretty well quashed by 1873.

Oregon was now beginning to profit by the arrival of better cattle from the east. Surpluses adequate to feed the gold-seekers stampeding into Idaho, Montana, and Nevada were accumulating, thanks to the abundant bunchgrass in eastern Oregon and southwestern Idaho, with fine grama and wheat grasses in the mountains—bunchgrass for summer, white sage and other desert plants for winter grazing.

During the three decades preceding 1890, the range-cattle industry of the Northwest prospered mightily. Farmers had not yet begun to fence and plow up grazing lands and importune national and state legislators for protection. Most of the herds were of modest size, a few hundred to a few thousand head. Hardly any exceeded five thousand.[12] John Day and Pendleton were cattle centers; also LaGrande and Baker, east of the Blue Mountains; Bend and Prineville on the east slope of the Cascades; and Burns at the edge of the eastern Oregon desert. The larger herds were in modern Lake and Klamath counties, with a few even larger located in what are now Harney, Grant, Baker, and Malheur counties.

The rugged Oregon winters bred strong, rugged animals, far better suited for breeding purposes in the intermountain territories, where settlement had to await the end of the Civil War, than Texas Longhorns, which were not inured to protracted cold. Some of the top herds of Montana, particularly those of Conrad Kohrs, Henry Sieben, and Robert Ford, got their start from foundation stock obtained in Oregon. Other famous stockmen who bred and distributed quality cattle included Miller and Lux, who ran as many as 100,000 head, scattered all the way from California across Nevada and Oregon, up to the Malheur and Snake rivers. Todhunter and Devine developed far-flung ranges in southeastern Oregon, with headquarters on Whitehorse Creek, and at their peak ran 24,000 head. Eighteen thousand to 20,000 head were owned by Glenn and French, a father-in-law, son-in-law firm, operating near Steen's Mountain.[13] T. M. Over-

---

[12] J. Orin Oliphant, "The Cattle Herds and Ranches of the Oregon Country, 1860–1890," *Agricultural History,* Vol. XXI, No. 4 (December, 1947), 217–38.

[13] This is commonly misspelled "Stein's" Mountain, but Lewis Ankeny Mc-

felt, in the east central part of the state, held about 7,500. And there were Benjamin E. Snipes, with 3,500 head, and William Leslie, with 4,000 head, on the Owyhee; Harper and McMahon, 2,000, on the Malheur; Charles Becker, 1,500, on Cow Creek; Dressler and Clara, 1,000, on Burnt River.

Written history fails to confer recognition on these Northwestern herds. Historians dealing with this period have been more interested in telling of missions, churches, schools, music, minerals, railroads, and theaters, and the thousand and one amenities that bring spiritual and physical comfort to life. And so it is that writers of the Southwest and the High Plains have captured the popular fancy with their sagas of the wild Longhorns and their herders. Buffalo Bill's Wild West Show and its imitators came out of the Northwest, but the show people thought too well of the imported cattle located there to chouse them around the arena. They maintained the "wild" traditions by using Longhorns.

In due course the federal government began to exercise stronger controls over the public lands of the Northwest. This cramped the range cattlemen's operations a full decade ahead of such activities in the Southwest. By 1900–1905 the great reservoir of cattle which had endowed western Montana, Wyoming, and the Dakotas with their beefiest stocks was a matter of memory, and the movement of Northwestern steers to Mississippi, Platte, and Kaw River feedlots could provide nothing to equal the spectacular characteristics of the Longhorn trail herds being "pointed north" year after year. Yet the great western cattle industry which today lies tributary to the thriving livestock markets of St. Paul, Sioux City, Omaha, and Denver was founded and developed on an open-range basis. Incidentally, the ability to pull through the vicious winter of 1948–49 traces back to the sturdy hardihood nurtured by Oregon's invigorating environment.

Arthur, in *Oregon Geographic Names*, 490, says it was named for Major Enoch Steen of the United States Army.

CHAPTER 21

Trailing in the Far Northwest

PIONEERS SCUFFING their dust-begrimed way across the plains to California and Oregon in the 1840's and 1850's did not think much of the country west of the one hundredth meridian. To these gold chasers and home seekers, coming from regions of twenty-five- to forty-inch rainfall, the arid wastes of sage and sand were indeed the Great American Desert. A few, it is true, sensing stock-raising possibilities in the foothills, had begun to develop small herds of cattle. But when the Civil War erupted, forcing the withdrawal of troop protection from frontier outposts, the Indians took over, repeating many of the bloody forays of prior decades. Not until after the treaty of 1876 with the Sioux and Cheyennes were the rich grasslands north of the Platte River and east of the Bozeman Trail made safe for stock growers.

Many Texas herds were immediately trailed north, particularly into the Powder River region of eastern Montana and Wyoming. Right on their heels, pointing east, came thousands of Oregon and Washington cattle. These were third- and fourth-generation descendants of the old family cows from the Corn Belt, veterans of the Oregon Trail, whose bulging udders had nourished the west-bound emigrant youngsters of the 1840's. Mated to quality Shorthorn or Devon bulls and fattened on the fertile grasslands of the Snake, Yakima, Columbia, and Willamette valleys, in less than four decades their progeny had swelled to unmanageable proportions. Actually the Pacific Northwest had more beef on the hoof than a few far-flung mining camps could consume and stock growers were looking for a market.

The quality of what they had to sell was high. These so-called "American," in contrast to the California, Texas, or "Spanish" cattle, were appraised by a government expert as "more uniform than the cattle of any other of the contiguous states and territories, having been less exposed to interbreeding with either the California or Texas stock."[1] Even in the 1840's and 1850's purebred stock had been brought in by individuals and by organizations like the Oregon Stock Importing Company of Benton and Marion counties. Stock improvement had so progressed by the 1870's that in 1878 a Congressional Report quoted Governor Hoyt of Wyoming Territory as saying that Oregon cattle were so much superior to the Texans that at all markets east of the Rockies, higher prices were paid for them for stocking ranges than for even the best Texas animals.[2] This claim was verified by Gordon, who reported in 1880 that American slaughter beeves in Wyoming averaged $9.50 more per head than Texas fat stock. For two- and three-year-old steers to be turned on grass, the margin was $9.00 in favor of the Northwesterners; for yearling steers, $6.00; and for she-stock, ranging from cows to yearling heifers, $5.50.[3]

This Oregon beef surplus was just the thing to fill the range vacuum created by the conquest of the Sioux, Cheyennes, and Bannocks west of Fort Fetterman and north of the Platte. Wyoming buyers, as early as 1875, began to gather dry stock in the Walla Walla district of Washington to be turned loose in the western part of the present state. Later, with newly built Union Pacific railheads affording easy access to grass and markets, breeders realized that real money could also be made by raising young stock on the range. They learned that worn-out oxen, turned loose by freighters, had wintered well on the bunch and grama grasses, some coming out in the spring fat enough to butcher.

[1] *Tenth U. S. Census, 1880* (Agriculture), 1080.
[2] 45 Cong., 3 sess., *House Ex. Doc.*, Serial No. 1850, p. 1160.
[3] *Tenth U. S. Census, 1880* (Agriculture), 1017.

Also in the mining camps of Montana, where even a poor, worn-out ox brought $100 in gold, shrewd cattlemen were not slow in introducing Oregon livestock to the Ruby, Deer Lodge, and Beaverhead valleys. Here they developed their own peculiar method of handling cattle, quite different from the open-range system of eastern Montana, which did not get under way until the late 1870's. High mountain ranges, rapidly flowing streams, and steep divides all provided natural barriers that kept the cattle within a comparatively small area. One observer thus described a typical stock ranch of those days:

"A fence six miles long, running across the valley, connects the steep rocky ranges on either side. Five miles above is another fence from mountain to mountain, forming an enclosure 30 miles square, containing 19,200 acres. Through this, another fence along the creek separates the pastures of 15 square miles each into one for summer, and one for winter range. Beyond is a range so hemmed in that cattle never get out in winter and seldom do in summer."[4]

After the Indians had been subdued and confined on reservations, such men as Floweree, Davis, Hauser, Stuart, Kohrs, Fergus, and Sieben drove Oregon cattle to the ranges along the Yellowstone and Musselshell. Even in 1880 central and eastern Montana were practically uninhabited. One could travel for miles without seeing even a trapper's bivouac. Thousands of buffalo darkened the rolling plains. In the whole territory of Montana there were but 250,000 cattle, including dairy stock and work oxen. By 1883 there was not a buffalo on the range; antelope, deer, and elk were scarce. "In 1880," said pioneering Granville Stuart, "no one had heard tell of a cowboy and Charlie Russell had made no pictures of them; by 1883 there were 600,-000 cattle on the range and the cowboy had become an institution."[5]

Those thousands of tough dogies who first tackled the lava-

[4] Charles Wayland Towne, *Her Majesty Montana*, 81.
[5] *Ibid.*

cursed, river-riven, sage-girt trails through sparsely settled eastern Oregon and Idaho, created scenes which were unique, possibly surpassing anything the Texas trails could show in the way of variety and color. But as one writer complained, "of cowboys and *longhorns* leading northward from Texas, historians have told us much; but of cowboys and *shorthorns* on trails leading eastward through Idaho they have told us virtually nothing. Yet—the overflow of the cattle country of the Pacific Northwest was a phenomenon of no slight significance."[6]

In the spring of 1883, the Bay State Livestock Company sent a crew including men from its headquarters at Kimball, Nebraska, and others from Cheyenne, under Manager John A. McShane to Baker Valley in Oregon to make a drive to Dakota Territory, a 1,200-mile, three months' journey shared by eleven men and 2,130 two-, three-, and four-year-old steers.

After eleven weeks of shoeing and breaking broncs, gathering cattle, throwing and branding them, the big FF herd started east in July. On the fifth day the outfit reached Olds Ferry. Here the men carefully worked the cattle onto a long bar where they stood and drank in belly-deep water. Two men who had already crossed showed up on the opposite bank driving seven or eight head of the ferryman's milch cows and cripples to serve as decoys. Two waddies at the "point" cut off the leaders and prodded them into swimming water. Then, as all hands sent up a yell, the lead steer, wearing a bell, looked across the river, saw the ferryman's cattle standing in the stream drinking, and led off. Keeping the rest on the move, all made the opposite shore without having to swim the treacherous Snake for more than forty yards.

In the rough country ahead there were still three rivers to cross. When they reached the Weiser, the cattle were warm and thirsty and it wasn't hard to get them into the water. Red O'Neil, an Oregon cowpoke, crossed to the other side on his strong

[6] J. Orin Oliphant, "Eastward Movement of Cattle from the Oregon Country," *Agricultural History*, Vol. XX, No. 1 (January, 1947), 19.

swimming horse and rode out to the end of the sand bar to act as a marker to which the animals could swim. At a low spot on the opposite bank a tripod was set up, and, at some distance behind this, another was placed. This helped the men to direct the herd on a course affording the greatest length of wading and the smallest amount of swimming water.

At the Payette River, dogs in a small village near the crossing caused a lot of trouble, barking and snapping at the cattle. As Jack Porter, one of the trail hands, says, "It seemed like there were three dogs to every inhabitant, and that went for every Indian camp on the river below; likewise for travelers we met! This made our cattle nervous and hard to bed that night. After dark, we heard several pistol shots. . . . I have an idea that some of the more persistent cattle-chasing dogs failed thereafter to greet their owners. The next morning we were at the crossing early . . . and the cattle were crossed, but not without some trouble, for the dogs again barked, and as there was some drift-wood in the the river, the steers became nervous and it was quite a while before we could get our old work oxen up toward the end of the bar. Red O'Neil put his rope on the big bell steer and led off. . . . With help from some of the men from the town, who were mounted, we finally made the crossing, losing one steer which got caught in some drift logs before we could get the animal loose."

Two days after the Payette crossing, an electrical storm hit the outfit. In the heat of the early evening the cattle would not bed down, but kept up an ominous lowing. The hair on their tails stood straight up, or clung to their bodies when they switched them about. The manes of the horses stood wildly erect and their hair seemed to "lay the wrong way," as Porter describes it. When the storm struck, the horses humped up and the cattle bunched together. Although the men were fearful of a stampede, none occurred. Porter thought that the roughness of the lava ground, painful to hoofs beginning to get footsore, was the reason they did not run. At the Boise River, eight miles west of the city, the sand bar that jutted into the stream provided an easy crossing.

Farther on, instead of taking a long detour north, trail boss Ford decided to make a two-day short cut across from Lost River to the mouth of the Blackfoot. "Few of us will forget the torture of those two days and nights," says Porter. "It was through lava-ash and lava-dust country, covered mostly with sagebrush. It was the hottest weather we had experienced and a blistering, dry, scorching wind blew out of the southeast. . . . Our lead cattle stirred up clouds of hot dust which blew into the eyes, ears, noses, and throats of men and beasts following in the long herd strung out for a mile and a half." The only water was in a few small depressions, but being brackish, it was only an aggravation. Every steer's tongue hung out, every face expressed hopelessness. Driving into the night, the herd seemed less thirsty. At dawn, with the wind moderating, the cook prepared the simplest kind of breakfast, but few had any appetite. The water in the two kegs was as hot as though they had been placed over a fire.

"By nightfall of the second night," Porter's story continues, "our two big lead steers, Tom and Jerry, . . . threw up their heads, sniffed the hot air, made low moaning sounds, and hastened their pace. We knew they had scented the water of the Snake River [of which another crossing loomed ahead], although we judged the stream must be at least ten miles distant. The other cattle heard the lead bell and in turn quickened their pace. It was then up to the men to ride at the point to try and check the lead animals. . . . The cattle were strung out for fully five miles or more.

"We stopped the cavvy, set up the ropes, and caught out a change of horses. Then half of us rode to the point in the rim-rocks where the trail came down to the river. . . . When the lead steers came along, with the trail bell ringing, we were able to head them into the cut where they followed one of our riders down the steep trail, with the others coming after in single and double file. The heat lightning had flashed all night, and that helped us.

"Dawn came about the time the middle of the herd was in the cut. The leaders had long since reached the river's edge and watered and were now standing on a shallow sand bar. The herd was strung out in the rear a great distance and some of the cripples were a long time getting to the cut in the rimrock and from the rim to the river. Some of the weaker never did reach the water. We never rode back over the trail, but by tally a few days later, we counted eleven steers short."

Weeks later, when the herd debouched from the Lander Road, it descended to Stump Creek by a terribly steep declivity known as Terrace Canyon, or "Tear-Ass" Canyon, as it was called by cowboys who felt they knew the facts of life. It was so steep that one old cowhand swore that "sheepherders had to rough-lock the legs of their dogs in order to go down safely."

On November 3, 1883, trail boss Ford delivered to Agent McGillicuddy at Pine Ridge Agency, Dakota Territory, 2,021 FF steers—just nine short of the number which had left Baker City on July 24. "We had lost several head," recounts Porter, "but the law of averages and the keen cow sense of our foreman and his men had about made good that slight loss . . . and we also delivered a fine string of sound, well-broke cow horses, with but very few sore-backed or thin ones."[7]

In contrast to these highlights of trailing an old-time Oregon herd was the far less arduous experience of rounding up a beef herd in southeastern Montana forty-four years later. As a "dude" participant, one of the authors recorded his adventure in a newspaper story published in Montana newspapers, under the heading "Riding Range in Powder River Country":

"Roll out, cowboys!"

Beneath the light of a smoke-dimmed lantern hung from the center pole, something stirred in the four white "tarps." There

[7] John K. Rollinson, *Wyoming Cattle Trails,* 83.

was a smell of meat, frying in lard. Wood crackled in the stove whose black pipe pierced the tent-top through a protecting square of sewed-in steer's hide. Bossman Sam, cooking breakfast, was booming "reveille."

Yawns and grunts from under the tarps. Then six brown, tousled-headed caterpillars crawled from white cocoons into the chill of early morning in the hills of Custer National Forest, Powder River County, ninety miles from Milestown, Montana. Six pair of legs struggled into high-heeled boots—spurs still attached—and six uncurried cowpokes were dressed for the day.

"Better get in the hosses, Pistol!"

Into the dawn that was yet half-night vanished the youthful wrangler. In the corral he caught and saddled his "jingle horse" and loped off to locate and drive in fifty head of more or less halter-broke animals that were grazing somewhere in the 300-acre pasture.

Another youngster grabbed two five-gallon pails and ambled off to the spring for water. Wash-basin, soap, towel, and hair-comb eased the ablutions of beardless youth and stubble-chinned middle age. The cow camp's roster spanned many milestones, from one and twenty to three-score years and three.

Suddenly two hundred pounding hoofs mingled their thunder with the tinkling tocsin of the old gray bellmare as the horses were hazed into the corral. Once inside, the gate was swung to, and Roger, the wrangler, joined the others for breakfast.

Tin plates, cups, knives, forks, and spoons, thick slices of unbuttered bread, fried meat, fried spuds, and coffee carrying authority, despite dilution by sugar and canned milk—this was breakfast, wolfed by punchers with appetites "sharp set" by perfect health, as they sat cross-legged on their rolled-up bed-rolls.

Dishes washed and cigarettes alight, all hands trooped to the corral. Here each cowpoke, rope in hand, caught his chosen animal and with more or less alacrity saddled and bridled it, depending on the orneriness of the beast. All mounts finally being ready, the gate swung wide, and the band, scenting escape, snorted and thundered its way to freedom—with the ancient switch-tail clanging the Liberty Bell suspended from her neck.

Morning in the piney hills! Sunrise, like a red prairie fire, lighting the distant buttes, purple in the shadows. Muffled staccato of horses' hoofs; creaking leather, tinkling spurs, flapping chaps; smell of dew along the creek bottoms; wind murmuring in the balsams. God's in his heaven! All's well with the world! The Dude starts singing:

> *Over hill, over dale,*
> *As we hit the cattle trail,*
> *Keep them white-face a-movin' along—*

Sam the Bossman spurs his big bay.

"C'mon boys, let's git along!"

We break into a run. The Dude's mount leaps from under him; he keeps his seat only at the cost of an abraded rump, the cantle shaving off a piece of skin the size of a silver dollar. Another tenderfoot learns that a cow pony is alert, capricious, and sudden.

But that's just what makes a cow pony fit for his job. We're "riding circle" this October morning in the Hanging Woman Creek country. We shall know some of the jolts and jerks, the toil and heat and dust and sweat and thirst that go to make up a ten-day beef roundup on the range. And we may know mishaps. For shale is slippery, holes are hidden, and a bounding bronc, chasing a mad, flying thing with horns may mire in a bog or stumble in a gopher hole and pitch his rider into most anything, from rider's cramp to a broken neck.

Didn't Charley's appaloose, madly chasing a dodging cow and calf in a creek bottom, stumble into a treacherous hidden bog and throw this seasoned rider, landing on Charley's right leg and thoroughly mashing him, hip and thigh?

Also broncs can buck. Remember when Sam, getting off to open a gate, tried to remount, the saddle slipped, and he found

251

himself half-perched on a ewe-necked knothead that resented the situation, forcefully? As they "broke in two," Sam hit the ground sudden and hard, earning a sprained ankle for souvenir. However, such mishaps are all in the day's work; and they add the necessary allure to make men want to punch cows and "live dangerously."

Twelve miles from camp we reach the rendezvous. This is a high plateau, a splendid starting-off point, commanding a view in all directions. Thirty miles to the west are the barrier buttes bordering the Cheyenne Indian Reservation. Eastward the terrain flattens to the billowy valley of Powder River. Southward the piney hills of Custer Forest trail a lengthening chain of beauty to the very edge of Wyoming.

Near by lies winding, brush-lined Home Creek, fed by a number of tributaries. These and other small gulches and coulees must be combed for cattle. The riders are told off by Sam the Bossman.

"Johnny, you and Lee ride this coulee"—pointing the direction with a gloved forefinger.

"Tom, you and Chuck take Little Punkin," adding, "Charley n' me'll ride Three Mile. We'll meet up at the fence by the reserve pasture."

Dispersing in three directions, the watchful waddies begin their quest. Starting at the dry head of a stream, each pair explores the surrounding country. Riding downstream, first efforts are fruitless. It begins to look as if no cattle were grazing here. Then all of a sudden, in a clump of bushes in a miry creek bottom, shaded from the hot sun, a dozen head—heifers, cows, calves, and a solitary bull—are uncovered.

"Yeh-hoo!"

"Whoop-e-e-e!"

Two shouting pokes and two snorting ponies discover them all at once. Unurged, the broncs plunge into the thorny thicket. The affronted family puts itself in motion, protestingly. An old cow, separated from her young, turns defiantly and bawls out the riders. The bull bellows. Your excited mount tears into the brush.

Hawberry thorns scratch your legs. Boggy ground slows up the stumbling pony. A box elder bough brushes your hat off. But the drive goes on relentlessly. Finally the last remaining critters are ousted from the bottoms and started at a "cow-puncher's jog" down the easier trail on the high bank.

Finally, at the rendezvous by the reserve fence, you halt your bevy of bovine beauties. The other riders have preceded you, and the day's take falls under the appraising eye of Sam the Bossman. Half a thousand beeves, matured or potential, mill around aimlessly on the grassy plain, loose-herded by alert riders.

Sam and Charley ride into the bunch for the "cutting." Sam owns a large part of the F–T stock and Charley is the "rep" for the KK outfit. The job now is to cut out and drive to pasture such animals as the owners shall decide should be shipped for sale in Chicago. Sam is after dry cows and yearlings—the newly popular "baby beef" of city epicures.

As the selected individuals are worked toward the outer edge, other riders worm their way in, segregate them, and head them for the solitary rider who is holding the shippers. Inside of two hours the job is finished. The main bunch is hazed off toward the hills and a hundred hog-fat hostages to the stock-yards are headed toward the detaining pasture, the ninety-mile trail to Miles City and the railroad.

"Never saw any better-lookin' beef," comments old Tom through the dust of the trail herd.

"They's worlds of grass this year, sure-nuff," agrees Sam. "Fact is, the supervisor wants to issue more permits. Grass is so long even now, he's afraid o' fire!"

"Humph!" groused old Tom, "First he makes it harder to git a permit, then he's a hollerin' 'cause they ain't enough cattle here to use up the feed! Great system!"

Munching the cud of discontent, the old cowman rambles on,

"cussing out" the whole National Forest set-up from A to Izzard.

Sam is more amenable.

"Guess I'll get winter permit and keep the stoutest of the stock in here till spring."

That ends discussion. For the pasture gate looms just ahead, and after thirty miles of hard riding, the "morning circle" comes to an end with the turning in of the herd.

A hard, fast gallop brings the hungry gang to camp, where saddles and bridles are quickly shed. Freed of their gear, hot, lathered horses roll on the grass, scratching sweaty, itching backs, with little nickerings of joy. Stiff-legged cowmen lurch toward grub-box and stove, intent on nourishment.

Afterwards there's a ride to the pasture with ropes and branding irons. A sagebrush fire offers unique incense as ropers and throwers heat the irons for applying the heraldry of owner-ship to a dozen unbranded calves. Undesirable males are emascu-lated.

Back to camp at dusk, with night falling sudden and cold, and a bit of vocalizing by the visiting minstrel and his twanging banjo. Then into the cocoon warmth of the tarps, with nothing to do till the break of day and the inexorable call of Sam the Bossman—and Cook:

"Roll out, cowboys!"[8]

[8] C. W. Towne, in six Montana Sunday newspapers, November 20, 1927.

CHAPTER 22

When the Cow Jumped over the Moon

U NTIL THE DAWN of the seventh century before Christ, trade in the ancient world was a matter of barter and exchange. There was little or no credit or coined money. In Homer's *Iliad* the prizes in a wrestling match were evaluated in terms of cattle. Thus Ajax wrestles Ulysses, for which

> *A massy tripod for the victor lies,*
> *Of twice six oxen its reputed price;*
> *And next, the loser's spirits to restore,*
> *A female captive, valued but at four.*

It remained for the Romans, mulling over the twelve-ox tripod and the four-ox slave and having a flair for semantics, to add a bit of padding to their word *pecus* (cattle), and come up with *pecunia*, meaning money. From that day to this, man's interest in livestock has been chiefly pecuniary—that of the American cattleman one of boom and bust.

Seventy years ago Governor Crittenden of Missouri, addressing the first national convention of cattlemen in St. Louis, put it this way: "Two by two, cattle went into the ark with man, and from that time to this they have been the objects of trade, commanding at all times—from the day when Jacob outwitted his father-in-law Laban down to this convention—the shrewdest and most refined intellects. . . . Our immense herds, scattered from Maine to California, are the offspring of a single bull and one or more cows imported into this country in 1493 by Christopher Columbus a few days before a custom house had been established upon our soil and officers appointed to vex travelers by inquisitive questions. They came in on the free list as raw material and some acquisitive [persons] still think they are on the free list—only convinced to the contrary by a 'short shrift and a long rope' at the hands of [those] who still believe in that old, solemn law of mine and thine."[1]

In February, 1887, two years after the Governor's speech, the United States Department of Agriculture reported that in the fourteen Plains and Pacific Coast states government-owned pasturage totaled more than 685,000,000 acres; that of the 152,-000,000 farm animals in the country, 74,000,000, or nearly half, were west of the Mississippi, and of these, the 28,000,000 "oxen and other cattle" numbered five times those east of the Mississippi.[2] At the same time, Norman J. Coleman, commissioner of agriculture, painted this picture:

"If a solid column should be formed, twelve animals deep, one end resting at New York City, its centre encircling San Francisco, and its other arm reaching back to Boston, such a column would contain about the number which now forms the basis, the capital stock, so to speak, of the cattle industry of the United States." Another expert claimed that the amount of money invested in cows exceeded by forty million dollars the amount invested in bank stocks; still another estimated that if all the livestock in the land were equally distributed, each family would have a horse, a cow, four pigs, and three sheep.[3]

Such was the rose-colored picture when grass was king, promotors extolling the "boundless, gateless, fenceless pastures" and inviting Americans and Europeans to "come and get it." The man of means was assured of doubling his capital, and the adventurer with a branding iron was encouraged to convert acres of free grass into steers at top prices. As humorist Bill Nye, writing in the *Laramie Boomerang*, solemnly asserted, "Three years ago a guileless tenderfoot came into Wyoming, leading a single steer and carrying a branding iron; now he is the opulent pos-

---

[1] William M. Thayer, *Marvels of the New West*, 537–38.
[2] *Ibid.*, 535–36.
[3] *Ibid.*, 538.

sessor of six hundred head of fine cattle—the ostensible progeny of that one steer."[4]

By 1883 the Union Pacific and Northern Pacific railroads were both offering convenient shipping points; the Indians had been suppressed; the panic of the seventies had evaporated; territorial legislatures, country newspapers, Eastern stock journals, and railroad literature were all promoting stock raising. The Northern Pacific, in its official *Guide*, estimated that "the average cost of raising a steer, not counting interest, or capital invested, is from sixty cents to one dollar a year, so that a four-year-old steer raised from a calf and ready for market costs about $4. A herd consisting of yearlings, cows, and bulls, will have no steers for the market in less than two or three years. Taking into account the loss of interest on capital invested before returns are received, besides all expenses and ordinary losses, the average profit of stock raising in Montana during the last few years has been at least 30 per cent per annum. Some well-informed cattle men estimate it at 40 or 45 per cent."[5]

A Dakota editor thought that few people besides stockmen realized how rapidly cattle multiply when all the females are allowed to breed; and he proceeded to enlighten them by saying that if 100 cows and their female offspring were kept at breeding for ten years, the total progeny at the end of that time would be 1,428 cows and the same number of bulls. "[Such] is the rate at which capital increases in the livestock business on the plains, where the cost of keeping a beef from birth to maturity is less than six dollars."[6]

"A good-sized steer," reported the *Breeder's Gazette* in 1883, "when it is fit for the butcher market will bring from $45 to $60. The same animal at its birth was worth but $5. He has run on the plains and cropped the grass from the public domain for four or five years, and now, with scarcely any expense to its own-

[4] Quoted in *Rocky Mountain Husbandmen*, Great Falls, Mont., June 14, 1883.
[5] Henry J. Winser, *The Great Northwest: A Guide Book and Itinerary*, 172.
[6] Thayer, *Marvels of the New West*, 548.

er, is worth $40 more than when he started on his pilgrimage."

Even the Eastern tenderfoot often cashed in handsomely on such cajolery. An Illinois merchant visiting in southern Colorado was so impressed by possible profits in the cattle business that he invested all the money he had laid by—only $800—and entered into partnership with a reliable local man with the understanding that he would continue to run his Illinois business and visit Colorado once a year. At the end of eight years, he sold his $800 interest for $10,000 to the partner who had run the herd and done all the work.[7]

A Massachusetts manufacturer in poor health was ordered to Nebraska, where he became interested in the cattle business and its opportunity for work in the open air. He bought out at a low figure a local stockman with 4,000 head and drove 5,000 more from Oregon the next year, which at the ranch were worth double what they had cost in Oregon. Four years later, for his investment of $110,000, he refused an offer of $300,000 in cash, declaring that he would not sell the herd for $500,000 because "in ten years—yes, in less time than that—it will be worth a million."[8]

Another Massachusetts man bought a Wyoming ranch which included 12,000 cattle, 700 horses, and other stock, for $230,000. This was in the spring of 1883. In December he answered a query about his ranch business by saying: "In October I sold my beef, and since that 6,000 head of cattle, the whole amounting to $180,000. I have 6,000 head of cattle and 700 horses left, which are worth at least what I paid for the ranch in the first place."[9]

English and Scottish capitalists were heavy contributors to the "beef bonanza." A Scotsman, J. S. Tait, issued a small brochure entitled "The Cattle-Fields of the Far West." His estimate of the business included possible profits of from 33⅓

[7] *Ibid.*, 556.
[8] *Ibid.*, 557.
[9] *Ibid.*, 558.

Texas Longhorns

From a photograph by Roy E. Heffner

A. P. Borden with some of the Shanghai Pierce cattle, apparently
early descendants of the O'Connor-Pierce Estate importation.

American Brahman Cattle Breeders' Association

A group of Hereford cattle bred by the Swan Brothers of Indianola, Iowa.

Henry Swan

A Grand Champion Shorthorn Steer

A Champion Hereford

An Aberdeen Angus Champion

A three-year-old white Charolaise registered bull, weighing 1,950 pounds.

Roger Brown and "Rajah," champion Brahman F.F.A. steer, Great Western Show, Los Angeles, 1951.

Crossbred Steer (Brahman bull and Hereford cow)

Santa Gertrudis Bull

The Cattleman

Grand Champion Brangus Bull

The Cattleman

Champion animal in Highland Cattle class, Smithfield Show, Earl's Court, London.

British Information Center and *The Cattleman*

And Back to Aurochs

Aurochs cow claimed to be resynthesized by Lutz Heck.

Paul Parey & Company, Berlin

to 66½ per cent.[10] This he followed up with individual "success" stories. Here are five whose profits, which Tait reckoned in pounds sterling, are expressed in American money, the pound then being worth five dollars:

"The Hon. Moreton E. Post, member of Congress and banker of Cheyenne informed the writer that Mr. Searight of Wyoming had invested $150,000 in the cattle business of that Territory in 1879, and having taken no money out of the business nor . . . put any in since, the property in the fall of 1882 was worth $1,500,000. . . . Colonel Slaughter, president of the First National Bank of Dallas, Texas, . . . has made a similar sum in the business and he has not yet reached middle life. . . . Mr. Charles Goodnight (Goodnight & Adair), the Pioneer of the Panhandle, has made (without any original capital of his own) $600,000 in ten years. His partner, Mr. Adair of Rathdairs, Ireland, . . . has put from $360,000 to $370,000 into the cattle business in Texas during the last six or seven years, and has taken out from $60,000 to $70,000. The $300,000 representing the balance of his money left in, is now worth $3,000,000. . . . Messrs. Post, Searight, Slaughter, Goodnight, and Adair may be surpassed in wealth by many of the cattle kings, but they have no superiors in standing and probity."

To the above might well be added such names as Iliff, Lux, Lytle, Snyder, Brush, Lawrence, Head, Kohrs, Carey, Kendrick, and Stuart. These pioneers of the Plains actually worked physically and mentally at the job, riding the range daily and supervising every minute detail. They were succeeded by great corporations whose stockholders hired managers while they themselves merely "talked shop" over Scotch and soda at their London Club or played poker in Cheyenne or Miles City. In the spring of 1884, hearing that a friend had just bought 3,000 two-year-old steers in Texas for his range in Montana, Granville Stuart asked him if he was going south to come up with the drive. To which came the reply, "Hell no! I'm going to

[10] *Ibid.*, 558.

Miles City and play poker and be comfortable until those steers arrive."

In Cheyenne everybody seemed to be dabbling in steers. Even the chief justice of the Supreme Court of Wyoming succumbed and bought a $40,000 herd, according to the *Laramie Boomerang,* which also reported that "large transactions are made every day in which the buyer does not see a hoof of his purchase and very likely does not use more than one-half of the purchase money in the trade before he has sold and made an enormous margin in the deal. . . . A Cheyenne man who don't pretend to know a maverick from a mandamus has made a neat little margin of $15,000 this summer in small transactions and hasn't seen a cow yet that he has bought and sold."[11]

Pioneer cattlemen with herds and a good range might sell out at their own figure for cash or, if they preferred, accept capital stock in a newly organized company which promised to contribute additional money for further expansion. Eastern money could not resist a happy plunge into such an adventure. The formula was simple: Uncle Sam provided the free grass, the East the capital; the Western cowman the know-how. As a result stock companies multiplied by the score. In a single year, twenty corporations with over $12,000,000 capitalization were organized under Wyoming laws, initiating leathery-skinned cowmen into new and strange accounting practices. "The time has come," said Secretary Sturgis of the Wyoming Stock Growers' Association, "when our business can no longer be done by the old rule-of-thumb method. In former days we had only to brand our calves, when dropped, and ship our beeves, when fat. The calf tally could be kept on a shingle and the checkbook was the only book kept, and the balance or the overdraft at the bank showed the whole of the business. Times are changed."[12]

Not only did the East eagerly swallow the bait, but London

---

[11] Quoted in the *Miles City* (Mont.) *Daily Press,* August 2, 1882.

[12] Ernest Staples Osgood. *The Day of the Cattleman,* 96-97 n.; John Clay, *My Life on the Range,* 245.

and Edinburgh also poured their pounds sterling into the speculative pot to equal, if not exceed, Yankee-dollar investments. Before they quit, thirty-six British companies between 1870 and 1900 had sunk $40,000,000 in herds and ranches located in a dozen Western states, from which they salvaged perhaps $15,-000,000 after the bubble had burst. For the fever of speculation had created what John Clay called a "minor South Sea Bubble," especially attractive to British investors. "In Edinburgh the ranch pot was boiling over. Drawing rooms buzzed with the stories of this last of bonanzas; staid old gentlemen, who scarcely knew the difference between a steer and a heifer, discussed it over their port and nuts."[13] Young aristocrats with a yen for adventure had no trouble in tapping the family funds for such an alluring investment, and Western cattlemen were only too happy to unload their holdings at fancy prices. All the evils of uncontrolled speculation cropped up. Swindlers flourished, as paper companies without an acre of land or a solitary Longhorn steer sold stock to unsuspecting buyers. Even when the seller was honest, the numbers of cattle written in the tally book were quite unreliable, since no account was taken of the losses in the calf crop or in stock which failed to survive the severe winters. Investors seemed to think they had to buy "sight unseen" or the golden opportunity would be lost. A story going the rounds in Cheyenne was related by John Clay. There had been a blizzard, and some of the cowmen lined up at the bar in Luke Murrin's saloon were gloomy, wondering what their livestock losses would amount to. "Cheer up, boys," said Luke, "the books won't freeze!" And forthwith set up drinks for the crowd.

Some Western newspapers issued warnings against crooks, pointing out that wild visions of wealth in the cattle business led many Easterners to invest in anything that happened to have a brand on it. Too late they discovered that the unreasonable dividends promised were but "a clever bait to catch suck-

[13] *Ibid.*, 101.

ers."[14] Even reputable cattle companies often sold off a larger beef herd than the calf crop warranted, thus reducing capital in order to declare a larger annual dividend.

But while some Western editors warned against the risks, others touted the opportunities for making a fortune. Declared a Colorado livestock journal, "Cattle is one of those investments men cannot pay too much for, since, if left alone, they will multiply, replenish and grow out of a bad bargain."[15] This prophecy seemed vindicated by market quotations of a previous year. The price for beef cattle on the Chicago market had reached the highest level since 1870, when on May 24, 1882, top-quality steers touched $9.35 a hundred. This seemed to justify the claim that profits would "grow out of a bad bargain." It was a bright but fleeting interlude, when "Steers, ready for fattening on the northern range, brought thirty-seven, forty, and even fifty dollars in Texas, and these might be sold to a Wyoming speculator for sixty dollars. . . . The story was about that the Prairie Cattle Company had announced a dividend of 42 per cent for 1882. Montana stockgrowers were, according to the livestock journals, reaping a profit of from 25 to 40 per cent."[16] With Texas steers selling for sixty dollars in Wyoming and the female of the species rated at thirty-five, 1882 must be regarded as the year "the cow jumped over the moon." Although she was already on her way back to earth, most of her joy riders were unprepared for the giddy descent and the unhappy landing.

Despite high prices, warnings against the demon of speculation could be heard in early 1882. The editor of the *Drovers Daily Journal,* in February, November, and December of that year, predicted "widespread catastrophe" as an aftermath to "a vast amount of over-trading." The latter was one cause of the bust following the boom. But there were other contributing

[14] *Denver News,* quoted in *Breeder's Gazette,* Vol. V, No. 21 (May 22, 1884), 797.

[15] *Colorado Livestock Record,* quoted in *Breeder's Gazette,* Vol. V, No. 25 (June 26, 1884), 998.

[16] Osgood, *The Day of the Cattleman,* 94, 95.

factors—overstocking of the range, bad management of the larger outfits, absentee ownership, and wholesale stealing by cattle rustlers.

"Cattle, cattle, more cattle," came the cry from the grass country, all the way from Texas to Canada. As if in answer, 420,000 head, the largest number since 1871, trudged north from Texas in 1884. At the same time, to aggravate the situation further, more Eastern stock, or "barnyard" cattle, than ever before were shipped west from farms in Illinois, Wisconsin, Michigan, Iowa, and Missouri. The Northern Pacific alone hauled 98,219 of these "pilgrims" to the wide open spaces, from which they transported to Chicago only 75,000 head. Other railroads reported the same trend.[17]

The purchase of these "barnyard" animals was a wise move from the standpoint of breeding up the range herds, but turning them out to shift for themselves increased the hazards of the business. For one thing, they cost more than the Texas stuff— $35 cows as against $24 for Longhorns. In Wyoming alone, $2,000,000 worth of blooded bulls were bought and turned loose in 1883. Having no experience or instinct at "rustling," Eastern stock stood around the ranch buildings in winter bellowing their heads off for someone to come and feed them. Another hazard was the possibility that these imported cattle would spread pleuro-pneumonia, which was prevalent in the East at the time. Finally, crowding cows on the range far beyond its feeding capacity, the stockmen saw them crop the spring grass so closely that there was hardly any summer feed left. Thus these underfed cattle were in no shape to go through the winter. "Before the boom, a section [640 acres] of good grazing land in southern Texas might feed 150 cattle, but after the grass had been injured by too heavy a stocking, it took ten acres to pasture one animal."[18]

[17] William McLeod Raine and Will C. Barnes, *Cattle*, 238; Osgood, *The Day of the Cattleman*, 93.
[18] Raine and Barnes, *Cattle*, 239.

The factor of incompetent management adversely affected many of the British-owned outfits. Brilliant exceptions were such men as John Clay and Murdo Mackenzie, two Scots who resolutely applied themselves to learning every angle of the business. Through character and ability they achieved success. In contrast, several of the foreign properties were entrusted to the inept supervision of callow youths, the sporting, big-game-hunting sons of titled Englishmen. Some were well-intentioned, hoping to save an imperiled family fortune by hard work and quick profits; others were black sheep, or remittance men, shipped to America to save the family further embarrassment at home. The *Pall Mall Gazette* pictured the Earl of Aylesford languishing on his 37,000-acre ranch in Texas, owner of twenty or thirty horses, thirteen dogs, and five servants, but no money to buy cattle. Known as "the Jedge" by his neighbors, he, as the story went, always opened a fresh bottle whenever a visiting cowboy dropped in. One of these reported that "he don't stop at one, neither. I've been to the ranch many a time to stay all night and woke in the mornin' to find the bottles lyin' around as thick as fleas, the boys two deep on the floor snorin' like mad buffalo and the Jedge with a bottle in each hand over in the corner."

Even the industrious, trying to manage a ranch in Wyoming under orders coming from an office in Europe, were frequently doomed to frustration. Moreton Frewen, British founder of the Powder River Land and Cattle Company, started to buy many of the state's larger herds. The greatest gathering of beeves ever seen in Wyoming was finally made up from the Frewen cattle by Fred Hesse, the foreman, and driven to Fort Fetterman. The plan was to ship from Douglas as soon as the railroad, then building, should reach that city. But, at Fetterman, Hesse received a cable from London, telling him to turn the beef herd back and ship from Medora, a loading station near the old Teddy Roosevelt range in Montana. From there they were to be railed direct to Duluth and shipped from there to Liverpool.

The herd was turned back on the long, weary trail across the waterless desert to the Northern Pacific Railroad. Before they could reach it, winter had set in and the cattle were loaded in a blinding snowstorm. When they finally arrived at Duluth, it was too late for loading aboard ship, as the lakes had frozen over. After more cablegrams, back and forth, the steers, which had been turned loose in the snow and were eating the leaves from the trees, were at last ordered shipped to Chicago, where they were sold for a song. Many stockmen figured the loss on this fiasco was at least $200,000.[19]

Frewen's $1,500,000 cattle ranch on the Powder River, located in a great game area, was the scene of lavish hospitality, with a guest book filled with illustrious names. One entry read: "There were four guns in this party and the ground shot over was the other side of the Range looking over the Big Horn basin —game was very plentiful. . . . Of bears there were bagged 26, and of sheep 14 rams and 1 ewe—The party left the Big Horn Ranche the beginning of September and returned in about six weeks, the weather being beautiful. Attendants included five camp hustlers, one black cook, and Pauline (French maid). All satisfactory."[20]

American cowmen were overjoyed whenever they could outsmart a Britisher. This same Frewen of the Powder River outfit was once reported to have bought the same herd of cattle twice.[21] As the animals were driven through a counting chute, located at the foot of a hill, past the talley men, and out, the cowboys merely drove the critters around the hill and back again for a second tally—a somewhat expensive "run-around."

Finlay Dun, secretary of the Swan Land and Cattle Company, once insisted on personally counting 100,000 head just purchased by his company. As each animal entered the counting

---

[19] *Memoirs of Bryant B. Brooks,* 174–75.

[20] Herbert O. Brayer, "The Influence of British Capital on the Western Range Cattle Industry," Denver *Westerners Brand Book,* 1948, p. 17.

[21] This story was told at the expense of Eastern or foreign investors in every Western cattle state. This one is found in the Denver *Westerners Brand Book,* 1948, p. 71.

chute, Dun smeared it with a blob of blue paint. By the time he had daubed 40,000, the first that had been counted had rubbed or worn off the paint. With nothing to tell the counted from the uncounted, further exterior decorating was called off.

Absentee ownership handicapped the big companies. The loyalty of the waddy to his American employer was a matter of common knowledge, but this quality depended largely on the daily assocation of cowboy and boss, often working the range together. On the other hand, loyalty to a "syndicate," with the directors lounging in London clubrooms, was something else again. With little at stake, managers became indifferent to the condition of the cattle. Cowboys ruined good horses by hard riding and careless handling. "Cowhands, out of work during the winter, gravitated to ranches where a reputation for generous hospitality had been built up at the expense of an owner thousands of miles away. The calf crop was far below what the prospectuses had promised. Small bands of cattle belonging to cowboys seemed to grow beyond the natural rate of increase. Somehow, a calf belonging to a company with offices in Edinburgh or New York did not seem quite as much a piece of private property as that of a neighbor on the range."[22]

Normally, the Western cowman was an individualist; he preferred to be let alone. But wholesale cattle thievery drove him to join others in forming stock growers' associations. In an effort to stop rustling, some of these persuaded the legislatures of their states to pass laws decreeing that all mavericks found on the range were the property of the association, and not of an individual, that they must be sold and the money put into the treasury. A bonus was offered every rider who so branded a maverick. Instead of making the cowhand more loyal, this legislation further alienated employer and employee; the temptation for the cowboy to put his own iron on the calf instead of that of the association was in many instances too great to be resisted.

[22] Osgood, *The Day of the Cattleman,* 104.

Hostility grew between the small operator and the big outfits. Also, many a homesteader, drifting in and locating along a creek, was sometimes hungry. When a steer wandered into his garden patch, he felt justified in killing it. It was almost impossible to convict rustlers. "A former sheriff and stock inspector of Weld County, Colorado, arrested a man for having seven calves in his barn that belonged to the Pony Cattle Company. Several witnesses swore in behalf of the accused that it was quite common for calves to leave their mothers and break into a barn."[23]

Finding no justice in the courts, the association hired inspectors or detectives and warned rustlers and suspects to leave the country. If depredations continued in spite of the warnings, the guilty were shot or hanged. In a campaign covering parts of Wyoming, Nebraska, Dakota, and Montana, seventy-five thieves were put to death; from one railroad bridge, according to the National Livestock Historical Association, thirteen men were hanged. Defending such methods, John Clay in his *My Life on the Range,* asks, "What would any man do if a burglar broke into his house, repeatedly stole property, regardless of remonstrance, and the courts laughed at complaints made against the thief? He would do as the cattlemen did, if he had a spark of manhood in him." On the other hand, not even Clay could justify the method of some of the Wyoming cattle barons who invaded Johnson County in 1892 in an attempt to run out settlers whom they claimed were cattle thieves, or the Lincoln County cattle war in New Mexico, perhaps the bloodiest of all, including some infamous killings by Billy the Kid.

Despite overstocking, incompetent management, and wholesale thievery, most of the big outfits managed to turn up with paper profits in 1884. But it was the last gasp. In 1885 came the crash. Values tumbled as everybody tried to sell and few wanted to buy. "One man who had refused $1,500,000 for his holdings in 1883 sold after the deflation for $245,000, all of

[23] Raine and Barnes, *Cattle,* 241.

which went for indebtedness incurred. Hundreds of stockmen were wiped out. . . . In '84 Col. Ike T. Pryor offered to buy a herd for $25 a head. He bought the same herd in 1893, loaded on the cars at Uvalde, no calves counted, for $6 a head."[24]

Those whom inflation did not ruin were hardly able to survive the winter of 1886–87, marked by the most calamitous blizzard in Western history. Practically one-half of all the northern stock were wiped out, largely on account of undernourishment the previous summer, and almost as many perished on southern ranges. In Montana, Granville Stuart wrote, "It was impossible to tell just what the losses were. . . . We did not get some of ours for a year. Our entire losses . . . were 66 per cent of the herd. Others lost from 75 to 80 per cent. In the fall of 1886 there were more than one million head . . . on the Montana ranges, and the losses in the 'big storm' amounted to twenty million dollars. This was the death knell to the range cattle business on anything like the scale it had been run on before. . . . A business that had been fascinating to me before, suddenly became distasteful. I wanted no more of it. I never wanted to own again an animal that I could not feed and shelter."[25] It was during this catastrophe that the young cowhand Charlie Russell received a note from his boss in Helena asking, "How's the herd getting along?" For answer, Charlie drew his famous sketch entitled "The Last of the 5,000," which started him on a career which ultimately marked him as the greatest of all Western range artists.

Among the heaviest losers was Stuart's friend and one-time partner, Conrad Kohrs, who salvaged only 3,000 animals out of a herd of 35,000. But he, along with several other operators, was enabled to recoup through the unique magnanimity of a Chicago livestock commission man, Joseph Rosenbaum. Following the disaster, a number of Montana cattlemen, to whom Rosenbaum loaned approximately a total of one million dollars,

24 *Ibid.,* 245–46.
25 Granville Stuart, *Forty Years on the Frontier,* II, 236–37.

were struck speechless when their creditor called them to Helena and announced he would not foreclose, but would actually loan them an additional million. This double indebtedness they eventually paid in full. Twenty years later, when the Chicago man faced ruin on the Grain Exchange, Conrad Kohrs and other beneficiaries pooled their resources and loaned their benefactor more than one million dollars. With this, Rosenbaum was enabled to stage a comeback, continue solvent, and reap a large profit.

CATTLE & MEN

Nutrition

CHAPTER 23

The Path to the Prime Rib

EVER SINCE HE DWELT IN A CAVE, hunted with a bludgeon, and wolfed the raw flesh of the aurochs and the wisent, man has been a meat eater. Monuments to his carnivorous habits in prehistoric times survive to this day in the kitchen-middens of central France. Here the remains of thousands of wild cattle, bison, boars, reindeer, antelope, and horses conjure up a vision of the Neanderthal trencherman, at those great open-air gatherings of fifteen thousand years ago, splitting well-gnawed bones for their marrow, then throwing them over his shoulder—like Charles Laughton as Henry VIII in the movies—leaving the rest of the job to the wolves. They further reveal that even our iron-jawed and snaggle-toothed ancestors preferred tender flesh. Most of the bones are those of young animals, easier to hunt and not so tough to chew.

As for the farmers of one thousand years ago, they were scarcely any better off. They worked their oxen until they were muscle-bound before slaughtering them for food. Actually such flesh was probably tougher than that of their wild ox forebears, quite immune from lifelong toil under the yoke. Nor had the sturdy yeomanry of England ever heard of the Japanese trick of massaging the older animals before slaughter in order to tenderize the cuts.

It was only a scant two centuries ago that the idea of improving meat animals for eating purposes first entered the British mind. In 1750, Robert Bakewell, Leicestershire farmer and trained anatomist, developed certain principles of breeding which have been summarized as: (1) Like begets like; (2) select an ideal type; (3) breed the best to the best; and (4) inbreed to produce early maturity.

Of great practical help were such contemporary agricultural innovations as those of Jethro Tull, who introduced the idea that tillage-grain and roots should be drilled instead of broadcast; Lord Charles Townshend, who stressed the value of turnips and other root crops for fattening cattle; Thomas Hoke, large-scale farmer who, in finishing Scottish cattle for the London market, emphasized the role of the fattening bullock in maintaining the profitable cultivation of his fields. Finally, there was Sir Arthur Young, indefatigable traveler and prolific author, whose *Annals of Agriculture* and other writings became by far the most important agency in publicizing those advanced methods which constituted the agricultural revolution of eighteenth-century England and stimulated better husbandry on the Continent and overseas. Young was an intimate and regular correspondent of George Washington, and his judgment was sought and often followed by our first gentleman farmer. To this class posterity was in large part indebted for improved cattle both here and abroad. Henry Home, writing in 1802, said:

"I cannot finish . . . without warmly recommending agriculture to gentlemen of land-estates. . . . In view of pleasure, it is of all occupations the best adapted to gentlemen in private station. . . . In former times, hunting was the only business of a gentleman. The practice of blood made him rough and hard hearted; he led the life of a dog, or of a savage; violently active in the field, supinely indolent at home. Consider the present mode of living. How delightful the change; from the hunter to the farmer, from the destroyer of animals to the feeder of men!"[1]

To this class belonged the half-dozen Englishmen already mentioned. As for Bakewell, his objectives were summarized by his widely-quoted slogan, "All is useless that is not Beef." This brings to mind the fact that at that time writers carefully distinguished between "flesh" and "beef." For example, George Culley reported that "our heaviest and largest oxen when properly fed victual the East-India ships, as they produce the thick-

[1] Henry Home, *The Gentleman Farmer* (5th ed.).

est *beef*. . . . Our Royal navy should also be victualled from these; but, by the jobs made by contractors, and the abuses lately crept in, our honest tars, I am afraid, are often fed with *flesh* rather than that valuable *beef*."[2] Perhaps it is not altogether whimsical to conclude that "while his forebears furnished flesh, it was Bakewell who brought us beef." Another writing idiosyncrasy of those days was to lump everything on a critter aside from beef under the word "offal." Today this former wastage yields a hundred and one indispensable and profitable "by-products."

Modern cattle breeders regard as most significant to them Bakewell's contributions to the science of breeding, overlooking the fact that without the new sources of fattening feeds, especially root crops, there could have been no development of the characteristics on which he based his system. Because Bakewell was completely reticent about his actual matings and because his published principles seemed too simple to produce the proven results, many suspected that he had "secrets" of breeding which died with him. Among his colleagues he excited envy and distrust. But when breeders elsewhere applied successfully to Angus, Herefords, Shorthorns, and other strains of cattle Bakewell's methods with the old English Longhorn, it became obvious that he had told them all he knew.

It was to his country estate of Dishley, in Leicestershire, that Bakewell first brought some long-horned cows known as the Caneley stock, which, after crossing with a Northumberland bull, produced a race hailed at the time as "the celebrated Dishley breed." In the decades that followed, his shepherd was his only confidant. He alone knew what cows had been bred to what sires. Not even such young gentlemen as the Earl of Leicester and George Culley, who lived for extended periods in Bakewell's home, shared these secrets. Perhaps the thing they most vividly remembered was the sight of the old *Maestro* cutting up, pickling, sealing in glass jars, and depositing in his library the prin-

[2] Culley, *An Essay on the Breeding of Livestock*, 14. Italics ours.

cipal cuts of meat from his sires, dams, and offspring. With these he could compare his results directly and find out whether he was moving ahead or backward.

According to Culley, the kind of cattle that were most esteemed before Bakewell's day was "the large, *long-bodied*, big-boned, coarse, gummy, flat-sided kind, and often lyery or black-fleshed. . . . This discerning breeder introduced a small, clean-boned, round, short-carcased, kindly looking cattle, and inclined to be fat."[3] Another reported that the "Dishley breed" ("Bakewell's Longhorns") were long and fine in the horn, had small heads, clean throats, straight, broad backs, wide quarters, and were "light in their bellies and offal." The chief improvements effected seem to have been in their "aptitude to fatten early, on the most valuable points, and in the superior quality of the flesh."[4] Among other objectives, Bakewell strove to lessen the amount of "offal." He tried to breed animals large in the parts which were of the greatest sales value—shoulders comparatively small, hindquarters proportionately large, smallness of head, neck, and extremities, round, blocky body, and fine boned. He disregarded or made light of size. He particularly aimed at early maturity and readiness to put on fat.

It is not easy for the present generation to realize the enormous demand for fat a century or two ago, before the discovery and processing of mineral and vegetable oils. Most everybody worked at physical labor outdoors. As a source of energy for hearty appetites fat was superior to starches and sugar in a ratio of nine to four. Furthermore, tallow was needed for candles, the most efficient illuminants then available. Bakewell with his long-horned cattle sought chiefly fattening ability.

Working with Shorthorns at the farms of Ketton and Brampton in Durham, the Colling brothers tried to combine fattening and size. This new type of cattle needed advertising, and bigness appealed to the popular mind. A calf, sired by his great bull,

3 *Ibid.*, 23.
4 Charles A. Goodrich (ed.), *A New Family Encyclopedia: Neat Cattle*, 247.

Favorite, dropped in 1796, and fattened by Charles Colling, at the age of five weighed 3,024 pounds. This weight put the Durham Ox in the show business, with a specially built carriage moving him from place to place. For the next six years this trouper visited the principal city and farming sections of England and Scotland after his owner had refused offers as high as $10,000. A dislocated hip bone which failed to heal sent the beast to the shambles, where he wound up as 2,322 pounds of carcass, 156 of tallow, and a 142-pound hide.

Long before this mammoth meat animal took to the road, prize cattle had been exhibited at various English fairs. The oldest fair was at Smithfield, near London, chartered in the reign of Henry II in 1133. Of it a nobleman named Fitz Stephen reported: "Every Tuesday . . . many come out of the city to buy or look on; to wit, Earls, Barons, Knights, and Citizens. . . . In another part stand the country people with cattle . . . large swine and kine with their udders strutting out, fair-bodied oxen and woolly flock."

This granddaddy of all fat stock shows, in England and America, got off to a slow start. It took the leisurely British four and one-half centuries to get the market ground paved. And it was not until 1798 that the Smithfield Club was organized to sponsor an annual Christmas show, with the Duke of Bedford as president and Arthur Young as secretary-treasurer. An early pronouncement pledged the show to hold prices down, stressing that "the only true object of the farmer is to profit, not by high prices, but by *great products*." The Duke (Sir John Sinclair) pointed out that it would be an essential service to prove "what breeds of cattle there are which give most food for man from given quantities of food for animals." Which was sound Bakewell doctrine. And in the ensuing century and a half, this has been the goal of conscientious breeders on two continents.

Cattle sent to Smithfield market in the thirteenth and fourteenth centuries weighed only about two-thirds of what they do now. It was not until the 1700's that the big-framed imported Flemish strains produced any pronounced effect either in sending younger stock to market or in actual slaughter weights. The best ox at the Smithfield show in 1808, a six-year-old, weighed 1,700 pounds. Throughout the 1830's the champions averaged a little over four years old, with weights increased to about 2,200 pounds. By the 1860's British exhibitors had reduced the age of their entries to about two years and ten months, albeit the weights were still excessive from today's point of view.

Even before Bakewell and others had begun their work of improvement, England's bards had forestalled the breeders in extolling the virtues of beef. Fielding, in *The Grub Street Opera*, rhapsodized about "the roast beef of England, And old England's roast beef," while poet Dick Leveridge hailed the day "When mighty roast beef was the Englishman's food, / It ennobled our hearts and enriched our blood, / Our soldiers were brave and our courtiers were good." A hundred years earlier, an etymologic "boner" gave us the word "sirloin." Instead of spelling the French *"sur"* ("above") correctly, some word-juggler wrote "sir," alleging that a particularly fine cut of beef had been knighted by King James I and dubbed "Sir Loin."

All the discussions about cattle and beef in the mother country caused repercussions in her American colonies. In the seventeenth century the first importations were Devons, a fact in later years noted by Chief Justice Jay, who, returning from abroad, reported the close resemblance of the New England stock to the Devonshire cattle. But Colonel Timothy Pickering of Massachusetts observed, "Although I suppose the Devon race of cattle to be *predominant* in New England, I doubt not that some of the other breeds were early introduced by our ancestors; some Herefords unquestionably, whose descendants are yet distinguished by their white faces."[5]

[5] *Ibid.*, 251. Undoubtedly these cattle were not Herefords as understood nowadays, but mixed descendants of white spotted Flemish cattle, introduced first to England, to produce the broken colors of Longhorns, Herefords, some two-century-old breeds of eastern Wales, and local varieties that have become extinct.

The importation of cattle from England ceased early. The *Massachusetts Agricultural Journal* believed that few cattle were imported after 1650, since at that time, and for the next one hundred years, English agriculture was in low estate. However, by the time Bakewell's brilliant experiments were bringing results, the *Journal* was forced to concede that "the cattle of England at the present time are far superior to our own." In this connection a spirited controversy arose between Colonel Pickering and Colonel John Hare Powell, both of whom once operated Pennsylvania farms and specialized in animal husbandry.

Powell was so convinced of the superiority of English cattle that he and several of his friends had imported many improved Shorthorns (Durhams) and other foreign breeds. These gentlemen stoutly maintained that native cattle could be bred to superior quality more quickly by crossing them with these blooded strangers than by selecting only the best of the native breeds and improving on them. Colonel Pickering differed. He told the editor of the *New England Farmer* that if only two or three farmers in every township in Massachusetts would give zealous attention to the business, the object would be realized within only a few years; "whereas," concluded the Colonel, "half a century or more might elapse before a general improvement by foreign crosses would be effected."[6]

As in England, leadership in the improvement of cattle came from a few wealthy men interested in progressive farming. Most of them seemed inclined to agree with Powell rather than with Pickering, preferring to import English stock rather than try to better the "native" animals by selective breeding. Among Virginia planters, there was George Washington, for example, who in the 1780's encouraged Richard Parkinson to bring over blooded cows, calves, and bulls; General Gough, who imported Teeswater stock; a Mr. Lloyd, who bought a bull and two cows from Bakewell; a Mr. O'Donnell, who paid 1,000 pounds sterling for

[6] *Ibid.*, 252.

279

a bull and two cows; Colonel Archibald Cary, who introduced stock of the old Shorthorn-Durham breed; and notably Matthew Patton, Sr., who in the last decade of the century imported an English bull which, when crossed with native cows, produced greatly improved strains. The operations of a Mr. Miller, who bought some of the Patton stock, a number of short-horned Maryland cattle, and several imported English bulls also contributed to the "better beef" crusade.[7]

In Maryland, Virginia, and Kentucky the long-horned "Patton stock" were the reigning favorites until the famous "importation of 1817," when Lewis Sanders of Kentucky brought over four short-horned bulls, four short-horned cows, two long-horned bulls, and two long-horned cows. From these sprang the notable American Shorthorns, or Durhams. Although Henry Clay imported some Herefords into Kentucky in this same year, and he and others experimented with them extensively, by mid-century Shorthorns were the popular preference. As for Virginia cattle, Hugh Jones claimed that the beef and veal were "small, sweet, and fat enough." And Washington wrote Sir John Sinclair that in northern Virginia "good pastures and proper attention can, and does, fill our markets with beef of seven, eight & more hundredweight the four quarters; whereas from 450 to 500 (especially in the states South of this . . .) may be found about the average weight."[8]

The obvious improvement of American herds by animals brought to this country by the landed gentry continued for forty years before there was any general cattle betterment by judicious crossing of selected native strains. Meanwhile sizable consignments of important English beef breeds—including North Devons, Herefords, and especially the Improved Durhams or Shorthorns—had reached our shores and were being kept with great care and frequently exhibited at annual cattle shows by their

[7] Gray, *History of Agriculture in the Southern United States to 1860*, II, 848ff.

[8] *Ibid.*, I, 204.

wealthy owners. Auction sales were social events in New York, Philadelphia, and elsewhere, at which distinguished persons bid against each other to pay fancy prices for pedigreed animals.

There was occasional group buying. An association of Ohio breeders and feeders, the "Ohio Company for Importing English Cattle," sent cattleman Felix Renick to England in 1833 to buy blue-blooded cows and bulls. He returned with some twenty head of the Shorthorn breed. Additional purchases during the next two years brought the company's total importations to sixty-one head. Their object accomplished, their holdings were disposed of in 1837 at public auction. Two bulls sold for $2,500 each and the cow Teeswater and her calf brought $2,225.

Up to about 1840, improved cattle were largely owned by prosperous, well-to-do farmers. By that time, however, there was growing a rapid and nation-wide desire for fat stock among all classes of agriculturists. Selective breeding and better feed, shelter, and care produced such a stuffing of steers as to glut the public markets of the North, South, and Middle West with champion beeves of sufficient stature to blaze for America an ever broadening path to the prime rib.

CHAPTER 24

"As an Ox Goeth to the Slaughter"

ALTHOUGH the Psalmist penned the words in connection with a vastly different situation, their impact has hurdled the centuries, eventually landing on all four hoofs in the shambles and the show rings of England and America.

Back in the fourteenth century the average weight of four- and five-year bullocks at London's Smithfield Market was a mere 500 or 600 pounds. By 1808 the best ox was a six-year-old, weighing around 1,700. Throughout the 1830's the champions averaged a bit over four years, with weights approximating 2,200 pounds. By the 1860's the British had reduced the age of their entries to an average of two years and ten months, albeit from the modern point of view the weights were excessive. With some exceptions, these ages prevailed in the British Isles until quite recently.

In the United States, the preference for big cattle continued from the beginning up to the last quarter of the nineteenth century. In the public markets of Boston, New York, Philadelphia, and later in Chicago, butchers bragged about the bigness and the fatness of their beeves. At the Bear Market in New York, as early as 1794, Samuel Winship advertised for sale "the finest beef now in the City," and at the same time Washington Market featured a bullock which, in carved meat, weighed 1,100 pounds.[1] For the next thirty years news of much tallow continued to glut the columns of the newspapers.

In March of 1810, New York readers were reminded that

[1] This and other incidents having to do with the New York markets can be found in *The Market Book,* by Thomas F. De Voe.

at the Oswego and Bear markets "the fattest beef" offered for sale that season was from "twins, a steer and a heifer, fed by Mr. Hezekiah Powell of Orange County, New York." And on an April morning in 1813, the *Daily Gazette* carried this paid advertisement:

EXTRAORDINARY
To All Lovers of Fat Beef
Joseph Blackwell takes the liberty of informing them that he
will have on Saturday, the 10th inst., beef of the most
superior quality ever offered for sale in
this country.

This bombastic prediction seems to have been realized. The next edition of the *Gazette* reported that the animal proved to be "the heaviest ever known before in New York City—the weight of his four quarters, in beef, near 1,900 pounds."

The following year the *Press* advertised a beef "of superior quality to any ever offered for sale in this city and it is believed that it never has been equalled in the U. S. . . . It is allowed by old, experienced butchers that this steer will weigh 1,800 and have more fat than any beast has ever produced in the U. S. . . . N. B. This is the ox that was exhibited through the streets on the 27th inst."

Five years later, down in Baltimore, an animal was slaughtered which might appropriately have been labeled "the ox that made Manhattan jealous." It was a monster—weighing alive 2,962, and after slaughter yielding 2,090 pounds of "neat beef," besides 783½ of "offal," which included 218 pounds of "rough tallow."[2] In March of 1821, among the sixty-four fat cattle exhibited at the New York County Agricultural Show, twenty first premium winners were taken to the Fly Market and thirty-two second prize winners to Washington Market. The *Press* boasted that "Philadelphia cannot furnish at this season 64 head of fat cattle superior to those now offered at our fair."

[2] Goodrich, *A New Family Encyclopedia: Neat Cattle*, 245–46.

Often there was great fanfare in the papers about "the carrying of beef to market." Once sixty carts, accompanied by music and flags and streamers, conveyed through the streets "32 head of cattle fatted by Philip Fink of the Washington Market." These cattle averaged 188½ pounds of rough fat each. To conclude the performance, a note of thanks was read from Debtors' Prison for the gift of "excellent steaks from P. Fink, Esq.," adding, "He that giveth to the poor lendeth to the Lord."

One February day in 1829 there was great excitement among New York's butchers, or "fleshers," as they were often called. It was the day on which they had all agreed to withdraw from business provided someone would purchase the celebrated ox "President" and have his beef sold in the market. George Clinch and William P. Varian bought him. Although his estimated live weight was above 4,000 pounds, the dressed weight was less than 1,900. A quantity of this prime beef was sold at $1.00 a pound. An exceptionally fine cut was sent to President Jackson with a note from the butchers of Centre Market claiming this ox to be "the fattest ever raised in this country." To which Old Hickory replied, "I have received the piece of beef . . . which you have been pleased to present as a token of respect for my character. I accept it with pleasure and promise tomorrow to give it a place on my table, as not an inappropriate emblem of the hospitality and solid prosperity of your citizens."[3]

One of the most enterprising of the contemporary New York establishments was Centre Market. Besides managing the purchase and sale of the ox "President," it later exhibited what was purported to be "the largest and heaviest bullock ever produced in the United States, perhaps in the world." William Lalor bought this animal from E. Haxton of Dutchess County. It was named "Union" and boasted a weight at home of 3,452, and the day before killing, 3,419 pounds. Its quarters were hung for ten days in the slaughter-house—far too long, compared with the customary two to four days—and so lost probably fifty

[3] De Voe, *The Market Book,* 468.

pounds in weight. Even so, after the ten days the four quarters tipped the scales at 2,319 pounds.

Those were the days when men were proud of their jobs, with none more eager to advertise their craftsmanship than the butchers. When the United States Constitution was adopted in 1789, New York held a great "Federal Procession," in which, mounted on spirited horses, rode one hundred representatives of the "Art and Mystery of Butchering."[4] Another, a colorful "butchers' " parade, was held on November 4, 1825, with even more participants. According to the newspapers, the marshals, riding four abreast, preceded two mounted trumpeters, followed by a float handsomely decorated with laurel, drawn by four horses, and portraying a farmer and his stock—a calf and several sheep. In front of the float marched two boys with a banner, decorated on one side with the emblem of the profession—a knife and steel crossed; above, the pole-ax; below, on one side the saw, on the other, the chopper; in the circle, an ox and a sheep. The inscription read, "We Preserve by Destroying." On the reverse was a pastoral scene, flocks and herds grazing, a plow, harrow, and other implements of husbandry, inscribed "Agriculture our Nation's Wealth."

Twenty boys followed, dressed in white frocks and carrying the traditional tools of the trade. A white standard, inscribed "The Butchers' Benevolent Society," preceded fifty of the profession in white aprons and check sleeves, all mounted on gray horses. Centered on the platform of a large vehicle drawn by six horses was a stall, at which a handsome white ox was feeding. The ends of the platform were enclosed by white palisades and were sodded, representing shrubbery and a field where sheep were grazing. Next came another palisaded platform displaying a full-sized ox decked out with ribbons and other furbelows, and attended by four boys in beribboned white frocks—the whole exhibit representing grazing, feeding, and preparing the animal

---

[4] Described in Charles W. Towne and Edward N. Wentworth, *Pigs: From Cave to Corn Belt*, 142–43.

for the knife. Finally, on lively black horses rode 150 white-aproned butchers, carrying at intervals four standards bearing appropriate legends. The first showed a heart above the words "Devoted to Our Country"; the second, an ox head inscribed "Liberty is Our Head"; the third, a steak, proclaiming "To All we Divide a Part"; and on the fourth were the words "Internal Improvements are Chains to Strengthen the Union of the States." The papers reported that the butchers got a great hand from the bystanders. No wonder! Those were the days of the five-cent lamb chop and the twenty-five-cent steak.

By the mid-1850's, many Eastern markets were being supplied with the fat cattle of Middle Western breeders and feeders. Among the most enterprising was an operator already mentioned, John D. Gillett of Illinois. Handling some 3,000 grade Shorthorns of his own raising, he turned out about 300 head a year, weighing from 1,800 to 2,400 pounds. By the 1870's he was marketing beeves at Chicago, Buffalo, Albany, Montreal, and New York. In 1872 he sent 83 head of three-year-olds to Albany, averaging 1,891 pounds each; the next year, 75 head of the same age, averaging over a ton, reached Buffalo, and 800 three-year-olds averaging 1,531 pounds were sent to markets in other cities. Gillett's methods of feeding his steers outdoors and growing them out on pasture, without shelter, produced hardy cattle on low investment and fattening costs.

In September, 1876, he made a bold move to capture some foreign business by shipping to England 100 head averaging 2,100 pounds apiece. During the next four years the London and Liverpool markets received—with mixed emotions—some 1,400 head of Gillett steers. In 1881, the 122 bullocks who crossed on the steamer *Thanemore* averaged in weight 1,936 pounds, in price $200 a head. Gillett figured that the proceeds of $24,400 were $5,000 more than he could have realized on the domestic market.

These moves caused a flurry in British livestock circles.

Already frightened by the competition of cheap refrigerated American beef, British raisers and drovers saw in these large, well-fattened bullocks the greatest threat to domestic agriculture since Polish wheat had taken over thirty years before. Health authorities placed import restrictions on this brash Yankee's cattle, claiming they were diseased. All animals from the United States had to be slaughtered within five days after arrival, and none could be removed to the interior.

But what upset the British most was America's low cost of production. They hurried experts to the United States, charged with the task of minutely examining the whole prairie and corn-belt set-up. One of these, James MacDonald, devoted single-handed attention to John Dean Gillett. Although critical of his tough, outdoor methods, he conceded that the Gillett operations were conducted on a large and efficient scale. He concluded his sapient verdict by reassuring his fellow-Britons that they had nothing to fear, either in chilled beef or live animals, on account of the generally inferior quality of the American beef and the high cost of ocean transportation.

Indifferent to British criticism, Gillett sent 180 Shorthorns across in 1883. Not only was this the pinnacle of his achievement, but it wrung from Sir Walter Gilbey's *Agricultural Gazette* the concession that they were in prime condition despite the long voyage, and were "most admirably finished, never to have tasted a turnip." They were particularly esteemed for their "wealth of meat, grandeur of scale, similarity of type, and extraordinary numbers."

But Gillett already foresaw the day—along with other Illinoisans, such as B. F. Harris, John T. Alexander, Lafayette Funk, and William Rankin, and Adams Earl and Moses Fowler of Indiana—when heavy three- and four-year-olds would be outmoded. Without abandoning his ideal of scale for his own personally bred steers, he shifted his goals to two-year-olds that would weigh around 1,700 pounds, stopped his shipments to

England, where discriminatory regulations wiped out profits, and in general bowed to the competition creeping toward him from the newer lands to the west.

By 1878, although big cattle were still the predominant favorites with the public, they were on their way out. Classes were offered at the Chicago show for steers over four years of age, but the farm editors worried because Gillett's champion had not turned four yet and weighed only 2,185 pounds. They seemed to fear he would prove "vealy." This class commonly brought out 2,200- to 3,000-pound steers. During the 1880's a great pre-Christmas event was the parade of these steers through the Loop area. In well-to-do Chicago homes prime Christmas beef was as traditional a dish as Thanksgiving turkey, and most folks thought that only from animals of this sort could a succulent, flavorful roast be obtained.

But the tide was turning. The leisure class—who had been the chief consumers of prize-winning beef—were finding that this was too rich a diet for their lessened activity. In addition, many a housewife felt, as had her English sister fifty years before, that this heavy-weight beef was "too dear to buy, too fat to eat." Thus it came about that the breeders began to concentrate on more compact types. The short-legged Angus, the newly imported Anxiety Herefords—critters described as "two ends and a middle"—and the Scotch Shorthorns were types which could mature for market and exhibit at ages under two years and weights between 1,000 and 1,200 pounds.

The country was getting ripe for the International Livestock Show—an institution with a primitive prototype dating back at least 1,600 years.

CHAPTER 25

"The Lowing Herd Winds Slowly"

ANCESTRAL TO THE great International Show at Chicago were the great mediaeval trade fairs of Europe.[1] These were originally religious festivals—mass pilgrimages of the faithful to famous shrines. As far back as the reign of the Emperor Constantine in the fourth century, Christians and Jews foregathered to perform their several rites at a tree in Palestine —reputedly the oak under which Abraham entertained the angels and received assurances of the fertility of his seed. Here the multitudes were so great they could not be supplied from the meager resources of the region.

Lacking any New Testament miracle of loaves and fishes, they were lucky to be serviced by opportunists who set up small shops stocked with food and clothing. Soon baggage-laden camels and ox-drawn carts began to arrive, bringing Asian and European merchandise. By the end of the sixth century the smells of the livestock and the shouts of hucksters had so polluted the odor of sanctity and drowned out the prayers of the sanctified that church authorities vigorously protested this profanation of the sacred shrines.

But priestly protest had little effect. As late as the eleventh century, fairs were being held every year on the fifteenth of September at Mount Calvary, outside Jerusalem.[2] This event was especially important in promoting commerce between Italy and the Near Orient. Those who question the persistence of zebu traits in Italian cattle, from the prehistoric Neolithic invasion

[1] The name "fair" apparently has a dual origin in the Latin words *forum*, or market place, and *feria*, or holiday. It came from Latin into English via the Norman-French word *foire*.

[2] Joseph François Michaud, *History of the Crusades*, I, 11.

to the founding of Rome, point out that eastern blood could have been reintroduced through the surplus cows transported by returning Italian mariners as a source of milk and meat.

During fairs all hostilities were suspended, since even when wars were actually being waged, these gatherings in the Eastern nations were always guarded by soldiers, and herds of cattle could be driven to market with reasonable security. The introduction of Eastern fairs into northern Europe and Great Britain is credited to Rome. At the earliest of these, cattle for slaughter or fattening were offered for sale. The stock distributed were usually suitable for breeding draft oxen or milch cows or, to a lesser extent, herd bulls.

When Theodoric, king of the Ostro-Goths, took over the fallen Roman Empire, there was a vigorous revival of fairs. To stimulate commerce with other countries, several were held in Italy by 493 A.D., where there were impressive sales of cows and work oxen. The great, royally sponsored gatherings at Aix-la-Chapelle and Troyes brought together traders all the way from the Mediterranean to the North and Baltic seas. The receipts from cattle sales at Aix-la-Chapelle usually exceeded those from the luxury goods. To the Flemish exhibitions at Bruges, Courtrai, Torhout, and Mont-Casel, cattle contributed indirectly from the traffic in hides and fine leather rather than through the sale of breeding or work animals.

Among the many mediaeval fairs, perhaps France did the most for the improvement and dissemination of cattle. Her greatest, founded in the early part of the fifth century, were in Champagne and Brie. From the fifth to the seventeenth centuries, French fairs were authorized by the department prefects. After that, cattle and food markets became permanent institutions which the prefects could neither abolish nor re-establish. They had become a national necessity.

Russia, too, contributed cattle to her famous fairs. Asiatics and western Europeans brought in processed and manufactured goods. Southern Russia enjoyed the bulk of the trade, with fairs at Berdichev, Elizabethgrad, Karkov, Orel, Poltava, Rostov, and a great six-week's annual exhibition at Nijni-Novgorod—this last probably the greatest in Europe in age and size. Russia's annual cattle and sheep traffic at all such markets probably totaled between one and two million dollars in the seventeenth and eighteenth centuries, bringing a few hard-earned rubles to the pockets of the local *mujiks*.

In a word, European commerce in cattle, from Palestine to Petrograd, for hundreds of years reverberated to the multi-lingual voices of drovers, in harsh contrast to the desultory droving of nineteenth century Yankees.

ANY PICTURE of "thund'ring hoofs of cattle," trail-choused by those "chaps-clad knights" of Texas, should be painted by a muralist wielding a whitewash brush. On the other hand, to portray a beef-cattle drive in New England a century ago, a lady miniaturist pin-pointing her pigments on ivory would suffice. If Edna Ferber's *Giant* epitomizes out-size Texas, perhaps the Deacon's "One Hoss Shay" of Holmes's poem might symbolize the old-time, one-man drover of pocket-size Massachusetts. Two thousand Longhorns on a thousand-mile, three months' drive from Mexican border to Kansas railhead; ninety-eight head in a mixed herd hoofing it one hundred miles from backwater Maine to bustling Boston—here are the contrasting raw materials for mural and miniature.

Ever since Revolutionary times, at historic Brighton just outside Boston there have been weekly cattle fairs. Hither have come cattle from inland Massachusetts, Maine, New Hampshire, and Vermont, driven by farmer-drovers, some of whose descendants are still operating at the same old stand, buying, selling, and bartering—like Adin Putnam, who breeds and drives cattle from the same Connecticut Valley farm in Vermont as did his grandsire a hundred years ago. Adin ships his stock by train and goes to market once a week. His grandfather took a month to drive his animals to Brighton, which he visited only once or twice a year.

Adin's story of his grandfather's leisurely progress from farm to market is worth retelling here:

"Granddad Putnam generally figured on two trips a year to Brighton market. He wanted a price, so he waited until some traveler brought word that mebbe meat was getting a little scarce. Then he'd set out one morning before sun-up with a dozen head of cattle and a couple of helpers. It was a great day, I'll tell you, when one of the boys got big enough to go along. If grandma was bothered—and she was—by that first trip, it wasn't because she was worried, but because it meant another boy growed up.

"The helpers walked up front and grandpa followed, riding or walking his horse—depending on which part of him needed a rest. Three men and a dozen animals and a boy didn't look too efficient, but grandpa always counted on picking up a load on the way. Mayhew, over to Bellows Falls, generally had another dozen, so did Bartlett at Keene, and Eaton, down to Fitchburg.

"They'd see grandpa coming and stop what they were doing in the fields and come down to the gate for a talk. First they'd exchange what news they had—who'd been born or died since the last trip, and who'd got married, and how, seemed like, there was more rain—or less—this year than anyone in these parts could remember. Then Mayhew'd say, 'Buying or selling?' and grandpa'd say, 'Both; trading, too.' And Mayhew would look at our stock and grandpa'd look at his. And Mayhew'd talk like he hadn't oughter sell and grandpa'd say prices down to Brighton was so low he hadn't oughter buy. Sometimes the talk would go on all afternoon and grandpa'd help drive his stock into Mayhew's pasture—and he'd give 'em supper and then they'd spend the night in the barn. There was never much hurry; grandpa liked to give the stock plenty of rest and feed, so they wouldn't be all skin and bone time they got to Brighton.

"Mayhew would mebbe come to the barn just when every-body was getting ready for bed to say if he did decide to sell what'd grandpa pay? 'Course they traded by the animal, not by the pound those days, and the bargaining kept up till they agreed on a price; and Mayhew would say goodnight—he hadn't oughter sell—and grandpa would say good night—he hadn't oughter buy.

"So by the middle of the trip down—that's after three weeks on the road—there'd be mebbe fifty or a hundred head of cattle, and all hands were kept busy keeping them to the road, keeping them moving, and keeping them from fighting. Eight to ten miles was a good day's traveling. And every second or third day they'd stop to graze. Half a day, or even a day, away from Brighton grandpa'd know if trading was going to be brisk. If it was, the buyers would meet him along the road. If nobody came, he was pretty disappointed; but you'd never know it, to look at him or hear him talk. He always acted like he didn't care whether he sold or not—and he always fetched as good a price as any.

"Grandpa would never hurry. He knew what he'd paid and he knew what he had to get, though he never mentioned it. No sir! He thought it was a sin, or bad luck, to set a price; that had to come natural—two people, one to buy, the other to sell, coming to agree on a price that had to be fair because it was based on how bad one wanted to buy—and how bad the other wanted to sell.

"Then a trade was made, and another, and another, and after a while grandpa had his leather pouch full of money, and nothing left but his horse. He'd sell that, too, if he got a good price. If it was before bank closing, he'd go over to the bank, shake out the silver dollars on the counter, and trust the bank to put the right amount on the books. And of course some of the silver dollars stayed right in his pocket, to buy a bolt of gingham for grandma, or shoes for aunt Ella; or to spend at the hotel, or in the square where there was a Punch and Judy show, and people—lots of them. Not what you'd call crowds today, but plenty for a boy from Chester, Vermont. It was a good life, I'm telling you—traveling, seeing people, talking, trading, and finally the excitement of the Cattle Fair, the Hotel, the puppet show, and the crowds."[3]

When interviewed in 1952, eighty-five-year-old Frank Wentworth of Norwich, Vermont, described the drives his great-uncles John and Daniel Ames,[4] used to make from Parsonsfield, Maine, close to the New Hampshire line, to Brighton Market, shortly after the Civil War. He reports:

"The first drive of the season was usually started soon after haying; the second, between Thanksgiving and Christmas, before there was a real hard freeze. The Ames brothers would start with some forty head, including their own and others picked up on near-by farms. For example, Aunt Maria Ames's husband, John Towne, would consign sixteen to eighteen head, and three families named Doe would offer four to eight, and up to twenty head, selling direct. By further trading along the way, the Ameses might have a herd of two hundred or more by the time they were halfway to Boston. Their route lay from Parsonsfield, Maine, west past Province Pond, well across the line to New Hampshire, thence through the Wakefields, Union, Milton, Rochester, Gonic, Dover, and Exeter, into Haverhill, Massachusetts, with one more stop before reaching Brighton.

"The first halt was made between Union and Milton, a seventeen mile drive. Brighton was 110 miles from Parsonsfield, and was usually made in seven or eight days. Nearly all drovers' night stops were on the farms of relatives and friends, or occasionally at fields where the farmers made a business of serving the passing herds. The cattle would fill up at night and were hardly finished eating when they were started at daylight the

---

[3] *Livestock and Meat,* film script for Swift and Company, 1945, courtesy of F. M. Simpson.

[4] Most of the people mentioned by Frank Wentworth were relatives or connections by marriage. The Ames, Page, Towne, and Wentworth families included antecedents, near or remote, of the authors of this book. These drives to Brighton twice a year became family visits as well as business excursions.

next morning. Speed depended on how much trading was done along the way. Uncle John liked to trade young steers for old— straight, with no cash difference. For example, he would replace a yoke of older work steers with younger ones, these to be worked for another season or two, when he would return, again exchanging a younger pair for the older. This was fair for both parties. The farmer got young, strong stock for work oxen, the traders the larger, more mature, firmer fleshed cattle for beef.

"The Ames caravan would try to reach each day's destination by afternoon, so local butchers could buy what they wanted and farmers could sell or exchange their older steers. Uncle John also traded in cows, heifers, and calves, one of his best customers being Daniel Cotton of Cotton Valley at Wolfeboro who needed calves to keep his big stock of wet cows milked. It seems there was no market for fluid milk as almost everybody kept a family cow or two. Cotton would sell the Ameses steer calves for fattening or for work oxen.

"When Uncle John reached Dover, he would turn his cattle —ably assisted by his little black-and-white, well-trained shepherd-type dog—into George Page's field and spend the night with his nephew, John Norris Wentworth, on Dover's Broadway, near the foot of historic Garrison Hill. Page, who was a relative by marriage, fed a lot of calves and traded in wet cows. In those days drovers figured that by pasturing their cattle for one night in a farmer's field, their livestock made up by manure any loss of feed or damage to meadow. In spite of this, they usually had to pay up to fifty cents per head for such 'overnight parking.'

"Most of the cattle driven were Durhams, the milking type of Shorthorn—dark red, red and white, or roan, with an infrequent white individual. There were also some Devons and various mixed types. Mature, hard-fleshed oxen would weigh 2,800 to 3,200 pounds per pair, mature cows from 1,500 up. Such cattle had no difficulty in walking the distance, especially the work oxen. The Ames brothers were skilled swappers, and before they reached Brighton they would have gotten rid of all the soft cattle and reduced their stock to a smaller and more marketable herd. Once when at the last stop Uncle John had sold all but two head, he recklessly swore he'd rather lose money than put only two animals over the one day's drive to Brighton. But Yankee caution prevailed and he went on to sell the pair at a profit.

"When Uncle John Ames stopped off at Norris Wentworth's in Dover on his return trip, my Aunt Ettie May would often come down on the train from Parsonsfield and ride back with drover John, his horse, buggy, and dog. The two boys who regularly helped him would be sent back on the train. John and Daniel Ames were shrewd buyers, close traders, and both left substantial estates."[5]

The Putnams and the Ameses having made their records, it remains for that observant reporter and eminent novelist Nathaniel Hawthorne to give us a pen picture of Brighton Cattle Market in 1840:

"Thursday of every week, which by common consent and custom is the market day, changes the generally quiet village of Brighton into a scene of bustle and excitement. At early morning the cattle, sheep, etc., are hurried in and soon the morning train from Boston, omnibuses, carriages, and other 'vehicular mediums' bring in a throng of drovers, buyers, speculators, and spectators; so that, by 10 o'clock, there are generally gathered as many as two or three hundred vehicles in the area fronting the Cattle Fair Hotel. The proprietors thereof throng the spacious bar-room for the purpose of warming themselves in winter, and in summer 'cooling off'—the process for effecting both results being precisely the same. The portico of the hotel is occupied by hawkers and peddlers, who sell clothing, jewelry, soap, watches, knives, razors, etc. (to say nothing of their customers), at astonishingly low rates. An 'English hunting lever eighteen carots fine' is frequently sold for five or six dollars and,

[5] Interviewed by Edward N. Wentworth at Chesterton, Indiana, August 19, 1952.

296

of course, is a genuine article. In the region round about, 'Mammoth Steer,' 'Living Skeletons,' 'Snakes,' etc., are on exhibition at reasonable prices.

"One of the outside features of the market is the horse auction. A Brighton horse has become a proverb. Here are gathered all the old, worn-out, broken-down, and used-up omnibus, cart, and livery stable steeds, and these are knocked down (if they don't tumble down) at sums varying from five to forty dollars. These sales are productive of a deal of merriment, and the mettle, speed, and fine points of the animal are exhibited (the 'points' perhaps being sufficiently prominent already).

"All this time the butchers and drovers are busily engaged in their traffic. The fattest and best of the cattle in the pens find ready sale, and long before all the drovers are in, select lots begin to be driven from the grounds. Men and boys hurry up and down the lanes and through the pens, each armed with a stock which is sort of a shillelah, shouting to the half-crazed cattle, and with screams and blows directing them where they should go. Occasionally a drove of cows and calves come along, the latter muzzled, and the former looing and bellowing in chorus to the shouts of their drivers. Farmers from the neighboring towns are selecting 'stores'[6] from the large number of that class in the pens, and dairymen carefully examining the 'milky-mothers' that are so anxiously seeking their young from the midst of their companions. Working oxen are driven in by farmers from the vicinity, who sell, only after much banter, to buy again when prices are low. In the midst of these, dogs and goats and mules are offered for sale, and near by are the hog pens, containing, at this season, only stores, which are sold singly and in pairs to small farmers, mechanics and others who think they can afford to 'keep a pig.'

"The forenoon is busy enough. At high noon the huge bell

---

[6] "Stores" are animals taken to the farm or feedlot for fattening. The use of the word in this connection is obsolete in the United States, where such animals are called "feeders," but is still used in the British Isles.

of the hotel announces dinner, and for a brief period there is a breathing spell for man and beast. After dinner, business again resumes its sway. The voice of the hawker becomes hoarse, but it is by no means silenced. Drovers who have not made many sales get nervous, and pens are cleared out without much regard to profit on the part of the seller. The butchers begin to turn their faces homewards, and the drovers, generally with well-filled wallets, start for Boston. A few, not liking the prices, and hoping for 'better times' make arrangements to turn out their cattle to pasture, and hold over to another week. By five o'clock the business of the day is over, and Brighton subsides once more into a quiet, matter-of-fact Massachusetts village, till another Thursday brings round another market day."[7]

Statistically, Brighton Cattle Market—by far the largest in New England—sold annually two million dollars' worth of cattle, hogs, and sheep, according to the 1844 report of the United States Patent Office. And Henry Colman, in the 1841 *Report of Agriculture in Massachusetts,* totaled the various kinds of animals sold each year at Brighton in the ten years 1831 to 1840 as follows: beef cattle, 36,600; stores, 12,900; sheep, 97,793; swine, 22,700. He further commented: "The cattle principally consist of young stock for wintering, working oxen, milch cows with their calves, and fat cattle for barrelling and for the retail market in the city and vicinity. . . . The butchers who come from a distance in order to get supplies for the small and remote villages and towns, of course drive their cattle to their respective homes to be slaughtered; and large numbers go from hence to Lowell, New Bedford, Fall River, Providence, R. I., and other considerable towns. The number of head of cattle, of all descriptions, brought here frequently exceeds eight thousand on a market-day. . . . They are often sold on the hoof—which is, on many accounts, a preferable mode for both parties, as it leaves no room for fraud or suspicion of fraud in regard to their

[7] Nathaniel Hawthorne, *American Note Books (Collected Works,* 11th ed., 1887), IX, 248.

weight." The cost of droving neat cattle to Brighton from points one hundred miles away was two dollars per head, plus the loss of about one hundred pounds in weight.[8]

Droving developed along the Atlantic because the population in the coast-line settlements grew faster than that in the near-by pastures. The desire to escape tribute to European manufacturers led to urban expansion to the degree that appetite overran acreage. The droving adventures of the Putnams and the Ames brothers were repeated in dozens of families clustered in the Hudson hinterlands of New York, among the Quaker and German farmsteads radiating from Philadelphia, far up the watercourses converging around Baltimore, and over the mountain passes and down the green valleys of Virginia, the Carolinas, and Georgia.

[8] Percy Wells Bidwell and John I. Falconer, *History of Agriculture in the Northern United States, 1620–1860*, 225n.

CHAPTER 26

That "Oiled and Curled Assyrian Bull"

A T THE CLOSE OF THE LAST CENTURY, nation-wide interest in purebred meat animals had reached such a pitch that breeders and exhibitors were eagerly demanding an exhibition or fair where judges of competence and integrity could award to steers, bulls, and cows grand championships of national and international significance.

In the fall of 1899 at the great Canadian livestock and agricultural show in Toronto, four well-known authorities from the United States—Robert B. Ogilvie, G. Howard Davison, Mortimer Levering, and William E. Skinner—conceived the idea of starting an even greater show in Chicago. They wanted something that would outstrip the specialized fat stock shows, which since 1878 had been held in the old Exposition Building at the corner of Michigan and Adams, present site of the Chicago Art Institute. They convinced Arthur G. Leonard, then general manager of the Union Stock Yards and Transit Company, of the worth of their idea, and under his forceful direction the project was brought to fruition. Here at the Yards the first International Livestock Exposition opened on the Saturday following Thanksgiving Day in 1900.

Several reasons determined the choice of this date. First, state and regional fairs were all over and their champions chosen. By bringing them together, a national, or even international, winner could be named. Second, the beef from the cattle slaughtered at the show would have time to ripen and develop the aged flavor traditional for a holiday roast. At that particular date, also, there would be no other great source of Christmas beef anywhere else in the United States, hence markets all over the nation could be made available in developing a strong supporting demand for the show. Happily, down to this day, unfailing support has been forthcoming from hotels, restaurants, dining car services, and exclusive retail shops.

Hollywood make-up artists have nothing on the specialist who prepares a prize bovine for the International. Ten months before the show opens, huge rations of barley, corn, and oats are shoveled into the pampered animal. With the coming of summer heat, he is confined to a cool, dark stall in the daytime and let out at night, in order to keep the hair from bleaching and coarsening. By July or August it is washed twice a month with castile soap, carefully rinsed, and brushed so as to avoid excessive dandruff. Just before show time, the hair is curled and the tail brush "waved." At the last minute before entering the ring, the critter is sprayed with a mixture of mineral oil and denatured alcohol to give his coat luster and bloom. At long last, oiled and curled, Tennyson's "Assyrian bull" is dressed "fit to kill."

Pedigreed beef animals are the machine tools of the cattle industry. Although they number only about 3 per cent of the cattle population of the United States, they furnish the seed stock, the basis for improvement in the remaining 97 per cent. The biggest buyers are the ranchers, who require purebred bulls to improve their calf crops. Although the mothers, being run-of-the-mill cows, do not beget prize youngsters, their calves are superior in gaining weight and producing better beef. There is a smaller market among breeders of pedigreed stock. Buying from one another to improve their own lines, they pay phenomenal prices—$100,000 for a single bull not being unusual. Total annual sales of blue-blooded animals at the big livestock shows are in excess of three hundred million dollars.[1]

The small breeder aspiring to national honors usually starts at his local county or state fair. If successful, he moves on to any one of the six top expositions: the American Royal at Kansas

[1] John S. Cooper, "Bull Market," *Wall Street Journal,* December 4, 1951.

City; the Eastern National at Timonium, Maryland; the Grand National at San Francisco; the National Western at Denver; the Southwestern at Fort Worth; and the International at Chicago, the "world series" of competing bovine royalty. Here grand championships have always been won by representatives of one of these three breeds: Aberdeen Angus, Hereford, or Shorthorn.

The grand champion steer at the first International was an Aberdeen Angus known as a "senior yearling," or an animal that had just reached two years old. He weighed 1,430 pounds. The champion carcass came from a grade Shorthorn that weighed 1,495 pounds alive. The carlot grand championship went to Aberdeen Angus steers averaging 1,492. In 1906 the show awarded its first calf championship to a 970-pound Hereford. The next year it was a 1,080-pound Shorthorn. From 1916 on, in the adult classes few very heavy steers have succeeded in winning championships. Most of them have weighed between 1,000 and 1,150 pounds. In developing lighter cattle, the carloads have led the way. In 1910 the grand champion load weighed 1,156, and only once since then has this weight been exceeded.

Two classes of fat cattle have been recognized at most shows. One was fed under outdoor commercial conditions, usually on such rough feeds as grass, hay, roots, silage, and the like. The other was hand- or stall-fed under cover on grain and protein concentrates. The first cost the grower less in financial investment, but the second made tenderer, tastier beef. At the International the carlot exhibits in the Yards represent the outdoor, rougher treatment, and the single steers, housed in the Auditorium, the sheltered, individual-care methods.

To an outsider, contests of this kind may seem to be only a competition between exhibitors to determine which breed has the best beef type or the best qualities for beef production. Actually it is something more. In awarding championships in the three great classes—single steers, carcasses, and carlots—the International sets the standard and leads the way for type, quality, and weight in market toppers for years to come. For it is axiomatic that the steer which puts on weight the fastest is almost always the one with a pure-blooded sire, the actual difference sometimes amounting to a pound a day.

The three major beef-cattle breeds are promoted and serviced by associations run with the efficiency of a great department store or nation-wide mail-order house.

Starting the alphabetical order is the Angus, a coal-black breed, originated in the highlands of Scotland with distinguished progenitors. On the female side there was Old Grannie, who dropped twenty-nine calves during her thirty-five-year career, also Black Meg and Kinochtry Princess. Around 1880 the first purebred bulls began to arrive in this country, notably Field Marshall, Nicolas 1102, and Basuto 1101 of Blackbird of Corskie.

Angus cattle were first backed by a group of Chicago businessmen. Today pure-blood breeders number more than 20,000, most of them in the Midwest, and calf registrations in the association's herdbook at $2.00 a head total more than 140,000 a year. Life memberships cost $20.00. Between three thousand and four thousand new breeders get into the business annually. Average price for a purebred Angus has mounted from $611 in 1950 to around $900 today.[2] Notable purchases of famous sires include those of Dr. Armand Hammer of Red Bank, New Jersey, who paid $100,000 for Prince Eric of Sunbeam; of W. G. Mennen, of shaving soap fame, who operates Hide-A-Way farm at Chester, New Jersey; and a sale at Pleasant Plains, Illinois, where breeders paid an average of over $10,000 each for fifty head to improve their own herds by introducing some of the famous Eileenmere strain.

Three-fourths of all registered beef cattle are Herefords. Of all the pure-blooded animals in the United States—including milk cows, sheep, horses, hogs, and goats—Herefords number 25 per cent of the total. Calf registrations are at the rate of

[2] *Ibid.*

303

more than 500,000 a year, and the average auction price per animal has jumped from $200 to about $900. At the association's big Kansas City building, several hundred girls and batteries of IBM machines process two thousand registration cards a day. Each entry admits to the socially elite a white-faced calf whose genealogy can be traced back at least three generations to an impeccable blood line, which began in the early nineteenth century with such names as Sir David, Sir Richard, Lord Wilton, and Anxiety.

At each of the two recent Hereford sales more than one million dollars worth of beef animals changed hands. One bull, M. W. Domino the 107th, lured $80,000 from the pocket of J. S. Bridwell of Wichita Falls, Texas, for a one-half interest, the other half going to the Milky Way Hereford Ranch of Phoenix, Arizona.

More than sixty-five volumes now comprise the sixty-nine-year-old association's herdbook, and the annual herd bull edition of the *Hereford Journal*, totaling more than 900 pages, is as fat as a Sears-Roebuck catalog. Among its various sources of income are calf registrations at $1.00, life memberships at $50.00 for member breeders, and the sale of record books, ear tattoos, branding irons, and other business gear. It offers $150,000 in prizes at annual fairs and keeps twelve field men on the road popularizing the breed.

The red, white, or roan-colored animals known as Shorthorns (originally Durhams) are the oldest breed in the United States. Its association staff registers about 60,000 purebreds a year. Average prices paid for this type are around $600 a head, up from $113 in 1950.

In Houston, Texas, the American Brahman Breeders Association registers more than 17,000 of this breed annually, compared with 2,500 a year in 1939. Especially valued for their immunity from tick fever, they are much esteemed by ranchers of Texas and the Southwest.

Winners of championships at the great expositions derive

their chief satisfaction from the advertising value. Monetary rewards are insignificant. At the International, the championship in each breed brings only $50 to $100. If a show animal were to make a clean sweep of its class, the most it could win would be $1,200 or $1,400—perhaps not enough to pay the cost of handlers and transportation.

The big reward comes when the owner of an International grand champion steer puts up his entry for auction. This is the high point of the show. Some of the recent winners are listed here. In 1950, a young Texan named Lloyd Robinson, whose 1,025-pound Hereford, "Big Spring Special," brought him $12,-300, or $12 a pound. The purchaser was Albert Pick of the Pick Hotel chain. In 1951 the winner was Iowa State College, whose 1,200-pound black Angus, "Toby," went to Triangle Packing Company of Chicago, the high bidder at $6.75 a pound. Ohio State University won the 1952 grand championship with its 1,100-pound roan Shorthorn, "Ohio's Leader 2nd," which Miller's Steak House, Chicago, bought at $4.55 a pound.[3]

The highest price ever paid for a grand champion sold at auction was in October, 1946, at the American Royal in Kansas City, when a 1,200-pound T O steer brought $35.50 a pound, and put $42,600 in the pocket of young Jack Hoffman of Ida Grove, Iowa.

It is noteworthy that champions owned by individuals, especially youngsters, rather than institutions always bring the top prices. Bidders value the added publicity when the purple-ribbon winners has been conditioned for the show by a young 4-H Club or Future Farmers of America member. This was strikingly apparent at the 1953 show when an eighteen-year-old Texas girl walked away with the grand championship and more money in her poke than had ever been paid for an International fat steer.

As reported by the *Chicago Daily Drovers Journal* of December 2, 1953: "Fully 10,000 pairs of eyes were glued to the amphitheatre as Judge Weber went through the routine that

[3] *Ibid.*

led to the selection of the top winners. . . . Everything was quiet and tense as he carefully inspected each of the four steers in the final lineup. But the spell broke and a roar went up from the crowd when he motioned the TO-bred Hereford senior calf Lone Star shown by Sue White of Big Spring, Texas, to the coveted grand championship spot." On the following morning at the auction, "the grand champion steer brought $20.00 per pound to set a new, all-time high price for this show." The purchaser was the Congress Hotel of Chicago, whose check for $20,100 was handed to the Texas girl while she was "giving free flow to her tears of joy."

On the advice of her county agent, Sue had rationed her steer on cracked corn, crimped oats, prairie hay, and cottonseed pellets. The agent and several members of the 4-H Club were on hand to root for Sue, among them being Lloyd Robinson of Big Spring, the 1950 winner. With another two years of 4-H eligibility remaining, Sue thinks she may feed cattle again, as the returns help finance her education. She is a business administration major in junior college. A farmer's daughter, she says she wouldn't mind owning a cattle ranch of her own some day, but that is far in the future. Just now getting an education is her major project.

The next highest honor, the reserve championship, for 1953 also went to an eighteen-year-old, Carlyle Greathouse of Hindsboro, Illinois, for his Angus summer yearling, "Little Stuff." He is using returns from his 4-H projects to found a breeding herd.

The International and other big shows are of great help to these youngsters in getting started in cattle business. Members of the 4-H Club and Future Farmers of America are particularly active in this field, and many promising youngsters are given calves to fatten by adult breeders who are not unmindful of the favorable publicity which follows the winning of a championship.

CHAPTER 27

All Beasts Come to the Pole-ax at Last

OR YEARS, great herds of cattle and hogs were choused over transmontane trails by professional drovers. Then came the railroads, which did the job quicker and handier, and centralized markets, providing facilities for penning livestock awaiting sale. Cincinnati, St. Louis, and Chicago had all the essentials—stockyards, commission men, packers.

Incidentally, probably no large American industry other than meat processing suffers from as comparable a misnomer as "packer." Before refrigeration, cattle and hogs were slaughtered and the carcasses cut up to be cured and packed in barrels for storage or shipment. Nowadays "packing" has all but ceased. To pin the word "packer" on Armour, Swift, or Wilson is about as appropriate as equipping an automobile with a whip-socket. Fruit and vegetable canners are the real packers of today, although as more and more processed and frozen meat products appear on the market, "packing" seems to be regaining some of its lost ground.

It was Massachusetts that gave to the industry two historic figures—one the first, the other one of the most famous, of the nation's long line of meat packers. One was the product of the seventeenth, the other of the nineteenth century.

In 1636, to better the condition of their livestock and themselves, William Pynchon and family left Roxbury, near Boston, and, like Abraham with his flocks and herds, hit the wilderness trail for greener pastures farther west. On the banks of the Connecticut, Pynchon and his son John located a settlement that later burgeoned into the city of Springfield. By driving stall-fattened cattle from here to Boston markets in 1655, Pynchon established himself as America's first drover. And when seven years later father and son began a twenty-year career of slaughtering and barreling beef and pork, they won a second honor—that of the nation's first meat packer.

In the mid-nineteenth century, down on Cape Cod a tall, lanky youth named Gustavus Franklin Swift borrowed $400 from an uncle, hustled off to Brighton Market, and ten days later returned with thirty-five head of hogs. In one hand were a rope and steelyards; in the other was a pole. On this, supported by his own and a customer's shoulder, "Stave" could hang the steelyard and a pig. A democrat wagon hauled by an old horse held a few lame or travel-weary shoats with their legs tied together. This was the lad and the outfit which founded Swift and Company, now one of the world's largest meat processors.

In Pynchon's day most of the New England farmers killed their own stock for local use. "Killing time" came somewhere between Thanksgiving and Christmas. It was then that the barn floor was cleared, tackle fastened to stout, overhead beams, and the bullock hoisted and dressed. About this time the Puritan revolt against Charles I in England ruined the British trade with the West Indies. This gave the colonists a chance to enter a profitable business. Their success was noted in the quaint language of Governor Winthrop of Massachusetts: "Now the country doth send great store of biscott, flour, peas, beef, pork, butter and other provisions to the supply of Barbadoes, Newfoundland and other places."

With the Dutch, who settled New Amsterdam in 1626, cattle pens and slaughter houses were as common on lower Manhattan Island as windmills in Holland. Abattoirs spanned the ditch on the north side of the palisade that later became Wall Street. Odoriferous effluvia flowed downstream to the Water Gate into the East River. Butchers were subject to strict regulations. Cattle, hogs, goats, or sheep could not be slaughtered even by the owner himself until he had given notice to the local magistrate and received an official permit. For this permit the "slaughter farmer" had to pay a fee in proportion to the value of the "critter" being killed.

Besides these "farmers," sworn butchers were licensed and required to serve in butchering and cutting up, "and to provide, have, and possess their own ropes, hand barrows, troughs, and other articles requisite for slaughtering," with fees fixed by law. Up to 1676, cattle were slaughtered below Wall Street and on the Brooklyn shore. But in that year a public abattoir was built on the east side of Pearl Street between Pine and Wall. After 1749 no cattle could be killed outside this public slaughter house.[1] In 1684, 400 beeves were required to feed the inhabitants; ten years later nearly 4,000 were necessary, besides 1,000 sheep and swine.

Philadelphia began to pack meats before 1729. And in that year the Pennsylvania Legislature passed laws aimed at preventing unfair practices, prescribing the size and material of casks, requiring that they be labeled with the marks of the coopers who made them, and ordering inspection of the contents before they were shipped or offered for sale.

The first Western packer was Elisha Mills, a Yankee who began business in Cincinnati in 1818. From then until 1860 the vast volume of meat processing earned for this city the name of "Porkopolis." Until the Civil War, it was the nation's largest center for the butchering of kine and swine. Meanwhile, packing houses were busily functioning in such Eastern cities as Boston, Providence, New Haven, New York, Philadelphia, Baltimore, and Pittsburgh; and at St. Louis, Missouri, and Alton, Illinois, in the West. Eventually all bowed to the domination of the lusty young metropolis on the southern shore of Lake Michigan.

When Carl Sandburg's "Hog Butcher for the World" was young, it was known as "Eschikagou." That is the way Colonel De Peyster, British commander at Michilimackinac, spelled the name in his letter of July 4, 1779, in referring to this "river and

---

[1] R. F. Clemen, *American Livestock and Meat Industry*, 29.

fort at the head of Lake Michigan." The Colonel also noted that the "first landed proprietor" was one Baptiste Point de Saible, "a handsome negro, well educated and settled . . . but much in the French interest." Fifteen years later a fellow French-man described him as "a large man . . . a trader, pretty wealthy, and drank freely."[2]

By the time the Indian spelling had been simplified to "Chi-cago," the tiny settlement was ready for its first shambles. The earliest slaughter house was built of logs in 1827. It was located on the north bank of the Chicago River by Archibald Clybourne, government butcher for the Indians and the soldiers at Fort Dearborn. For Eastern customers, Clybourne packed beef in the late fall and shipped it out by water before the lake froze.

The first frame building devoted to butchering was erected by George W. Dole, located at what is now South Water and Dearborn streets, in 1832. In that year Mark and John Noble slaughtered 152 animals "out on the prairies"—now Madison and Michigan avenues—and Dole packed the beef for shipment to Oliver Newberry at Detroit. "These cattle were purchased from Charles Reed of Hickory Creek for $2.75 per 100 lbs.— the hides and tallow being thrown in for the slaughtering."[3]

It was not long before the outside world became aware that the meat being doled out to soldiers, Indians, and settlers was good eating. Shipments began to the East, and later not only Boston but London was clamoring for beef packed in Chicago and paying high prices for it. Other early citizens who helped build the city's reputation for meat products included Gurdon S. Hubbard, Sylvester Marsh, R. M. and Oramel S. Hough, D. H. Underhill, Eri Reynolds, Oren Sherman, Nathaniel Pit-kin, Thomas Dyer, John P. Chapin, Julius Wadsworth, and George Steel.[4]

At first only mean tavern yards were available for the cattle

[2] A. T. Andreas, *History of Chicago*, I, 70.
[3] *Ibid.*, I, 122.
[4] Paul Gilbert and Lee Bryson, *Chicago and Its Makers* (not paged).

and hogs being delivered on the hoof or hauled in by the rail-roads. With the Civil War the streams of livestock multiplied so prodigiously as to force the formation of a centralized and unified market yard. In the summer of 1864 the Chicago Pork Packers' Association formally recommended the consolidation of the various small yards. The organization of the Union Stock Yards and Transit Company was followed by the purchase from Long John Wentworth of 320 acres of swamp at Halsted Street "in the town of Lake." Most of the money to finance the deal was subscribed by the railroads, and an act of the Illinois Legislature governing the enterprise was signed by Governor Oglesby on February 13, 1865. On December 26 the yards were opened for business.

Colonel Roselle M. Hough of Wooster, Hough and Company, packers, after superintending construction, appointed as general superintendent J. F. E. Bryant of the same firm. But livestock producers voiced such a protest at having as boss of the yards a "packer's man" that Bryant resigned. He was succeeded by John B. Sherman, a rugged character who, as manager of the old Bull's Head Yards, had promptly renamed them the Sherman Yards. On taking his new job, Sherman discharged a number of Hough's appointees and rechristened Hough House the Transit.

"Perhaps there have been more colorful hostelries than the old Transit House," wrote one historian. ". . . But you couldn't get a veteran of the yards to agree with you. . . . In color, if not in violence, it was Dodge City, Cheyenne, and Old Tascosa mixed with the flavor of the prairies and salted by the rich brogue of Emerald Avenue. The high-heeled boots of Texas, Montana, and Wyoming hooked on the brass rail of the . . . bar with the cowhide boots of the corn belt farmers and the stock-handlers of the yards. . . . The house featured a fifty-cent meal that really was a meal even in that period of husky appetites. If one steak wasn't enough the diner could have a second at no additional charge. . . . Another feature of the house was the staff of . . . redoubtable Irish waitresses, by both nature and experience equipped to cope effectively with the most obstreperous and woman-hungry cowhand from the wild and lonely hinterlands."[5]

Across from the lawn and the hitching rail for the buyers' and commission men's horses was Whiskey Row—where Halsted Street was either a sea of mud in wet weather or a cloud of dust in dry. Saloons ran the whole gamut from the decent dram shop to the dive in which a victim might take a drink and wake up in the alley with his pockets emptied. On the whole, however, law and order were fairly well enforced. Authorities rode herd on Whiskey Row, and the Transit House decreed "no women above stairs." The stock yard company saw to it that as far as it could control the situation, no visitor ever fell into the clutches of swindlers or strumpets.

Before refrigeration, packing activities in Chicago were strictly seasonal. The frosts of autumn and the thaws of spring determined just when "all beasts came to the pole-ax." When the prairie grass began to wither so that the steer could no longer feed on it, somewhere between October 15 and November 10, cattle slaughter began. At the same time frost also hastened the ripening of the corn that fed the hog, whose rendezvous with the butcher followed that of the steer.

Those were the days when the butcher was really a "packer," and the weather had a lot to do with his operations. A thaw or rain would throw him into panicky fear that the meat would spoil. When it was extremely cold, workers in the flimsy buildings couldn't keep warm enough to handle their jobs. Often the supply of animals was insufficient to keep the plants going, since stormy weather also ruined the roads and kept timid drovers at home. On the other hand, the packers often needed a large force of extra workmen in an emergency, such as an avalanche of drovers with livestock. Only a large city such as Chicago could provide this casual labor.

[5] Bertram B. Fowler, *Men, Meat, and Miracles,* 41–42.

Englishmen first welcomed American beef on a large scale in 1843, but were very particular. They would buy only fat cattle, with the whole carcass—except head, feet, and legs—cut into eight-pound pieces. The meat was first rubbed well with dry salt, then placed in vats containing pickle and enough saltpeter to give it color and proper consistency. In twenty-four hours, with the blood sufficiently purged out, the beef went into fresh pickle, and after a while into a third, where it stayed until packed for export. Thirty-eight pieces weighing 304 pounds went into huge tierces, to which the weight of the pickle and salt added several pounds more. After the barrel was packed and headed, two iron hoops were added to supplement those of wood. Through a hole bored in the head, four or five gallons of pickle were poured over the meat and the hole plugged. To the query, "On what meat do you feed?" the average Briton's reply of a century ago was "the barreled beef of Yankeeland."

Between the thirty-sixth and forty-third parallels and extending west to about the one hundredth meridian lies a zone that a hundred years ago was christened the "American beef belt." At that time it was found that cattle pastured there fattened in less time and mixed their lean and fat more evenly and fully than those fattened elsewhere. North of this area, intense cold caused unprofitable consumption of fodder in order to keep the animal heat up to standard, resulting in poor quality beef, dark in color and with inadequately mixed fat and lean. South of here tallow was not interlarded with the flesh, and the beef was stringy. Today the "beef belt" is practically coterminus with the corn belt. Millions of cattle and other livestock fatten on the corn, and millions still continue to jam Chicago's Union Stock Yards. Here five hundred acres contain twenty-five miles of streets and thirteen thousand pens, with open-air plumbing and running water for the visiting dogies.

Even before their opening in 1857 came the first important link between producer and packer, the commission man. By 1870 he was firmly settled as the fourth necessary factor in the economic picture, the other being the opening of a new source of supply in Texas and the Southwest, the expansion of the railroads to all livestock sources, and refrigeration.

The commission man was peculiarly fitted for his job. He was always in the market and thus knew what stock was worth. To increase his commissions, he tried for the highest possible price. Previous to his advent, livestock sales had been on a credit basis, often causing a loss. Now the driver could ship his cattle to market and draw on the commission man, a person of integrity, as soon as the livestock were delivered. After nearly one hundred years the same equitable arrangements still apply. There is no other large industry dealing with a perishable commodity in which merely the spoken word governs. When a packer's buyer completes a transaction with a commission man or the livestock owner, he simply says, "Weigh 'em." He writes nothing down, but carries the transaction in his head until he makes his daily report. Meanwhile, the pen of cattle is weighed by the Union Stock Yard Company and a weight receipt given the commission man, who pays the owner, then bills the packer. Or if they prefer, he and the commission man can take the weight ticket, mark on it the agreed price, and deposit it or get cash for it at the bank.

Refrigeration came in the late 1870's, along with two mighty business Titans—Swift and Armour—whose enterprise helped put dressed beef into "ice boxes on wheels" for transportation to and conquest of the East, which fiercely but unsuccessfully fought this invasion of its markets, for the battle to get dressed beef into the markets of the country continued for more than ten years. First, the consumers were obsessed with a mighty prejudice against it. Second, the railroads did not like this kind of new business, representing, as they thought, greatly reduced tonnage from that of live cattle. And third, local butchers everywhere fought it bitterly by every means at their command. But in the end, thanks to the establishment of a remarkable system of distribution through branch houses and car routings, Chicago won domination of the world and has held it ever since.

On arrival at the stockyards, cattle are separated into three major classes—beef cattle, butcher stock, and feeders and stockers. From beef cattle come carcasses suitable for the wholesale trade. Butcher stock yields only a minimum of marketable cuts. Feeders are those animals destined for immediate fattening at the feedlots; stockers are those so thin they have to be further built up on cheap feeds.

The largest single source of the American farmer's income in 1952 was from the sale of beef cattle, 19 per cent, compared with 14 per cent for dairy products and 11 per cent for hogs. The remaining 56 per cent came from a score of other sources. Out of every one hundred cattle marketed from June, 1951, through May, 1952, forty-four were rated choice or prime. The other grades included, in the order named, good, utility, cutter and canner, commercial, and bulls. The nation-wide demand for choice and prime roasting beef and steaks has greatly stimulated the raising of superior animals to meet this demand and, in one instance, the actual establishment of a new breed, the first in the Western Hemisphere.

CHAPTER 28

Breeds and Feeds

ATTLE BREEDS THROUGH THE AGES have been the product
of either uninhibited promiscuity or human planning, a
result of accident or design. Before man even thought of
such a thing as breeds, herds of wild stock for centuries had
been intermingling with those of neighboring districts. Where
a group had long been isolated, though most individuals were
alike in many respects, they were never exactly alike in all.
Where groups had not been isolated, their differences were even
greater.

With the planned crossing of varieties—prompted by a kind
of praiseworthy covetousness—man took the first step toward
cattle improvement. When he saw or heard of a strain which he
thought was better than his own, he bought or traded for the
best specimens, and, bringing them to the home byre or field,
he bred them to his own cattle. If the results were satisfactory,
he acquired more and continued to cross-breed through succeeding generations until he had mastered the process known as
"grading."

Eventually these graded animals, being almost as good as the
"graders," were mated with each other. But results were not
always uniform. In many cases the offspring were inferior. In
a few instances, however, some developed better qualities than
those of the grading stock itself. After breeding from the best of
these—again with many of the get showing undesirable traits—a
few, perhaps only one or two, were found to have inherited the
most desirable qualities of their parents.

These superior blue-bloods were then eligible for registration as pure-breds in the official herd book of their breed—of

which the English Shorthorn, started in 1811, is the oldest. Unfortunately, herd books record pedigrees only, never economic performance. And because early-day breeders believed that the capacity to throw good stock resided chiefly in the female, the sire was treated so cavalierly that before his contribution to posterity could be checked and recorded, he was dead and eaten!

For example, an Irish breeder had fourteen or fifteen three-year-old cows, each yielding two and one-half to three and one-half gallons of milk a day. A visitor, asking to be shown their sire, was told he had been sold to a breeder in England. In reply to a wire offering to buy the animal came word that the bull had gone to the butcher the week before. Another Irishman who had six or seven cows of about the same age, on being asked to show the sire, replied, "He is now in the Argentine."[1]

The undue prominence given to the direct female line was exemplified in the case of a well-known Angus cow belonging to the "Miss Burgess" family of Scotland. After naming the sire (Elation of Inchgrower), the genealogist went on to trace the lineage of Buxom Maid of Connage from the tenth female ancestor. As a result, the family tree bristled with such metronymic symbols of bovine snobbery as Miss Burgess, Bertha, Maid of Avon, Bonnie Maid, Buxom Maid, Beautiful Maid, Bonnie Maid of Ardoch, Bohemian Maid, Burmese Maid of Harviestoun, and Beaming Maid of Connage.[2] The desert Bedouin, boastful of the dam that foaled the Arabian mare which shares his sleeping tent, makes no greater obeisance to equine matriarchy than this.

In contrast to the popular trend, Webster of Canley, from whom Bakewell bought some of his foundation cows, used the prolific bull "Bloxedge" until he was quite old, in keeping with his determination to keep good bulls. Among others, his West-

---

[1] James Wilson, "The History of Stockbreeding and the Formation of Breeds," *Cattle Breeding: Proceedings of the Scottish Cattle Breeding Conference* (ed. by J. Cossar Ewart), 22; hereafter referred to as *Cattle Breeding.*

[2] James A. S. Watson, "Family Breeding and Line Breeding," *Cattle Breeding,* 177.

moreland bull was still in use at seven years; the grandson "D" at twelve or thirteen; "D's" son Shakespear" at eleven; the two Shorthorn bulls "Hubback" and Charles Colling's "Favourite" at ten. Bakewell also practiced letting out bulls and thus was able to gauge the breeding capacity of his animals by the stock they left in other herds, and to bring back the best ones for use at home.[3]

Probably few of the millions of T-bone addicts of today are aware of the debt we owe to the pioneering work of those old master breeders of England and Scotland—such men as Bakewell, Colling, Townshend, and Tull. A century and more ago hardly any beef was available that was not at least five, six, seven, or even ten years old. If the world today had to depend on that kind of beef, it is safe to say that there would now be a world shortage of meat. For the ox of that era was esteemed chiefly as a beast of burden, yoked to the plow and the cart. Only when he grew too old to be thus employed was he turned into beef, and tough beef at that.

Slow growing, late maturing, carrying a poor quality of flesh, he seemed hardly fit to serve as foundation stock for our modern, purebred herds. Yet such he was. And by a process of evolution, by careful selection and mating, the early-day breeders of Britain developed from this unpromising exemplar the purebred Angus, Hereford, and Shorthorn strains of today. According to one Scotsman, they "revolutionized the beef supplies of the world as surely as Stephenson revolutionized traveling by his invention of the steam-engine."[4]

Compared with that of a hundred years ago, this generation is living at such a rapid pace that whereas breeders could then wait six years for a mature bullock, they now have to turn over their money in two. As one student of animal breeding put it thirty years ago, "Each year sees a growing desire for yearling

3 Wilson, "The History of Stockbreeding and the Formation of Breeds," *Cattle Breeding*, 25.

4 W. F. McLaren, "Cattle Breeding Problems," *Cattle Breeding*, 107.

cattle (baby beef) on the part of the American consumer, while the American producer faces the changing problem of developing types of cattle that will make weights at younger ages."[5] Even earlier than that, the first fat stock show, held in Chicago in 1878, marked an epoch in the history of beef making in the United States. Here a tribunal was convened, not only for a comparison of the relative values of different breeds for producing profitable steers, but to try the general economic issue of *big bulk* versus *baby beef,* just then looming large "as a mooted question."[6] It was beginning to dawn on the breeder that it was poor economy to carry a bullock to great weight and age. To add the extra pounds as the steer advanced in age entailed too much expense. Even then, bold, progressive stockmen were trying to shift the basis of American cattle breeding from an old to a new dispensation.

Those were the days when the ambitious American stockman, planning an importation from England, was asking, "What is the best breed of cattle?" One of the shrewdest answers was made by Lewis F. Allen, whose *American Cattle: Their History, Breeding, and Management,* published in 1868, was a classic of his day and generation. Although he established the American Shorthorn Herd Book, he revealed his essential open-mindedness concerning breeds when he wrote: "It is vain to name any particular breeds as *best* for all our own localities, and all our own uses. That the adoption of some of these foreign breeds, in their purity, or the crossing of bulls of some one of them on to our native cows, is advisable, we cannot doubt. It is for the interest of every farmer and cattle-breeder throughout the country, *who takes any particular care of his stock,* to do so." Taking a crack at Texas Longhorns, Allen concludes: "For all such as take no care of their cattle, but let them mainly take care of themselves—the poorer the breed the better, so that they

---

[5] E. N. Wentworth, "Relations between Genetics and Practical Breeding," *Cattle Breeding,* 143.

[6] A. H. Sanders, *The Story of the Hereford,* 368.

can forage or steal a living out of others—the Texans can perhaps suit them. But as this book will never get into the hands of such people, nothing more need be said on that score."[7]

Allen insisted that choosing a breed depended on conditions of soil, climate, and location, suggesting that our "rich, level, or gently rolling lands, with abundant grasses, invite the imported Shorthorn, Longhorn, or Hereford. The stony, more hilly and less luxuriant pastures are better fitted for the Ayrshire, Alderney, Devon, or Galloway, while the proprietor of wild ranges, with thinner and shorter herbage, requiring more laborious seeking after, or the scantier plains of the Far West, would—if he could get them—better adopt the West Highland. As for the Texan, we do not name them as an economical beast at all. We have only described them to be shunned."

Among the imported cattle which in recent years have notably influenced American breeding is the *Bos indicus,* the so-called Brahman of India, or zebu as he is called by Brazilians and Europeans. For thousands of years these animals have been bred in their native land and from there introduced to so many far-flung countries that today in more than one-half of all the cattle in the world there is some Brahman blood. This is largely because Brahmans not only cross easily with other breeds, but in so doing have invariably improved the native stock. Among other virtues, Brahmans have proved to be tolerant of great heat, immune to tick fever and other insect bites, and to various diseases afflicting other breeds.

The zebu of the Orient is never found in an original wild form, being either feral or under man's control. Its original home was probably in the Indo-Malay region of southern Asia. Although its appearance in Egypt dates from about 3500 B.C., it was probably introduced from Mesopotamia. Aristotle mentions its being in Syria centuries before the Christian era. In southwestern Russia, Hungary, and Spain there have existed since prehistoric times breeds with marked zebu traits. In Asia, the

[7] Pages 181–82.

flesh of these animals was seldom eaten, although some tribes drank their milk and all agricultural races used them for draft. Two hundred years ago Buffon described the zebu's hump as an excresence, "a kind of wen, a piece of tender flesh, as good to eat as the tongue of an ox." Also, in India the hump helps to hold the yoke for zebu oxen.

There are many breeds of this animal in Asia and in Africa. One of the most useful is found in the northern provinces of India—tall, graceful animals surpassing in activity any of the European breeds of oxen. They are used for pack animals, as saddle mounts, harnessed to carriages, and for field labor. In many military campaigns they transported war materials and were gaily accoutered for the state processions of Indian princes, guided by a cord passed through the septum of the nose to which bridle reins were attached. While the wild Brahman-bull riders of American rodeos might not agree, the Orientals claim that their gaits are easy for riding, and that they trot and gallop as freely as a horse. Their endurance is remarkable, and there are authentic records of Brahmans having traveled sixty to eighty miles a day.

In place of the long-legged breed, many American breeders have selected types with shorter legs, developing a deep-bodied animal carrying plenty of good beef without making it exceptionally low set; they believe that for life on the range, cattle that can walk are preferable.

The distinguishing Brahman feature, the hump or crest, is larger in some Indian breeds than in others. It is thought by many geneticists that animals having the largest humps have survived repeated periods of drought or famine. Certain it is that when the animal is well fed, this crest fills out with fat and shrinks and shrivels when feed is scarce. The loose, pendulous skin hanging in folds under the neck, the prominent dewlap, and pronounced sheath and navel are a handicap to working zebu oxen. However, all this loose skin serves as a "radiator" since the amount of heat given off by an animal is proportional to its surface area. Large, drooping ears also help to some extent to rid the body of excess heat, as well as acting as a fly whisk when the beast shakes its head. Another aid in withstanding heat is the animal's dense, short, glossy hair, which permits a maximum escape of body heat.

Hair colors vary from black to white, gray predominating, although there are also red, fawn, dun, brown, and mottled. The Gir, with the greatest weight of any of the Brahmans, has all colors except gray and black. Girs and Guzarats have contributed the most to the range-beef type in the Americas. Gir cattle with solid red or sometimes brown hair are among the most popular of the "Red Brahmans" sought by United States breeders. Others are the Nellore, the Sahiwal, and the Red Sindhi. Regardless of the color of the hair, the skin of the zebu is usually black or chocolate colored. Another unique feature is the presence of sweat glands, an equipment much more highly developed in Brahmans than in other cattle. Most of these glands are located along the shoulder vein and on the neck. Sweat is often seen dripping from the dewlap. Instead of bellowing or lowing, zebus "grunt," somewhat as do the yaks.

Only within the last forty years have there been substantial importations of Brahmans to the North American continent, although James Bolton Davis is credited with having brought to his South Carolina plantation in 1849 two cows and a bull. The Civil War is believed to have contributed to the extinction of all purebred descendants. But from the arrival in Louisiana in 1854 of two Brahman bulls, a gift from the British crown to Richard Barrow, cross-breeding resulted in such high-grade cattle as to attract the attention of two Texans, J. M. Frost and Albert Montgomery. Impressed with their rapid growth, high quality meat, and grazing capabilities, the partners bought some of these cross-breds and shipped them to Texas. In 1885 they sent their own herdsman to Calcutta, who brought back two bulls—Khedive, a Guzarat, and Richard III, a Nellore type. These rank as the third importation to this country, the first to Texas.

In succeeding years, thousands of Brahmans have found their way from India to the Americas, including Brazil. Exports from that country to Texas by way of Mexico of 90 bulls of the Gir, Guzarat, and Nellore races were made in 1924, followed the next year by another consignment including 120 bulls and 18 heifers. One of the last importations to Texas, in 1946, was of 18 Brazilian bulls.

Commendation is due the American Brahman Breeders Association for maintaining open herd books. Registration is permitted after five top crosses of purebred Brahman bulls and an appraisal, which permits the admission of a large number of valuable animals. There are now about 10,000 owners of Brahmans in the United States and approximately 180,000 registered Brahman cattle. According to the association, "During the past quarter of a century cross-breeding experiments with Brahman (*Bos indicus*) and the English (*Bos taurus*) breeds have been carried out by government experimental stations and individuals. Reports to date have consistently shown that cross-breeding with Brahmans results in an improved market animal."[8]

The persistence of zebu traits in cross-breds was recorded thirty years ago by a Scottish authority who, after noting that the zebu had already been blended with British beef breeds (especially the Hereford) to a considerable extent in Texas, Jamaica, Brazil, India, and Italy, declared that "the results invariably show that as regards conformation and other characters the hybrid is intermediate between the parental breeds, and that even when grading back to the pure British breeds, as is commonly practised, the Zebu characters are discernible even when there is only one-eighth Zebu blood present."[9]

On the great, sprawling King Ranch of southern Texas, the mating of zebus and English Shorthorns began more than forty years ago. A famous cross-bred bull named "Monkey," product

[8] *Bulletin*, American Brahman Breeders Association, November 1, 1952.
[9] G. F. Finley, "The Inheritance of Milk and Beef Characteristics," *Cattle Breeding*, 70.

of a Brahman sire and a red Shorthorn cow with one-sixteenth Brahman blood, was found to have peculiar potency in transmitting to his offspring the best qualities of both types. In a patient, tireless crusade to develop an animal supremely fitted to withstand the rigors of the Southwestern ranges, the owners continued their meticulously selective breeding until their labors were crowned by the establishment of an officially recognized, entirely new breed, the Santa Gertrudis. It is the first new breed of beef cattle ever developed in the United States, and the first new breed developed anywhere in more than a century.

King Ranch sold at auction its first Santa Gertrudis bulls in 1950. In the severe drought year of 1952, the top bull brought $40,000. Today Santa Gertrudis cattle have spread to twenty-four states and eighteen foreign countries. At his new Winrock Ranch near Little Rock, Arkansas, Winthrop Rockefeller has recently contracted for a big consignment of these cherry-red beauties, whose blood is five-eighths Shorthorn and three-eighths Brahman.

When Alton Blakeslee, science reporter for the Associated Press, visited the King Ranch, he interviewed owners Richard and Robert Kleberg and their professional consultants, Dr. J. K. Northway, veterinarian, and Dr. Albert O. Rhoad, geneticist, Dubbing this vast enterprise "a meat factory," Blakeslee took three columns of newspaper space to tell the world what he had seen and heard.[10] He reported that on the real estate side the ranch now consists of 940,000 acres after dividing among heirs in 1895 the 1,250,000 acres owned by Captain Richard King, who had died ten years before.

Here from fifteen to thirty acres of the sparse grassland are required to support a single steer, whereas in Florida but one is necessary. In Texas the quest is ever for better and tougher grasses. Yet Santa Gertrudis animals thrive in this hot, arid environment and are said to do equally well in humid and semi-

[10] Alton W. Blakeslee, "Science on the King Ranch," *Los Angeles Times,* April 4, 1954.

tropical lands. They grow fast. Range cows weigh from 1,100 to 1,200 pounds and bulls 1,800 to 2,000 at maturity. They average some 200 pounds heavier than other breeds raised under the same conditions and dress out a higher percentage of carcass beef. They are good rustlers and easily travel long distances for water pumped from wells operated by the four hundred windmills on the ranch. Although many of the 60,000 head of cattle are of the Santa Gertrudis breed, special pastures contain herds of Hereford-Brahman crosses, purebred Brahmans, white French Charolaise, English Park cattle, and Afrikanders. From such as these, experiments in breeding have resulted in the founding of bovine families known as Brangus, Braford, Charbray, and Red Poll.

King Ranch, made up of four separate and rather distinct divisions that extend into five South Texas counties, covers an acreage equal to a strip of land half a mile wide reaching from New England to California—a fact once arrestingly brought home to an investigator for the United States Internal Revenue Bureau who had been sent down to check the Klebergs' claim of having lost seventy-five windmills in a tornado. After the agent had spent the night and breakfasted at the big headquarters ranch house, he stepped outside to be confronted by a string of pack horses saddled for a long journey; they were burdened with tents, blankets, food, and cooking equipment.

"Climb aboard," said Kleberg.

"Why?" asked the tax collector.

"We're going out to count windmills."

"No, thanks, I think I'll take your word for it," said the agent.

The origin of Afrikander cattle, with eighty head of which King Ranch has been experimenting since 1932, has not been positively determined. But as the first European colonists found them in possession of the Hottentots in the western and southwestern parts of the Cape province, it seems reasonable to conclude—as does Professor Bosman of Transvaal University College, Pretoria—that "the Afrikander is and has been for a very long time a pure breed of indigenous cattle." Others have conjectured that Arabs took Afrikanders east, from which India developed its Brahmans. Afrikanders now are widely distributed throughout Rhodesia and the Union of South Africa. Their ability to subsist on sour, coarse pasturage, their courage in scaling rugged mountains and steep hills in search of food, to "stand on their hind legs and eat tree leaves" have enabled the breed to hang on to life where others starved. Under severe conditions of the open range of Africa, only the fittest have survived. From these, offspring of great longevity have been bred. The Afrikander bull or cow at thirteen or fourteen years will breed healthy, normal calves. At a Pretoria show some years ago a twenty-one-year-old cow in calf was exhibited. As for beef qualities, butchers prefer Afrikanders as they yield a higher percentage of carcass weight to live weight, with a marked absence of paunchiness and coarse bone. In Africa, breeding for early maturity has had encouraging results. At a Bloemfontein agricultural show a young bull bred in the Vrede district weighed 1,100 pounds at sixteen months; a heifer, aged twenty-six months, bred in the Kroonstad district, weighed 1,200; and a three-and-one-half-year-old heifer in calf weighed 1,400 pounds.[11]

In Canada, purebred bison bulls have been crossed with purebred or grade Hereford, Shorthorn, or Angus cows, producing hybrids. The product of two hybrids was designated by the experimenter, the late Mossom Boyd of Ontario, as *cattalo*. Their claimed virtues are a thick, warm hide (from which excellent robes can be made) which enables the beast to face severe blizzards in the manner of bison, not drift with it and pile up against wire fencing and perish as cattle do; great rustling qualities; marked disease resistance; one more rib than ordinary cattle, so that there is a greater percentage of steaks and rib cuts; and a higher percentage of flesh along the back than is carried by domestic cattle. Difficulties, however, include a high

[11] T. G. W. Reinecke, "Africander Cattle," *Cattle Breeding,* 452.

percentage of mortality among calves on account of excessive amniotic fluids. The popular belief that deaths are due to the heavy shoulder of the bison calf is unfounded since pure bison calves themselves show no excessive shoulders at birth. Lack of fertility in male hybrids, particularly in the first cross, is also a discouraging factor for the breeder.[12]

According to Ottawa scientist Hamer, the missing link between bison and cattle is the yak, our friend with the trailing skirts from the high plateaus of central Asia. Experiments conducted several years ago by the Canadian Department of Agriculture were based on the hope that the hybrid resulting from a crossing of yak bull and domestic cow would in turn cross readily and safely with the bison, and thus assist in producing fertile males, overcoming the admitted difficulties of mortality and lack of fertility in directly crossing bison and domestic cattle. At first there was some success in hybridization, the initial calf crop including five heifers (yak sire and domestic dam); one bull of same breeding; two heifers (bison sire and domestic dam); and one heifer (yak sire, bison dam). But of late little has been heard of this attempt to breed stock especially fitted to thrive and fatten in the sub-arctic forests and on the ranges of the barren lands of the northern provinces.

THE BASIC ENTERPRISE of a cattle ranch is the conversion of grass into beef. Many a Southwestern state rates grass as its most valuable natural resource. In Texas it nourishes the cattle, sheep, and goats which produce meat, leather, wool, and mohair. Its champions even declare that grass not only supported Texas economy long before the discovery of oil, gas, and minerals, but that it is destined to be a key resource when the latter resources cease to be abundant. Yet here and in other states along the Mexican border there is a ceaseless quest for drought-resisting species. Although the perfect range grass has not yet been dis-

[12] R. S. Hamer, "The Canadian Bison-Cattle Cross," *Cattle Breeding*, 288 ff.

covered, scientists at agricultural colleges in California, Arizona, New Mexico, and Texas have long been at work on problems of heredity, growth and development, nutrition and reproduction of native and imported strains. Like the cattle breeder, they have cross-bred various types of grass in an effort to produce hybrids that will yield maximum amounts of forage.

More than thirty years ago, King Ranch introduced Rhodes grass from Rhodesia. When it was found to be sturdy and drought resisting, it was planted on 130,000 acres of the ranch and later on in other large Texas areas. Unfortunately, its survival has been threatened by a tiny insect, Chinese scale, which sucks the juices of the plant. Small wasps have been introduced which feed on the scale, but so far excessively dry weather has impaired their effectiveness. If science can lick this problem and a few others, the future of this and other range grasses will look much rosier.

One researcher claims that by applying "the knowledge we now have about the grasses to the management of grasslands it will make possible livestock population increases ranging from 50 per cent in the more arid regions of the West to 475 per cent in the Southeastern part of the United States." He calculated that over the country an average increase of 50 per cent in the number of units of stock could be obtained.[13] The significance of this claim is apparent when one realizes that grass, hay, and dry roughage now make up almost three-fourths of all feeds consumed by beef cattle. Without these "four-stomach wonders" there would be little use for over 40 per cent of the land in the United States that can produce only grass and other crops that people will not eat.

Droughts throughout the Southwest sometimes drive ranchers to extreme measures. On a number of Texas ranches, cowboys recently went into the desert equipped with flame-throwers to singe off the thorns of prickly pear cactus, a succulent fodder

[13] W. Gordon Whaley, "Grass the Economic Cornerstone," *Corpus Christi Call-Times*, July 12, 1953.

much relished by cattle. In less pampered herds, steers are often seen with muzzles as full of quills as a porcupine. Lacking cowboy first aid, they take their cactus straight. Supplemental feed in the form of cottonseed cakes is universally used in the Southwest. On the King Ranch the bill for this often amounts to $70,-000 a month.

An interesting new feed has recently been perfected in Arizona which gives promise of fattening cattle at less expense. Taking cotton-gin trash—the hulls, leaves, and stalks of cotton plants, always burned as waste at the gin—grinding it to a fine powder, adding molasses and minerals in proper proportions to retain the digestible cellulose and eliminate the indigestible lignin, the manufacturer's six-year experiments have shown favorable results. When substituted for as much as 50 per cent of the grain in livestock rations, this feed has produced rapid increases in cattle weights.

In experiments conducted by the Luling Foundation of Texas, it was shown that steers can be finished to earn "U. S. good" classification by feeding grain on grass much cheaper than by fattening them on harvested feeds. A group of 202 Santa Gertrudis yearlings averaging 505 pounds in nineteen months were brought to an average weight of over 1,400. Length of time required in the final finishing period ranged from 79 days for those on excellent grazing to 159 for those finished when pasturage was burned up in the hot summer of 1952. Out-of-pocket costs for feeds for finishing periods to supplement pastures were as low as $1.96 per one hundred pounds of gain for one lot on excellent grazing to $16.91 for a lot finished while pasturage was "burned up."[13]

As for the various grains used in trying to determine the best feedstuff for cattle, California barley-fed beef is being tested in competition with locally raised corn-fed flesh by a woman professor in food technology at Davis, California. Steaks will be cut from butchered animals of both types and the verdict rendered by expert tasters especially selected as jurors.

Yet despite sporadic efforts to by-pass the nation's corn feeding lots, it will probably be a long time before grass-fattened cattle in appreciably large numbers will reach the great packing houses in such shape as to be graded "choice" or "prime." As it stands now, about 85 per cent of all the corn raised in this country is fed to livestock. And 85 per cent of the native beef steers which reach Chicago and are bought for slaughter are the stockers and feeders which gained their eligibility for the shambles on corn.

CHAPTER 29

Man's Oldest Ration

IN THE VILLAGE MEAT SHOP the wife of the local doctor was having a conference with the butcher—one of the old-fashioned kind who hung his sides of beef in a walk-in cooler and carved off cuts to the customer's order.

"My husband says some people are reducing by eating beef," began the young matron, aged thirty-one, whose five-foot-six, 163-pound figure the doctor gallantly told her was "pleasingly plump."

"So," she continued, "I guess you can cut me a nice T-bone steak. By the way, how much is it?"

"One dollar a pound."

"Holy cow!" burbled the lady.

"Ma'am, it's no cow! Good steer beef from Chicago."

"Isn't there something cheaper that'll do just as well?"

"Yes, ma'am, I can give you sirloin at 88 cents, round at 77—"

"Goodness no, none of that. I'm round enough now!"

The humorless Mr. Schultz continued his sales talk.

"Rib roast at 65 cents, stew meat 56, chuck 55, hamburger at 42."

Finally settling for a boneless rump roast at 89 cents a pound, the lady departed for home and the opening engagement in the battle of the bulge.[1]

The incident points up two serious problems in the dietary

---

[1] Prices quoted in this chapter are from January, 1954, national advertising material released by the American Meat Institute, which stated that the retail prices quoted were averages for "all kinds of Chicago stores, including cash-and-carry, charge-and-deliver, in high rent areas and in low rent areas. Prices in some stores may be higher . . . in others lower."

life of today's meat eaters—their figures and their finances. For the befuddled consumer who asks, "How come one-dollar steak from twenty-five cent steers?" the American Meat Institute, spokesman for most of the nation's butchers, has an illuminating answer. It postulates a 1,000-pound steer bought from a stock grower by the packer for $258. This 1,000-pound animal yields 591 pounds of beef. This the packer sells to the retailer for $241.90, which is less than he paid for the live animal. It is now up to the packer to make up this loss and realize a possible profit from the sale of such by-products as hides, fats, hair, animal feeds, and pharmaceuticals.

As for the retailer, after suffering an average 140-pound loss of carcass weight from shrinkage and fat and bones not salable to customers, he sells his remaining 450 pounds of beef cuts for $291.40, or $50.00 more than they cost him. Such a mark-up must take into account the cost of rent, labor, depreciation on equipment, fixtures, and other expenses.

All cuts of beef are equally nourishing. If there were equal amounts of all with an equal demand for all, steak, hamburger, and stew meat would all sell at the same price. In the average carcass there are only 35 pounds of the one-dollar steaks, but 150 of the cheaper hamburger and stew variety. If consumers won't pay one dollar for steak but rush in large numbers to buy fifty-cent hamburger and stewing beef, the steak price drops and the cheap meat prices go up, following the unchanging law of supply and demand.

To put it another way, says the Institute, there are about three times more pot roasts in a steer than fancy steak cuts. That is supply. Most people like steak better than anything else. That is demand. Thus steak, in limited supply and subject to heavy demand, simply has to cost more, just as diamonds in scant supply cost more than turquoises, which are comparatively plentiful.

Before refrigeration, slaughtering was confined to the cold months, roughly from October to April. Now it is an all-year proposition, but with certain definite cycles. Beginning in late July or August, cattle marketings for slaughter are substantial, reaching peak levels in October and November. The rise from low to high is normally about 25 per cent, but varies from year to year. Animals killed in the fall are generally those just off grass and thus of lower grade compared with the spring slaughter of corn-fattened stock. Not only do cattle marketings vary from month to month, but from week to week and day to day. This is because it is impossible to tell in advance how many animals will arrive from one day to the next.[2]

Although the great centralized cash markets of Chicago, Kansas City, East St. Louis, Omaha, Sioux City, and Denver receive the bulk of the nineteen million cattle annually sent to some sixty-five public markets, they are not the producer's only outlets. If he prefers, the stock grower can sell his livestock through auction markets direct to many of the eighteen thousand meat packers and commercial slaughterers, to other cattle producers, or to independent buyers and traders.

It is well to remember the difference between *chilled* beef and *frozen* beef. The first is the kind sold to retailers, and is by far the largest part of the packer's output. Chilled or "dressed" beef is ready for sale or shipment to distant distributors within two days after the steer is slaughtered. Constantly maintained at 32- to 34-degree temperature, it reaches the packer's whole-sale branch houses in about five days. In a day or two thereafter it is hanging in the retailer's cooler, so that two weeks after the beast's rump has been processed into roasting meat, Butcher Schultz was able to sell the doctor's wife the first installment of her slenderizing diet.

As for the frozen beef, most of it is generally boneless and emerges from the packing plant as frankfurters, hamburgers, meat loaves, and other forms of table-ready meats. Because most housewives prefer fresh, unfrozen beef (according to the United States Department of Agriculture), only about 2 per cent of the

[2] Swift and Company *Agricultural Research Bulletin No. 15,* p. 12.

annual production goes into storage as frozen beef. The average journey of a beef from producer to consumer is about one thousand miles. Since it is perishable, it must be moved quickly and carefully. Only specialists in the meat business can do this.

It is estimated by the Bureau of Human Nutrition and Home Economics of the U.S.D.A. that eighty-eight out of every one hundred people in the United States eat beef. But they don't all eat the same kind. There are regional differences. In the Boston area they favor beef from cattle weighing from 1,300–1,500 pounds alive; in New York, those with weights ranging from 1,100–1,200. As one moves westward, it is discovered that in Buffalo the flesh of the 900-pound steer is preferred; in Chicago that of the 750–850 pounder. Among the Mississippi Valley cities, popular weights are anywhere from 600–900 pounds. From here to the Pacific Coast the best seller is beef from heavier cattle—800–900 pounds in Denver; and on the Coast, 900–1,200 pounds live weight.

Compared with that of beef, consumption of veal is inconsequential—only 6 per cent of the total meat supply. Of that which is sold, the weight preferences are quite the opposite to those for beef. In the Northeast the folks who prefer heavy beef clamor for light-weight calves. In the southern half of the country, the customer favors veal from heavy calves, locally known as "heavy veals."

Inasmuch as people in different sections and of different tastes demand different weights and grades, stock growers all over the land can raise and send to the packers the kind of cattle best suited to their farm or ranch conditions. It is the packing plant's function to process this meat, match the available supply and the various grades of beef to meet the demand, and ship it to areas where it will bring gustatory delight to the consumer and lucrative satisfaction to the retailer. It is the boast of the industry that in nearly every town and hamlet in the country the housewife can get the kind and quality of meat that she wants, when she wants it.

As has been pointed out, it is on the by-products that the packer depends chiefly for profits, but in a constantly changing industrial economy, markets for his by-products are often as unstable as water. One outstanding example is the outlet for fats and oils. Lard was long the nation's leading shortening. Within the past twenty years the packer has had to meet strong competition from popular vegetable-oil shortenings. Lard has suffered because the cheapest vegetable oils are used and hydrogenated, whereas if lard is hydrogenated, it loses its effect on skin health, which is its peculiar benefit. This has forced him to develop better lard products and wider uses for tallow, edible fats, and oils. Where the soap maker formerly depended upon these for his basic ingredients, chemical detergents now usurp one-third of the market, challenging the leadership of all laundry soaps and powders and detergents made from animal fatty acids, to say nothing of the substitution of palm oil for animal fats in the manufacture of soap itself.[3]

Animal hair, sterilized and processed, was once widely used in stuffing mattresses and upholstered furniture. As this market dwindled, the automobile industry came to the rescue. For a while its demand for upholstery stuffing for passenger cars more than made up for the loss of the furniture outlet. Now motor car manufacturers have turned to kapok, sponge rubber, and other materials. The latest possible cures for the packer's difficulties are air conditioning, with its large demand for air-filtering equipment, and iceless refrigeration, which needs an immense amount of insulation. For these, animal hair at present is meeting the requirements and doing a good job. Yet there is always the danger that a better or cheaper product may appear and wipe out this business.

Only the larger packers can afford to maintain laboratories and conduct exhaustive research, but the public and the smaller meat operators benefit from their liberal outlay of risk capital. This is strikingly apparent in what has been called the glandular

[3] Fowler, *Men, Meat, and Miracles,* 181.

therapy field. To correct maladjustments in human glands, the medical profession some years ago joined with the packing industry and from the glands of animals, salvaged and processed by the packers, eventually developed extracts for the treatment of such ills as Addison's disease, arthritis, rheumatic fever, and diabetes. In 1922 diabetes was conquered by the discovery of insulin. In 1926 liver extracts were perfected for treating anemia. Still later Addison's disease, an affliction caused by lack of the adrenal cortex, succumbed to the magic of adrenocortical extract. What was once incurable can now be cured, restoring the patient to a normal, useful life.[4] Offsetting the strictly practical and selfish motives of the industry are the heart-warming benefits bestowed on thousands of sufferers previously without hope of recovery. Pharmaceutical by-products may have brought profits to the packer, but they have also brought much permanent release from human pain and misery.

No less beneficial to the healthy are the proteins, B vitamins, and iron—besides significant quantities of copper and phosphorus—which are to be found in cooked meats, including beef, veal, pork, and lamb. Time was when nutritionists and housewives alike expressed opinions for and against "calories." It was claimed that if we got enough of these "heat units," all would be well with our general health, but the boom was lowered on the most zealous advocates by the paunchy and triple-chinned when they learned that excessive calories made people fat.

Presently the vitamin boosters moved in. When laboratory animals were fed on purified foods, they sickened and almost died. When a few wisps of lettuce or shreds of spinach were offered, the sufferers wolfed them and recovered. From these experiments a Kansas farm boy, at work at the University of Wisconsin, in 1914 identified the first vitamin, which was promptly labelled vitamin A. From then on up to the 1930's, the search for new vitamins continued. Now that the calorie and

[4] *Ibid.*, 184–86.

the vitamin craze are waning, the protein era holds the center of the dietary stage.

The richest source of protein is meat, man's oldest ration. And meat contains sufficient complete proteins—also to a lesser extent do cheese, milk, fish, chicken, and eggs—to aid in accomplishing results commensurate with some of the new wonder drugs. For cirrhosis of the liver, once regarded as inevitably fatal, patients are now given a high protein diet along with vitamins, bringing bright prospects for recovery. The toxemias of pregnancy, killing mother and unborn babe, have been overcome by feeding foods rich in proteins. Proteins are saving the lives of people severely burned; also restoring victims of surgical shock. For those about to undergo surgery, a high protein diet before the operation fortifies them against shock. As a result, there are fewer operative mortalities than ever before.

Because proteins hasten the rate at which the body burns calories, they play an indispensable part in most medically approved reducing diets, some of which permit a person to eat all the lean meat he desires.[5]

Proteins, the basic constituents of foods, of the blood, and of other body fluids, are not stored, as one might suppose, in the body. They are used as they are eaten, not stowed away as are sugar and some vitamins in the liver or in the form of fats under the skin and around many organs. When introduced to the system, they go to work immediately at building new tissue and repairing old. When a person's diet lacks proteins, his body begins to devour its own substance like a cannibal. Such was one of the cruel tragedies which smote the victims of Nazi horror camps.

The bloodstream cannot tolerate most proteins in a pure state. Injections of egg white, for instance, might be fatal. What the body does to the proteins in one's meat or eggs is to break them down into amino acids, which are the "building blocks" of

[5] J. D. Ratcliff, *You and Meat in This Protein Era*, 10.

proteins. Twenty-two amino acids have now been discovered, ten of them being essential to life in that they must be obtained from food. Complete proteins contain all of the essential amino acids. When a mouthful of beef enters the body, its protein is broken down into its component parts; these are amino acids which the blood picks up and moves as on a conveyor belt to all parts of the body. En route a wound in process of healing or older tissues needing replacement snatch from the blood the amino acids required for the job.

It has been proved that all the essential amino acids must be available simultaneously if full nutritional benefit is to be obtained. In one experiment, rats were fed five of the essential acids. Two hours later they were given the other five. During the weeks in which they were fed on this alternating schedule they wilted, lost weight, and sickened, showing that only complete proteins will bring beneficial results.

Another old theory, which has been exploded, concerns protein as a cause of high blood pressure and kidney diseases, as well as prompting something vaguely alluded to as "intestinal autointoxication," which no one has been able to define exactly. Careful study of Eskimos, who live almost exclusively on meat, has shown that they have no greater incidence of high blood pressure or kidney trouble than any other people.

It is now conceded that protein foods are among the most digestible and the most essential of all foods. The body cannot convert carbohydrates or fats into proteins, but proteins can be converted into carbohydrates or fats. This means that if there is an excess of proteins, they are burned to create energy. The Eskimo's diet of meat was once the sole support of Vilhjalmur Stefansson for a year. The famous explorer reported that at the end of the experiment he was in better physical condition than at the start.

The list of beneficiaries of a protein diet is a long one. Among those not already mentioned are patients suffering from stomach and duodenal ulcers; growing children, who especially need large amounts for the building of new tissue; and babies, who at six to eight weeks are given scraped or strained beef.

As for adults in normal health, it has long been common knowledge that the well-fed person is less subject to disease than the poorly nourished, but only in recent years has an explanation been forthcoming. It seems the body wards off disease through its antibodies or bacteria destroyers. In entering the body a bacterium finds ideal conditions—warmth, darkness, and a bountiful food supply—for promoting a devastating career. Only the antibodies, protein in character, can challenge the invader. If enough protein building materials are available, the enemy is defeated and human life and health are preserved. This is probably why disease rates mount in ill-fed, war-torn countries. Without adequate proteins in normal diets, disease takes over.

Our own national health grows steadily better. Life expectancy at birth continues to rise. Our average consumption of meat, richest of all proteins, has risen 14 pounds per person from the prewar rate to an annual total of 153 pounds. The generous protein allowance in the American soldier's ration is claimed by one prominent physician to have been a contributing factor in winning the late war, bringing to our front-line fighters greater vigor, quicker and more assured recovery from injury, and a higher degree of morale.[6]

But the profound changes effected by the beef animal in nutrition are only part of the picture. From beef-cattle raising and droving have come cultural influences upon the whole of America, which those now living are often least able to interpret. The romantic—even heroic—pattern set by the Mexican *vaquero* and American cowboy has become a part of our historical consciousness, and has won the interest of readers and students of cultural development in both hemispheres.

[6] James S. McLester, M.D., "Protein Comes into Its Own," *Journal* of the American Medical Association, Vol. CXXXIX, No. 14 (April 2, 1949), 17.

Bibliography

1. Manuscripts, Letters, and Interviews

Curtiss, C. F. (Ames, Iowa). Interviews in 1938.

Edwards, Philip Leget. Diary. Oregon Archives Building, Salem.

Fasman, Rabbi Oscar Z. Letter to the authors, October 16, 1952.

Lovell, Charles W. Letter to the authors, October 16, 1952.

Mackenzie, John. (Matador Land and Cattle Company). Letter to the authors, February 14, 1952.

Oregon State Historical Society Archives, Salem.

Shoemaker, Warren (Chicago). Interviews, 1929.

Skinner, Robert S. (Jordan Valley, Oregon). Interviews and letters, September and October, 1953.

Skinner, S. W. (Jordan Valley, Oregon). Letters, April and May, 1953; interview, August 15, 1953.

Smith, Arthur A. (Sterling, Colorado). Interview at Chicago, May 18, 1954.

Swan, Henry. (Denver). Interviews and letters, 1940–53.

Weadock, J. F. Interview, May 18, 1953.

Wentworth, Frank. Interview at Chesterton, Indiana, August 19, 1952.

Wyoming Stock Growers Archives, University of Wyoming Library, Laramie.

2. Government Publications: Federal and State

Fletcher, Robert S. *Organization of the Range Cattle Business in Eastern Montana.* Bozeman, Mont., Agricultural Experiment Station, June, 1932.

45 Cong., 3 sess., *House Executive Documents,* Vol. IX.

Ohio State Board of Agriculture Third Annual Report (1848). Columbus, 1849.

Population Reference Bureau (Washington, D. C.). *Population Bulletin,* Vol, IX, No. 1 (February, 1953).

Saunders, W. L. (ed.). *The Colonial Records of North Carolina, 1662–1776*. 10 vols. Pub. under the supervision of the Public Libraries. . . . Goldsboro, Nash Brothers, 1886–1907.
Tenth U. S. Census, 1880, III (Agriculture). Washington, D. C., 1883.
Thompson, James Westfall. *History of Livestock Raising in the United States, 1607–1860*. U. S. Department of Agriculture, Agricultural History Series, No. 5. Washington, 1942.

3. Newspapers
Chicago Daily Drovers Journal, December 3, 4, 1951.
Corpus Christi Call-Times, July 12, 1953.
Daily Missouri Republican (St. Louis), August 24, 1854.
Daily Western Journal of Commerce (Kansas City, Mo.), June 20, 1858.
Galveston (Texas) *Weekly News*, November 18, 1856.
Miles City (Mont.) *Daily Press*, August 2, 1882.
Philadelphia Independent Gazetteer, July 10, 1787.
Rocky Mountain Husbandman (Great Falls, Mont.), June 14, 1883.
San Antonio Western Texan, June 1, 1854.
Texas State Gazette (Austin), July 6, 1850.
Washington Post and Times-Herald, November 25, 1954.

4. Pamphlets and Special Bulletins
American Brahman Breeders Association *Bulletin* (Houston, Tex.), November 1, 1952.
Haley, J. Evetts. *A Bit of Bragging about a Cow*. Amarillo, Texas, Privately Printed, 1948.
Ratcliff, J. D. *You and Meat in This Protein Era*. Chicago, American Meat Institute, 1950.
Reports from the Scientific Expedition to the Northwestern Provinces of China under the leadership of Dr. Sven Hedin, *Publication 9*. Vienna, 1929.
Swift and Company. *Livestock and Meat*. Chicago, 1945.
———. *Agricultural Research Bulletin No. 15*. Chicago, 1954.
Warwick, E. J. *Cross Breeding with Braman Cattle*. Paper read before the American Society of Animal Production, Chicago, November 28, 1952.

5. Books
Abbott, E. C. ("Teddy Blue"), and Helena Huntington Smith. *We*

Pointed Them North: Recollections of a Cowpuncher. New York, Farrar and Rinehart, 1939.

Allen, Lewis F. *American Cattle: Their History, Breeding, and Management.* New York, Taintor Bros. and Company, 1868.

American Husbandry: Containing an Account of the Soil, Climate, Production, and Agriculture of the British Colonies in North America and the West Indies. 2 vols. London, J. Bew, 1775.

Andreas, A. T. *History of Chicago.* Chicago, Andreas, 1884.

Applegate, Jesse. *A Day with the Cow Column in 1843.* Chicago, Caxton Club, 1934. The volume also includes Jesse A. Applegate's *Recollections of My Boyhood.*

Atwood, Rev. A. *The Conquerors.* Glendale, Arthur H. Clark, 1907.

Avebury, Lord. *Prehistoric Times.* 7th ed. London, Williams and Norgate, 1913.

Bancroft, Hubert Howe. *History of the Northwest Coast.* 2 vols. San Francisco, The History Company, 1886.

———. *History of Oregon.* 2 vols. San Francisco, The History Company, 1886.

———. *California Pastoral, 1769–1848.* San Francisco, The History Company, 1888.

———. *North Mexican States and Texas.* 2 vols. San Francisco, The History Company, 1888.

———. *History of California.* 7 vols. San Francisco, The History Company, 1884–1890.

———. *The History of Washington, Idaho, and Montana, 1845–1889.* San Francisco, The History Company, 1890.

Bell, James A. *A Log of the Texas–California Cattle Trail, 1854.* Ed. by J. Evetts Haley. Privately published. (Copyr. Ned C. Bell), 1932.

Belloc, Hilaire. *The Bad Child's Book of Beasts.* New York, Alfred A. Knopf, 1924.

Bewick, Thomas. *A General History of Quadrupeds.* 5th ed. Newcastle-on-Tyne, Tyne, England, Tyne Publishing Company, Ltd., 1847.

Bidwell, Percy Wells, and John I. Falconer. *History of Agriculture in the Northern United States, 1620–1860.* New York, Peter Smith, 1941.

Blasco-Ibáñez, Vicente. *Blood and Sand*. New York, E. P. Dutton, 1919.

Bolton, Herbert Eugene. *Athanase de Mézières and the Louisiana–Texas Frontier, 1768–1780*. 2 vols. Cleveland, Arthur H. Clark, 1914.

———. *The Padre on Horseback*: *A Sketch of Eusebio Francisco Kino*. San Francisco, The Sonora Press, 1932.

Bradbury, John. *Travels in the Interior of America in the Years 1809, 1810, and 1811*. Vol. V. of Thwaites' *Early Western Travels, q. v.*

Branch, E. Douglas. *The Hunting of the Buffalo*. New York, D. Appleton, 1929.

Brayer, Garnet M. and Herbert O. *American Cattle Trails*. Denver, Smith-Brooks Printing Company, 1952.

Brayer, Herbert O. *Life of Tom Candy Ponting*: *An Autobiography*. Evanston, Ill., Branding Iron Press, 1952.

Breasted, James H. *Ancient Times*: *A History of the Early World*. 2nd ed. Boston, Ginn, 1935.

Brehm, Alfred Edmund. *Life of Animals*. Chicago, A. N. Marquis, 1895.

Brodribb, C. W. (ed.). *The Georgics* (Virgil). New York, D. Appleton, 1929.

Brodrick, Alan Houghton. *Lascaux*: *A Commentary*. London, Lindsay Drummond, Ltd., 1949.

Brooks, Bryant B. *Memoirs*. Glendale, Arthur H. Clark, 1929.

Brown, Jesse, and A. M. Willard. *The Freighter*. Ed. by J. T. Milek. Rapid City, S. Dakota, Rapid City Journal Company, 1924.

Budge, E. A. T. Wallace. *The Gods of the Egyptians*. 2 vols. London, Methuen, 1904.

Buffon, G. L. L. *Histoire Naturelle*. 44 vols. Paris, Repet and Company, 1750–1804.

Burt, Struthers. *Powder River, Let 'er Buck*. New York, Farrar and Rinehart, 1938.

Carrier, Lyman. *The Beginnings of Agriculture in America*. New York, McGraw-Hill Book Company, 1923.

Castañeda, C. E. *The Finding of Texas*. Vol. I of *Our Catholic Heritage in Texas, 1518–1936*. 2 vols. Austin, Von Boeckmann-Jones, 1936.

Chapman, Charles E. *A History of California*: *The Spanish Period*. New York, Macmillan, 1921.

Clay, John M. *My Life on the Range*. Chicago, Privately Printed, 1924.

Clemen, R. F. *American Livestock and Meat Industry*. New York, Ronald Press, 1923.

Cody, William F. *An Autobiography of Buffalo Bill*. New York, Cosmopolitan Book Corporation, 1920.

Collins, Rev. W. Lucas. *Virgil*. New York, John B. Alden, 1890.

Connelley, William Elsey. *Wild Bill and His Era*. New York, Press of the Pioneers, 1933.

Conner, Palmer. *The Romance of the Ranchos*. Los Angeles, Title Insurance and Trust Company, 1939.

Cook, James H. *Longhorn Cowboy*. New York, G. P. Putnam's Sons, 1942.

Culley, George. *An Essay on the Breeding of Livestock*. Kingston, Jamaica, Privately Printed, 1796.

Dana, Richard Henry. *Two Years Before the Mast*. Vol. 23 of *Harvard Classics, q. v.*

Darwin, Charles A. *Animals and Plants Under Domestication*. 2 vols. New York, D. Appleton, 1890.

Davies, Nina de Garis (with Alan H. Gardiner). *The Tomb of Huy*. London, Egypt Exploration Society, 1926. 4th Memoir in the Theban Tomb Series, ed. by Norman de Garis Davies and Alan H. Gardiner.

Davies, Norman de Garis. *The Rock Tombs of Deir el Gebrâwi*. 2 vols. London, Egypt Exploration Fund, 1902. 11th and 12th Memoirs in Archaeological Survey of Egypt, ed. by F. L. Griffith.

Denhardt, Robert M. *The Horse of the Americas*. Norman, University of Oklahoma Press, 1947.

De Voe, Thomas F. *The Market Book*. 2 vols. New York, Privately Printed, 1862.

———. *The Market Assistant*. Boston, Houghton Mifflin, 1867.

Dickson, Arthur Jerome. *Covered Wagon Days*. Cleveland, Arthur H. Clark, 1939.

Dobie, J. Frank. *The Longhorns*. Boston, Little, Brown, 1941.

Duflot de Mofras, Eugene. *Travels on the Pacific Coast*. Ed. by Marguerite Eyer Wilbur. 2 vols. The Fine Arts Press, Santa Ana, Calif., 1937.

Durant, Will. *The Life of Greece*. New York, Simon and Schuster, 1939.

Dürst, J. V. *Die Rinder von Babylonien, Assyrien, und Aegypten*. Berlin, G. Reimer, 1899.

Evans, Sir Arthur. *The Palace of Minos at Knossos*. 6 vols. London, Macmillan, 1921.

Evelyn, John. *The Diary of . . . .* Ed. by William Bray. 2 vols. Akron, Ohio, St. Dunstan Society, 1901.

Ewart, J. Cossar (ed.). *Cattle Breeding: Proceedings of the Scottish Cattle Breeding Conference*. Edinburgh, Oliver and Boyd, 1925.

Fairfield, Asa Merrill. *Fairfield's Pioneer History of Lassen County, California*. San Francisco, H. S. Crocker, 1916.

Farnham, Thomas J. *Travels in the Great Western Prairies*. London, Richard Bentley, 1843.

Fellows, Dexter W. *This Way to the Big Show*. New York, Halcyon House, 1936.

Felt, Joseph Barlow. *History of Ipswich, Essex, and Hamilton, Massachusetts*. Cambridge, C. Folsom, 1834.

Fessenden, Thomas G. *The Complete Farmer and Rural Economist*. Boston, Russell, Shaffner and Company, 1835.

Flint, James. *Letters from America*. Vol. IX in Thwaites' *Early Western Travels, q. v.*

Foik, Paul J. (trans.). *Ramon's Diary of Expedition into Texas in 1716*. Austin, Von Boeckmann-Jones, 1935.

Fowler, Bertram B. *Men, Meat, and Miracles*. New York, Messner, 1952.

Frazer, Sir George. *The Golden Bough*. 12 vols. London, Macmillan, 1924–26.

Gard, Wayne. *The Chisholm Trail*. Norman, University of Oklahoma Press, 1954.

Gent, J. W. *Systema Agriculturae: The Mystery of Husbandry Discovered*. 2nd ed. London, Privately Printed, 1675.

Ghent, W. J. *The Road to Oregon*. New York, Longmans, Green, 1929.

Gilbert, Paul, and Lee Bryson. *Chicago and Its Makers*. Chicago, Felix Mendelsohn, 1929.

Goodrich, Charles A. (ed.). *A New Family Encyclopedia: Neat Cattle.* 4th ed. Philadelphia, The Author, 1833.

Gray, Lewis Cecil. *History of Agriculture in the Southern United States to 1860.* 2 vols. New York, Peter Smith, 1941.

Gregg, Josiah. *Commerce of the Prairies.* 2 vols. 2nd ed. New York, J. and H. G. Langley, 1845.

Hackett, Charles Wilson (ed.). *Pichardo's Treatise on the Limits of Louisiana and Texas.* 4 vols. Austin, University of Texas, 1931–46.

Hagedorn, A. L. *Animal Breeding.* 3rd ed. London, C. Lockwood, 1948.

Hall, Capt. Basil. *Travels in North America in the Years 1827–28.* 2 vols. London, S. Westley and A. H. Davis, 1833.

Hall, H. R., and C. Leonard Woolley. *Ur Excavations al-'Ubaid.* 2 vols. London, Oxford University Press, 1927.

Hafen, LeRoy R., and Francis Marion Young. *Fort Laramie and the Pageant of the West.* Glendale, Arthur H. Clark, 1938.

Haley, J. Evetts. *Charles Goodnight: Cowman and Plainsman.* Boston, Houghton Mifflin, 1936.

———. *The XIT Ranch of Texas.* Chicago, Capitol Reservation Lands, 1929.

Harvard Classics. 50 vols. New York, P. F. Collier and Sons, 1909.

Haugen, Einar. *Voyages to Vinland.* New York, Knopf, 1942.

Hebard, Grace R. *The Path Breakers from River to Ocean.* Glendale, Arthur H. Clark, 1932.

———, and E. A. Brininstool. *The Bozeman Trail.* Cleveland, Arthur H. Clark, 1922.

Heck, Lutz, *Auf Tiersuche in Weiter Welt.* Berlin, Parey Company, 1941.

Herberstein, Baron Sigismund von. *Rerum Muscoviticarum Commentarii.* London, Hakluyt Society, 1851.

Herndon, Sarah R. *Days on the Road: Crossing the Plains in 1865.* New York, Burr Printing House, 1902.

Hill, J. L. *The End of the Cattle Trail.* Long Beach, Calif., George W. Moyle Publishing Company, 1924.

Hinman, Robert B., and Robert B. Harris. *The Story of Meat.* Chicago, Swift and Company, 1942.

Holman, Frederick B. *Dr. John McLaughlin, the Father of Oregon.* Cleveland, Arthur H. Clark, 1907.

Home, Henry (Lord Kames). *The Gentleman Farmer*. 2nd ed. Edinburgh, Bell and Bradfute, 1802.

Hughes, Thomas. *G. T. T. ("Gone to Texas")*: *Letters from Our Boys*. London, Macmillan, 1884.

Huidekoper, Rush Shippen. *Age of the Domestic Animals*. Chicago, Alexander Eger, 1904.

Hunter, J. Marvin (ed.). *The Trail Drivers of Texas*. 2nd ed. Nashville, Cokesbury Press, 1925.

Jameson, J. Franklin (ed.). *Edward Johnson's Wonder-Working Providence, 1628–1651*. New York, Charles Scribner's Sons, 1910.

Jones, Major. *The Emigrant's Friend*. Newcastle-on-Tyne, England, Tyne Publishing Company, Ltd., 1881.

Kellar, Herbert A. (ed.). *Solon Robinson: Pioneer and Agriculturist*. 2 vols. Indianapolis, Indiana Historical Bureau, 1936.

Kelly, L. V. *The Range Men*. Toronto, William Briggs, 1913.

Knight, Charles R. *Prehistoric Man, the Great Adventurer*. New York, Appleton-Century-Crofts, 1949.

Lattimore, Owen J. *The Inner Asian Frontiers of China*. New York, American Geographical Society, 1940.

Laut, A. D. *Pathfinders of the West*. New York, Macmillan, 1922.

Lawrence, Robert Means, M. D. *New England Colonial Life*. Cambridge, Mass., The Cosmos Press, 1927.

Logan, John H. *A History of the Upper Country of South Carolina*. Charleston, S. C. Courtenay and Company, 1859.

Lomax, Alfred L. *Pioneer Woolen Mills in Oregon*. Portland, Binfords and Mort, 1941.

Lord, Mrs. Elizabeth. *Reminiscences of Oregon*. Portland, The Irwin-Hodson Company, 1903.

Low, David. *The Breeding of the Domestic Animals of the British Islands*. London, Longman, Orme, Brown, Green and Longmans, 1842.

Lydekker, Richard. *The Ox and Its Kindred*. London, G. Allan and Company, 1912.

McArthur, Lewis Ankeny. *Oregon Geographic Names*. Portland, Binfords and Mort, 1952.

McCarty, John L. *Maverick Town: The Story of Old Tascosa*. Norman, University of Oklahoma Press, 1946.

Bibliography

McConnell, W. J. *Early History of Idaho*. Caldwell, The Caxton Printers, 1913.

McCoy, Joseph A. *Historic Sketches of the Cattle Trade of the West and Southwest*. Ed. by Ralph P. Bieber. Glendale, Arthur H. Clark, 1940.

Mallery, Arlington H. *Lost America*. Columbus, Ohio, The Overlook Company, 1951.

Merlin, Alfred. *Vases Grec in Librairie des Artes Decoratives*. Paris, Commission of the Piot Foundation, 1929.

Michaud, Joseph François. *History of the Crusades*. 2 vols. Philadelphia, G. Barrie, 1896.

Michaux, François André. *Travels to the West of the Alleghany Mountains*. Vol. III in Thwaites' *Early Western Travels, q. v.*

Morfi, Juan A. *History of Texas*. Trans. by Carlos Eduardo Castañeda. Quivira Society Publication VI. 2 vols. Albuquerque, The Quivira Society, 1935.

Neely, W. C. *The Agricultural Fair*. New York, Columbia University Press, 1935.

Olmstead, A. T. *History of Assyria*. New York, Charles Scribner's Sons, 1923.

Olmsted, Frederick Law. *A Journey through Texas; or, A Saddle Trip on the Southwestern Frontier*. New York, Dix, Edwards and Company, 1857.

Osborn, Henry Fairfield. *The Age of Mammals*. New York, Macmillan, 1910.

———. *Men of the Old Stone Age*. 3d ed. New York, Charles Scribner's Sons, 1924.

Osgood, Ernest Staples. *The Day of the Cattleman*. Minneapolis, University of Minnesota Press, 1929.

Paden, Irene D. *The Wake of the Prairie Schooner*. New York, Macmillan, 1943.

Palmer, Joel. *Journal of Travels over the Rocky Mountains . . . 1845–46*. Cincinnati, J. A. and U. P. James, 1847.

Pelzer, Louis. *The Cattleman's Frontier*. Glendale, Arthur H. Clark, 1936.

Pike, Zebulon Montgomery. *Exploratory Travels in North America*. Denver, W. H. Lawrence and Company, 1889.

Plumb, Charles S. *Types and Breeds of Farm Animals*. Boston, Ginn and Company, 1920.

Potter, Col. Jack, and Laura H. Krehbiel. *Cattle Trails of the Old West*. Clayton, New Mex., Laura H. Krehbiel, 1939.

Pumpelly, R. *Explorations in Turkestan*. Washington, Carnegie Institution of Washington, 1908.

Raine, William McLeod, and W. C. Barnes. *Cattle*. Garden City, Doubleday, Doran, 1930.

Reman, Edward. *Norse Discoveries and Explorations in America*. Berkeley, University of California Press, 1949.

Robinson, Roland E. *Danvis Folks and a Hero of Ticonderoga*. Ed. by Llewellyn B. Perkins. Rutland, Vt., The Tuttle Company, 1934.

Rollinson, John K. *Wyoming Cattle Trails*. Caldwell, The Caxton Printers, 1948.

Russell, Charles M. *Rawhide Rawlins Stories*. Great Falls, Mont., Montana Newspaper Association, 1921.

Rütimeyer, L. *The Fauna of Middle Europe during the Stone Age*. Washington, Smithsonian Institution, 1861.

Sanders, A. H. *The Story of the Hereford*. Chicago, Breeder's Gazette Publishing Company, 1914.

Schmid, A. *Rassenkunde des Rindes*. 2 vols. Berne Switzerland, Bentili, 1942.

Shepherd, Major W. *Prairie Experiences*. New York, Orange Judd, 1885.

Sienkiewicz, Henrik. *Quo Vadis*. Trans. by Jeremiah Curtin. Boston, Little, Brown, 1897.

Stefansson, Vilhjalmur. *Greenland*. New York, Doubleday, Doran, 1942.

———. *Iceland: The First American Republic*. New York, Doubleday, Doran, 1943.

Storer, John. *The Wild White Cattle of Great Britain*. London, Cassell, Petter, Galpin, n.d.

Stuart, Granville. *Forty Years on the Frontier*. 2 vols. Cleveland, Arthur H. Clark, 1925.

Tate, G. H. H. *Mammals of Eastern Asia*. New York, Macmillan, 1947.

Taylor, T. U. *The Chisholm Trail and Other Routes*. San Antonio, Naylor, 1936.

Thayer, William M. *Marvels of the New West.* Norwich, Conn., Henry Hill Publishing Company, 1888.

Thwaites, Reuben Gold (ed.). *Early Western Travels.* 32 vols. Cleveland, Arthur H. Clark, 1904–1907.

Torfaers, Thormodus. *History of Vinland.* New York, U. S. Catholic Historical Society, 1888.

Towne, Charles W. *Her Majesty Montana.* Butte, The Standard Press, 1939.

———, and Edward Norris Wentworth. *Shepherd's Empire.* Norman, University of Oklahoma Press, 1945.

———, and Edward Norris Wentworth. *Pigs: From Cave to Corn Belt.* Norman, University of Oklahoma Press, 1950.

Toynbee, Arnold J. *A Study of History.* New York and London, Macmillan, 1947.

Turner, Frederick Jackson. *Rise of the New West.* New York, Harper, 1906.

Vancouver, George. *A Voyage of Discovery to the North Pacific Ocean.* 3 vols. London, E. G. and J. Robinson, 1798.

Walford, Cornelius. *Fairs, Past and Present.* London, Elliott Stock, 1883.

Waltari, Mika. *The Egyptian.* New York, G. P. Putnam's Sons, 1949.

Weeden, William B. *Economic and Social History of New England, 1620–1789.* Boston, Houghton Mifflin, 1890.

Wellman, Paul I. *The Trampling Herd.* New York, Carrick and Evans, 1939.

Wells, H. G. *The Outline of History.* New York, Macmillan, 1930.

Wentworth, Edward Norris. *The Portrait Gallery of the Saddle and Sirloin Club.* Chicago, Union Stock Yards Co., 1920.

White, Bouck. *The Book of Daniel Drew.* Garden City, Doubleday, Page, 1911.

Wilson, John A. *The Burden of Egypt.* Chicago, University of Chicago Press, 1951.

Windels, Fernand. *The Lascaux Cave Paintings.* New York, Viking, 1950.

Winser, Henry J. *The Great Northwest: A Guide Book and Itinerary* (of the Northern Pacific Railroad). New York, G. P. Putnam's Sons, 1883.

Winship, George Parker. *The Coronado Expedition.* Bureau of American Ethnology *Fourteenth Annual Report,* Part I. Washington, 1896.

Woods, John. *Two Years' Residence on the English Prairie in the Illinois Country.* London, Longman, Hurst, Rees, Orme and Brown, 1822.

Wyllys, Rufus K. *Pioneer Padre: The Life and Times of Eusebio Francisco Kino.* Dallas, Southwest Press, 1935.

Youatt, W., and W. C. L. Martin. *Cattle: A Treatise on Their Breeding, Management, and Diseases.* London, Simpkin, Marshall, 1872.

6. ARTICLES

Braidwood, Robert J. "Jarmo: A Village of Early Farmers in Iraq," *Antiquity,* Vol. XXIV, No. 96 (December, 1950).

Brayer, Herbert O. "The Influence of British Capital on the Western Range Cattle Industry," Denver *Westerners Brand Book,* Vol. IV, No. 5 (May, 1948).

Breeder's Gazette, Vol. V, No. 21 (May 22, 1884); Vol. V, No. 25 (June 26, 1884). Editorials.

Coolidge, Harold J. "The Indo-Chinese Forest Ox or Kouprey," *Memoirs* of the Museum of Comparative Zoology at Harvard College, Vol. LIV, No. 6 (August, 1940).

Cooper, John S. "Bull Market," *Wall Street Journal,* December 4, 1951.

Dawkins, W. Boyd. "1. On the British Fossil Oxen. Part II. Bos longifrons, Owen," *Quarterly Journal of the Royal Geological Society* (London), Vol. XXIII (February 20, 1867).

Gates, Paul Wallace. "Cattle Kings in the Prairies," *Mississippi Valley Historical Review,* Vol. XXXV, No. 3 (December, 1948).

Gould, John. "The Pull in the Pulling Contest," *Christian Science Monitor,* undated clipping.

Holmes, Abiel. "The History of Cambridge," Massachusetts Historical Society *Collections,* VII (1801).

Kaufman, Kenneth C. "Research Charts Nation's Great Western Trek," *Chicago Sunday Tribune,* Book Review Section, October 24, 1943.

Bibliography

King, I. F. "The Coming and Going of Ohio Droving," *Ohio Archaeological and Historical Publications*, XVII (1908).

McLester, James S., M.D. "Protein Comes into Its Own," *Journal of the American Medical Association*, Vol. CXXXIX, No. 14 (April 2, 1949).

Myrick, Norman. "The Lord Made 'em Capable: A Story of Oxen," *Yankee Magazine*, Vol. XI, No. 5 (May, 1947).

Oliphant, J. Orin. "Eastward Movement of Cattle from the Oregon Country," *Agricultural History*, Vol. XX, No. 1 (January, 1946).

————. "The Cattle Herds and Ranches of the Oregon Country, 1860–1890," *Agricultural History*, Vol. XXI, No. 4 (December, 1947).

Sanders, A. H. "The Taurine World," *National Geographic*, Vol. XLVIII, No. 6 (December, 1925).

Sharp, Paul F. "Whoop-Up Trail: International Highway on the Great Plains," *Pacific Historical Review*, Vol. XXI, No. 2 (May, 1952). Reprint.

————. "The Northern Great Plains: A Study in Canadian-American Regionalism," *Mississippi Valley Historical Review*, Vol. XXXIX, No. 1 (June, 1952).

South Dakota Historical Collections, XIV (1928).

Turner, Frederick Jackson. "The Old West," Wisconsin State Historical Society *Proceedings*, XIV (1908).

Wentworth, Edward N. "A Search for Cattle Trails in Matto Grosso," *Agricultural History*, Vol. XXVI, No. 1 (January, 1952).

Whaley, W. Gordon. "Grass the Economic Cornerstone," *Corpus Christi Call-Times*, July 12, 1953.

Whitmore, Eugene. "John Jacob Myers and the Early Cattle Drives," Chicago *Westerners Brand Book*, Vol. IX, No. 8 (October, 1952).

Index

Abbott, E. C. (Teddy Blue): 181; experiences of in stampede, 178–79, 181; cowboy antics described by, 185–86.
Aberdeen Angus cattle: 72, 302, 310ff.; description of, 303
Abilene, Kansas: 145, 163
Abraham: 30–31, 289
Adams, John Quincy: 188
Africa: 18
Afrikander cattle: 325; characteristics of, 326
Agricultural Gazette, praises John D. Gillett's cattle: 287
Aguayo, Marquis of: 151
Aix-la-Chapelle: 14–15
Akhethetep, tomb of, engravings of cattle in: 32
Alabama: 156
Alaska: 117
Albany, New York: 146
Albrecht, Prince, of Prussia: 24
Alderney cows: 113
Alert, the (American sailing vessel): 126
Alexander, John T.: 223n., 287
Alexander the Second, czar of Russia: 24
Algeciras: 68
Allen, Lewis F., opinion of on breeds of cattle: 319–20
Allerton, Samuel: 223n.
Alsace-Lorraine: 13
Altamira, Spain: discovery of cave paintings at, 51; frescoes of bulls in, 51–52
Alvarado, Governor Alonso de: 231
Alvarado, Pedro de: 148
"American beef belt," early location of: 313
American Brahman Breeders Association: 304
American colonies: cattle in, 130ff.; frontier aspects of cattle raising in, 146
American Meat Institute: 332

357

CATTLE & MEN

Windsor, Connecticut: 136
Winnemucca, Paiute chief: 238
Winship, Samuel: 282
Winslow, Capt. Edward, first cattle brought to Massachusetts by: 133–34
Winter of 1886–87, disastrous effects of on cattle: 268
Wisconsin: 263
Wisent: *see* European bison
Women: on cattle trails, 182–84; with emigrant groups, 203ff.
Wood, William: 133
Worms, Forest of: 15
Wyeth, Nathaniel J.: 228–29
Wyoming: 71, 252, 262, 263, 264–65, 267
Wyoming cattle owners in Johnson County war: 267
Wyoming Stock Growers' Association: 260

Yak: 18; description of, 22–23; crossbreeds, 23, 327f.
Yellow Danish cattle: 134f.
York, England: 97
Young, Sir Arthur: 274, 277
Young, Brigham: 188, 192
Young, Ewing: 234; cattle brought to Oregon from California by, 231–33
Young, John: 238
Yuma Indians: 120
Yu-Nan: 21

Zaldivar, Vicente de: 149
Zebu: 18, 20, 21, 320f.; in Brazil, 78; Brahman bulls, 81
Zeus (Greek god): 48, temple of, 50, 57
Zo: *see* yak
Zuñi, New Mexico: 148

384

UNIVERSITY OF OKLAHOMA PRESS

NORMAN